QUARTZ FAMILY MINERALS

Section of polished agate, showing natural color at the lower end, and on the remainder various artificial colors. (*Courtesy of Field Museum of Natural History, Chicago.*)

QUARTZ
FAMILY MINERALS

A Handbook for the Mineral Collector

BY

H. C. DAKE

FRANK L. FLEENER

AND

BEN HUR WILSON

New York WHITTLESEY HOUSE *London*

McGRAW-HILL BOOK COMPANY, INC.

PUBLISHED BY WHITTLESEY HOUSE

A division of the McGraw-Hill Book Company, Inc.

*The quality of the materials used in the manufacture
of this book is governed by continued postwar shortages.*

DEDICATED

*to all those anonymous writers of the
past who have preserved mineral information of
great value to the present generation
Mineralogists*

Preface

With the manyfold increase during the past decade in the number of persons seriously interested in one phase or another of the mineralogical sciences, there has arisen a growing demand for one compact volume on the subject of quartz, where the most essential information would be made available for reference to the amateur and the professional student alike.

In culling the widely scattered literature upon the subject, the authors were overwhelmed with its profusion. They dared not even brief the greater bulk of it. They were reminded of Buckles's statement in his "History of Civilization in England": "We live in that predicament that our facts have outstripped our knowledge and now encumber its march."

Early realizing the futility of attempting a complete treatment of a mineral so diversified and abundant, they have set themselves to the task of producing a volume which will answer many of the more common, general, and perplexing questions about quartz minerals, yet give such perspective to the subject as will encourage the reader to set out on a line of further research and investigation for himself.

All books should be written with certain fixed limitations and objectives in mind. The authors adopted these:

1. They have tried to give the reader definite information concerning the typical, rather than the exceptional, examples. They are not interested particularly in freaks or curiosities of the quartz world, unless these emphasize some definite point or give a clue to the solution of some obscure or puzzling observation.

2. In general, they have attempted to allot space in proportion to the importance of the variety under consideration, though this, again, may be largely a matter of opinion. It will be

immediately apparent that the varieties (subspecies) of quartz are not all of like importance; therefore, an equal amount of space should not be devoted to each. Some lesser varieties, however, have been treated at greater length, because of unique features or some historical or economic value attached to them.

3. They have endeavored to render some distinct contribution to the literature of the field by listing many of the known contemporary American localities of interest to collectors—especially those of the western or newer sections of the country, which have been recently explored and remain comparatively unknown. At the same time, attention has been given to some of the less known of the older localities which are yet available and accessible to present-day collectors.

4. They have attempted to check from original sources as many as possible of the statements that are made. This proved most difficult, and the authors are indebted to many persons for assistance.

The readers may judge to what extent these aims have been achieved.

The authors have realized their inability to cover the whole field of important localities throughout the entire world, many of which are now exhausted, and many more of which are as inaccessible to the average collector, striving to make a modest collection of minerals for his own edification and pleasure, as though they were located on the planet Mars. To catalogue geographically a mineral as widespread and common as quartz would require a fairly complete gazetteer of the earth, which plainly is quite beyond the scope of this volume.

The central idea of the book is helpfulness. The intention is to help, more than anybody else, the fellow who is struggling along by himself, who knows minerals, appreciates their beauty, and understands that they can tell him something. If it is possible here to teach him the proper slant, or give him the clue to the correct interpretation of the meaning of minerals and the important part they play in the economy of things in nature, the authors will be amply repaid for their efforts.

Preface

To acknowledge indebtedness to every individual who has helped make this work a reality would be as impossible as to tell the whole story of quartz complete in every detail. The authors have drawn freely upon the general literature. Inferences have also been made from certain artifacts antedating recorded history. Some admirable observations which have found their way into print have been made anonymously, and so in many cases it is impossible to give credit. The books and texts on minerals which have been consulted in the preparation of the book are listed in the Selected References at the close of the book.

Many friends have generously lent a helping hand by answering numerous inquiries to the best of their ability, and thanks is hereby extended to all who have so assisted. The authors are especially grateful for special information and advice given by Dr. Esper S. Larsen, Harvard University; Dr. John R. Ball, Northwestern University; John Melhase, Berkeley, California; E. Mitchell Gunnell, University of Missouri; J. Lewis Renton, Portland, Oregon; George J. Huss, Marquette Mineral Society, Chicago; Edward Wigglesworth, Boston Society of Natural History; William Pitts, Sunnyvale, California; D. H. Newland, New York State Museum; Prof. George Beck, Washington State Normal College; Raymond C. Moore, University of Kansas; Dr. W. H. Over, South Dakota State Museum; Prof. Francis T. Jones, Pacific University; and George L. English, Gus Brockmann, and Harlow D. Grose for photographic contributions.

They are also immeasurably indebted to the files of the following mineral magazines which have made important contributions to the literature: *Minerals*, edited by W. M. Goldthwaite (discontinued); *Mineral Collector*, edited by Arthur Chamberlain (discontinued); *The American Mineralogist*, edited by Walter F. Hunt; *The Mineralogist*, edited by H. C. Dake; *Rocks and Minerals*, edited by Peter Zodac; and *Sands, Clays and Minerals* (British), edited by A. L. Curtis.

It might be of interest to some to know the parts of the book for which the joint authors were individually responsible. This would be hard to state precisely, for each has assisted the others. In a general way, Mr. Wilson was responsible for the early chapters of the book, up to and including the discussion of the crystalline forms; Mr. Fleener's voluminous notes, the product of a lifetime of reading and research, fitted him pre-eminently to prepare the chapters on the numerous varieties and subvarieties of amorphous quartz, including the part on opal; Mr. Dake's many years of experience as editor of *The Mineralogist* and his wide travels in the West have given him a valuable fund of information on the subject of agates, chalcedony, and petrified woods, and these chapters were arranged by him.

The authors realize the inadequacy of certain phases of the work and regret that lack of space has forbidden the pursuit of some of the lines of discussion to their full conclusion. It goes without saying that they would appreciate correspondence or criticism concerning any statements which might appear to be debatable, and they will also be pleased to answer any questions that may help to straighten out problems which seem troublesome to any reader.

H. C. DAKE,
FRANK L. FLEENER,
BEN HUR WILSON.

Contents

Contents

List of Illustrations

List of Illustrations

QUARTZ FAMILY MINERALS

CHAPTER I

Why Know Quartz?

We hear, today, much emphasis and stress being placed upon the value of a well-rounded, general education. In fact, practically our entire educational system, up to and in many instances including our liberal arts colleges, builds the curriculum on the basis of giving the student broad knowledge intended to integrate him thoroughly with his natural surroundings. Therefore, any person with a balanced education should be able to look the old world in the face, and say, "Earth, you and I are acquainted. I feel as if I have known you for a long time. We are friends and are going to live together in mutual harmony and understanding for the rest of my life."

Perhaps, from the standpoint of history, physics, chemistry, and the biologies, this may be actually true, but when the same student comes to the geological sciences, the "rock-bottom" foundation of them all, where is he? There is reason for doubting gravely whether even 1 per cent of our secondary school graduates can give the correct distinction between the meaning of the terms "rock" and "mineral," and quite as often college graduates can do little better. The ignorance of even our so-called educated class on the important subject of mineralogy is woeful, nor is the situation among our teaching profession much better. Look through the ordinary, meager collection of school minerals and notice in how many instances you will find calcite labeled "quartz." "It has a glassy luster, therefore it must be quartz."

Many years ago, Lorenzo Yates, in writing on the subject in *Minerals* magazine stated, "It is one of the most important of the 'ologies' in its bearings and relations. It is the foundation of the arts and sciences, for minerals are the prime source of everything we see, feel, eat, drink, wear, or take pleasure in. Our earth is composed of the so-called elements, in various combinations; these elements are all mineral substances, and the majority of them are solids. Mineralogy, in connection with chemistry, enables us to determine the component parts of these combinations, and to recognize the mineral species in all varied and often beautiful forms." In the entire mineral kingdom, no species is more abundant, widespread, varied, or beautiful than quartz, and so it seems almost needless to ask the question, Why know quartz?

ADVANTAGES OF KNOWING QUARTZ

For that matter, why know any mineral? Every mineralogist can point to outstanding instances where a knowledge of minerals has been decidedly advantageous. For example, many years ago a poor farm boy came to a small Iowa college with a knocked-down buck-saw in the bottom of his trunk, by means of which he hoped to help earn his way through school. Here he studied the rudiments of mineralogy, and learned to recognize the metals and their common ores. When the Civil War broke out and disrupted his plans for a college education, he drove a team to Colorado and started to work in a gold quartz mine, where from careful observation he gained some practical experience in mining and further knowledge of the nature of quartz ore bodies. In 1863 he joined the stampede to Horse Prairie Creek in Montana, where he quickly washed out $1,500 in gold. With this capital he went into business and soon amassed a modest fortune.

Relying solely upon his own judgment and his knowledge of mineralogy and mining he quietly acquired the Original, Colusa, Mountain Chief, and Gambetta mining claims at Butte. Feeling the need of greater technical training in mine operation, he attended the School of Mines at Columbia for one year. Returning to Montana, he built the Old Dexter stamp mill, the first of its kind in the Butte district. From then on, his mining properties expanded with remarkable rapidity, and so influential did they become in the political and business affairs of the nation, that at the time of his death, on January 8, 1925, Sen. William A. Clark, known as "the Copper King," was rated as one of the world's wealthiest men. Former president Herbert Hoover, another Iowa country lad, also owes his success in life directly to the thorough knowledge of minerals he acquired while attending college. Doubtless, we could truthfully say that many of the greatest fortunes in our country have been tied up in one way or another with the world's mineral resources, and that a knowledge of mineralogy helped to lay their foundations.

A full understanding of quartz and the quartz minerals is truly a prerequisite to the study of mineralogy and the geological sciences. However, it is not the intention of the authors of this book to overemphasize the economic or commercial value of minerals, important as they are. Rather, we desire to discuss quartz from the point of view of the average mineral student or collector. The person who enjoys minerals most is not usually the one who continually thinks of them as a source of profit. The mine owner or the manufacturer, unless he be exceptional, looks only to their value in dollars and cents, and therefore seldom realizes or appreciates their true beauty or their educational or cultural worth. As a delightful avocation, the collecting of minerals has no superior and but few close competitors.

The live, wide-awake collector is no longer satisfied to sit idly by and admire his most cherished specimens, but demands constantly to know more and more about them. There is no end to the lines of study and investigation he may pursue, even with respect to the most common mineral, and he is likely not to be satisfied until he has gathered the last bit of information available concerning his favorites. There is more popular interest, today, in quartz minerals and agates than in any other single mineral species. This statement is amply borne out by the great interest evinced in agates at the mineral exhibits of the numerous "hobby shows" held annually throughout the country. Moreover, a study of the genesis of quartz minerals, their mode of deposition, inclusions, crystal forms, and physical properties has added greatly to our common fund of mineralogical knowledge. We are glad to state unqualifiedly, in this connection, that important contributions are coming in from amateurs with ever-increasing frequency.

LOCALITIES AND NOMENCLATURE

Quartz minerals, including agates, are known to exist in nearly every part of the world. Over a period of many years, more than 200 varieties and subvarieties of quartz have been noted and listed by various writers. As in the case of other natural objects, it is not always easy to discern their true relationships, and therefore, an exact classification is sometimes impossible. Quartz also occupies a rather unique and prominent position in the field of semiprecious stones, as it is found in great profusion and in a wide variety of colors, patterns, textures, and combinations. For this reason, there is a long list of names which have been applied to the numerous varieties and subvarieties. Often these names are used only locally, but in other instances the local name later finds universal adoption.

For instance, the term "Herkimer diamond" is often applied to the remarkably clear, brilliant, and well-developed quartz crystals found in Herkimer County, New York. Again the terms "Medfordite" and "Oregonite" are applied to varieties of jasper found in southern Oregon, types distinctive enough to warrant a local name. The orbicular jasper of California is sometimes called "Egyptian jasper." Then there are the misnomers, like the Petoskey "agates" of Michigan and other Midwestern states, which are not agates but fossilized corals that do resemble some varieties of agates, superficially, just enough to fool the early settlers who first found them along the beach of Lake Michigan at Petoskey. Strange to say, these so-called "agates" are not even siliceous, but are composed chiefly of limestone (calcite). A type of water-worn agate

6

found widely distributed in stream gravels and on beaches may be termed "moonstone," since it resembles to some extent the feldspar moonstone.

It is only to be expected of any science like mineralogy, springing up piecemeal from an enormous bulk of hodgepodge observations and materials, that more or less difficulty in the matter of nomenclature will be experienced. The ecology of quartz presents no exception to this rule. Consequently, we are not surprised to discover that in the literature, both old and modern, there is some discrepancy in the employment of type names, also some duplication. One might without avail enter into a long discussion of this problem. Part of the confusion has resulted from attempts to identify solely from the literature "finds," scattered widely throughout the world. Finally, when the material has been brought together in some collection or museum, so that direct comparison is possible, distinct differences are immediately perceived. Some of these problems will be mentioned individually throughout the text.

On the other hand, it is observed by those who are working with large collections and who are thoroughly familiar with quartz that the individual variations or subspecies, like members of the plant and animal world, when systematically arranged, all tend to blend insensibly from one variation into another. Thus, when a series of specimens of hornstone, flint, chert, tripoli, etc., is graded and compared, it is almost impossible for anyone to put his finger on a certain point in the gradation and say: "This is the place where flint leaves off and where chert begins." In such cases, we are compelled to resort to such subterfuge terms as "flinty-chert" and "cherty-flint." The same might as truly be said of the jaspers and, for that matter, of nearly every other variety of quartz.

For this reason, there is apparent lack of agreement, and in some instances we find contradictions even in the same text— an occurrence which, under existing conditions, cannot well be avoided. Even the different editions of Dana present obscurities; and this is not to be criticised, for they can largely be accounted for by the natural growth of the subject and by the discovery and introduction of newer and more authoritative opinion. So complicated is this problem, even in the case of a single mineral species, that it will be some time before all the seeming discrepancies are entirely or satisfactorily rectified. Some of them will be mentioned in appropriate places throughout this book, and, if possible, an attempt will be made to "iron out" certain of the more obvious ones.

Since one of the main purposes of the present work is to stress some of the more popular phases of the growing interest in the minerals of the quartz family, much that is of general helpfulness may be added concerning a few of the various ramifications which this unbounded enthusiasm now displays. One branch in particular, worthy of special notice, is the present widespread, almost universal, awakening of the public consciousness to the great value and importance of mineral collecting as a desirable hobby. In our strenuous ultramodern living, the nerve-racking pace which must be kept up requires occasional complete relaxation and change from business cares and worries, if physical and mental equilibrium are to be maintained successfully. In few other ways can anyone detach or lose himself so completely, as by becoming a "rabid," deep-rooted mineral fan.

During recent years, literally hundreds of mineral devotees have become seriously engaged in the practice of cutting and polishing semiprecious stones. No common mineral (for reasons which will be developed later) lends itself, from the standpoint of variety, beauty, or durability, to these ends so well as quartz. One of the chief problems which confront the amateur gemmologist, is the source of supply for raw material with which to work. Fortunately, many new localities where quartz of gem quality may be found have been discovered and opened up within the past few years. Perhaps nowhere do fine "deposits" of agate and chalcedony occur in greater abundance or of better quality than in the Western states. Consequently, the working of semiprecious stones as a hobby, in this section of the country, has become so well established that many of the schools consider it worth while to put into their curriculums courses of training in lapidary work. In some places, the hobby has actually swept over whole communities like a great wave, and numerous clubs are springing up for the study of minerals and allied subjects. The more remarkable of these collecting localities will be mentioned later.

DEPOSITS OF GEM QUARTZ

A discussion regarding the nature of the occurrences of gem-quartz appears apropos at this point. Quartz is found in the rocks of all ages and of nearly every type, including igneous, sedimentary, and metamorphic. Cavities in lava (igneous) rocks, formed by gas bubbles known as vesicles, appear to be a favorite place for the deposition of agates and certain types of crystal-lined geodes. These fillings are brought about through the agency of percolating ground waters bearing silica in solution. Many of the finest examples of crystalized quartz and amorphous agate known occur in this manner. Granite rocks and the granite pegmatites are favorite places for the formation of large single quartz crystals and groups of crystals.

In general, quartz minerals, including chalcedonies, agates, and jaspers, are very resistant to weathering. Frequently, the hard rock matrix in which specimens occur will completely disintegrate long before the quartz is even slightly affected by the work of the elements. This is well illustrated at localities like Antelope, Oregon, Barstow, California, and similar areas throughout Nevada and Wyoming, where specimens in profusion were found thickly strewn about on the surface. Often the "mother rock" had disappeared, having long since succumbed to the attacks of wind, sand, sun, and freezing and to the chemical action of the atmosphere and ground water, but the splendid specimens of fine quartz remained unblemished.

At some localities in Oregon, Nevada, and California, in small areas, many tons of agates, jaspers, geodes, nodules, and moss agate were found lying loose upon the surface, or covered only by a thin layer of surface debris. At Antelope, Oregon,

it required about ten years to remove the many tons of specimens found upon the surface, but areas like these have not
ceased to yield, for the annual rains and the plowing in the
fields continually expose an additional crop of material. For
more than one hundred years, quartz geodes have been removed
from the world-famous beds of Iowa, Illinois, and Missouri
surrounding Keokuk, literally by the hundreds of thousands,
and yet an abundance remains today for those who go in search
of them.

Agates are found also in many localities throughout the
Midwest, but they are generally of smaller size, usually not
over several inches in diameter. This may be accounted
for by the fact that some of them were brought in from the
region far to the north on the train of glacial ice which once
submerged this entire region. Considering the fact that they
were ground together by the movement of the ice, under ice
pressures up to and even exceeding a half mile in depth, the
remarkable wearing ability of the stones is well illustrated.
Owing to the nature of their distribution, no large concentration of the materials is possible, but their presence is widely
disseminated over large areas. While small, these agates (for
the greater part, carnelian) and jaspers found in the glacial
drift of the Central states, are well colored and often present
pleasing bandings of layers of alternating color. Rarely do these
"drift" agates or jaspers exceed ten or twelve inches in diameter, while at desert localities of the Far West specimens of
agate, chalcedony, and jasper, weighing a ton or more, are by
no means unusual.

Again, someone may wonder why small specimens prevail
upon the ocean beaches, while huge examples of similar material
may be found in the desert areas of the interior. Beach agates
owe their presence in the sands to two distinctly different
sources. They may be carried in by streams that are entering
the oceans, or they may be eroded from the formations along the
shore. In either event, the ceaseless action of the waves
pounding upon the beach effects a scouring or eroding action
which through endless centuries tends to reduce or wear down

the larger agates and other quartz materials to smaller and yet smaller sizes, until they eventually become only a part of the great sand mass along the ocean shore line. The symmetrical, water-worn pebbles often present examples of unusual beauty and unique occurrence.

What is true of the western and central part of the United States is likewise true of the entire world. We shall now pass on to a discussion of the historical aspect of this great interest of the human race in these handiworks of nature.

CHAPTER II

The Historical Lore of Quartz

Considerable historical and archaeological interest is attached to the minerals of the quartz family, particularly to the noncrystalline forms. Flint, chert, and jasper were recognized long ago as being hard substances which could be fashioned into tools, weapons, and ornaments. Moreover, quartz minerals are found widely distributed throughout the entire world; hence, quantities of raw material were readily available whenever needed.

PRIMITIVE TOOLS, WEAPONS, AND ORNAMENTS

Quartz minerals, with their relatively high hardness—greater than that of steel—proved effective as tools and weapons, once an edge or a point was attained. Primitive man somehow learned that by flaking these minerals he could obtain any desired shape. The date when prehistoric man first learned of the superior qualities of the quartz minerals over those of common rocks has been lost in the obscurity of time. The utilization of metals and their alloys did not come until a relatively recent date, historically speaking.

The men of the Old Stone Age are known to have used flint, jasper, and crystal quartz, approximately 100,000 years ago. The ruins of the dune dwellers of Mongolia, those of the Swiss lake and cave dwellers of Western Europe, the predynastic period in Egypt, and numerous other areas occupied by Stone Age man, all yield worked fragments of flint or other quartz minerals. In all probability, neither paleolithic nor neolithic man engaged in the actual mining of quartz minerals; they doubtless merely picked up pieces of suitable size and shape for the work at hand.

Archaeologically, the Sumerians, the earliest inhabitants of Mesopotamia, were the first people, so far as we now know, who recognized the ornamental value of the semiprecious stones and had mastered the art of cutting and polishing these stones into cylinder seals, signet rings, beads, and other forms of jewelry. One of the commonest forms of ornament made in those far-off times, was that of beads, which were made in a peculiar cylindrical shape; some were two or more inches each, in length. The boring of these beads must have presented a problem to the Sumerian lapidary; but the task was done, perhaps with a bow-drill, so true as to make anyone pause and wonder how, with such crude tools, the work could be accomplished so well. Carnelian and agate beads seem to have been the most popular, judging from the number that have been found. Even though these stones are very old, some of them were engraved. The source of agate supply then was probably India.

AGATE VALUED BY THE ANCIENTS

The Sumerians also used agate for making ceremonial axheads, the purpose of which is conjectural. An exceptionally fine example of such an object, engraved with a three-line inscription, may be seen preserved in the Morgan Collection of the American Museum of National History in New York. Based upon a translation of the inscription, the date of the axe is set as between 3000 and 2300 B.C. Another Babylonian axhead, of still earlier date, is in the Metropolitan Museum of Art in New York.

Theophrastus (c. 372–287 B.C.), in his treatise on "Stones," was undoubtedly the first man to write about agates. He notes that agate is a beautiful stone which is sold at a high price. Besides, he gives the accepted derivation of the name as from the river Achates in Sicily, where the stones were first taken in quantity.

Pliny the Elder (23–79 A.D.), in his "Natural History," also discusses the agate. However, he notes that the discovery of the stone in numerous places other than Sicily seems to have detracted from its popularity. Besides Sicily, Pliny mentions Crete, India, Phrygia in Asia Minor, Egypt, Cyprus, the Oeta Mountains, Mt. Parnassus, Lesboa, Messenia, Rhodes, and Persia, as places where agates were known to occur in his day.

Neither Pliny nor any of the other ancient writers states definitely that the agate was cut into gems; however, some cut stones have come down to us from very ancient times. Some of these date back as far as the Mycenaean age of Greek culture

AXHEAD FASHIONED FROM AGATE

A Sumerian ceremonial axhead engraved with a three-line inscription. (*Morgan Collection, American Museum Natural History, New York.*)

So far had the lapidarists progressed in the art of cutting and polishing agates, even at that early date, that some were engraved with mythological figures.

In early times, agates were used for many objects, such as bottles, cups, and bowls, a few of which have survived to our time. One of the best examples, cut from a single agate, measures twenty-eight and a half inches in diameter. This piece fell into the hands of the Crusaders, who carried it to Europe. It is now preserved in Vienna. Probably the most striking object ever worked from agate is a two-handled wine cup, with a capacity of more than a pint, carved over on the outside with Bacchanalian subjects. History states that this cup was made for the Emperor Nero, and that, after passing through many hands, it was presented in the ninth century by Charles the Bald to the Abbey of St. Denis, where it was used for centuries to hold the wine at the coronation of the kings of France. This cup is still treasured by the French as one of the most highly prized mementoes of their past.

The Persians and the Arabs, as well as other Oriental peoples, were partial to the agate in its various forms, no doubt being attracted by its color and durability. The stone was chiefly used for finger and signet rings, upon each of which the owner's name, a verse from the Koran, or some magical or symbolical figures, were carved. Such rings were and still are considered as potent talismans, protecting the owners from a long list of calamities. That Mohammed wore a signet of Yeman agate has had much to do with popularizing agates from that locality.

THE QUARTZ INDUSTRY IN THE EAST

India has been the source of beautiful stones of the quartz family for many centuries. Pliny the Elder ascribed marvelous properties to some of these stones, "as they present the appearance of rivers, woods, beasts of burden, and forms even like ivy and the trappings of horses," alluding, of course, to undulated and moss agates. He also stated that the druggists of his time were accustomed to use these stones for grinding drugs, which reminds us of the agate mortar found as an indispensable part of the apparatus of any well-appointed laboratory. Moreover, it was believed that the stones had the power to allay thirst, when held in the mouth, and it is said that many a camel driver sucked one of them as he piloted his "ship of the desert" over the burning sands, little comprehending the psychological background of what he did.

It is not definitely known when India took the lead in the quartz mineral industry, but when Duarte Barbosa, a Portuguese traveler, visited Limodra early in the sixteenth century, he found that city to be the center of a very profitable industry. In the story of his travels he states: "Here is found an agate rock which is white, milky, or red stone, which is made redder in the fire." This is probably the first recorded account of any artificial attempt to change the natural color of the agate. Barbosa also reported that he found much activity in the cutting of the ornamental stones at Cambay. Soon after this, early in the seventeenth century, that city became the leading center for the cutting of agates. It is interesting to note that a considerable trade is still carried on from the same place, the material being readily obtained from the near-by Deccan traprock. Much of the semiprecious quartz mineral sold in Europe, outside of Germany, is exported from Cambay; and large quantities in the rough are shipped to China and Japan.

The organized mining of quartz minerals was probably first carried out about 3500 B.C. when the early Egyptians mined rock crystal north of Assuan and amethyst near Gebel Abu Diyeiba, and collected agates from the surrounding desert areas. By 500 B.C. agates had become an article of commerce among the Arabians, and it is possible that about this time the industry began in India, where good material could be easily obtained that had weathered from the igneous rocks. In 300 B.C. agates were being collected along the Achates River in Sicily, and for many years prior to the Christian era the Swiss Alps were the source of supply for quartz crystals for the Romans. Thus, like salt, gold, and silver, the quartz minerals became a medium of exchange value at a very remote period in ancient history. More recently, we find the aborigines of America bartering flint and chert with other tribes, the Far Western Indians exchanging agate and obsidian with the plains Indians for buffalo hides, which were greatly prized.

CUTTING AND SHAPING QUARTZ

Centuries ago, the cutting of quartz minerals reached a very high state of perfection, even without the aid of modern tools and abrasives. Advantage was taken of any figure or design seen in the stone, particularly if it had some religious significance. Such stones were highly prized. During the Roman period, the banded varieties of jasper were much used for cameos. Many specimens of the Roman cameos now adorn the collections of Europe and America. Some of them exhibit great skill and workmanship. In one instance, the lapidary, by taking advantage of the different colored layers, cut a piece showing the head of a warror in red, his helmet in green, and his breastplate in yellow. Some fine portraits of the Roman emperors were cut in this stone; a likeness of Nero and a head of Minerva, now in the Vatican museum, are considered the finest intaglios in existence. In that same collection, there are also two notable vases made of remarkably beautiful jasper; one is cut from a bright-red variety that is crossed by white veins, and the other from black jasper that is crisscrossed by fine yellow lines.

Seals and intaglios were early cut in designs very difficult to execute, and for this a small splinter of diamond was used as a tool. Diamond powder also was employed to charge the points of soft metal tools for engraving quartz. Probably the most painstaking work of all was done on the delicate vases, goblets, cups, and plates, carved from solid, single crystals of quartz or amethyst. Some of these goblets were eight inches or more in depth, the outside being embellished with elaborate engravings. The story handed down to us is that these cups of amethyst were used to deceive a nobleman, when "in his cups." The goblet was filled with water, but the purple color would lend the illusion of wine.

The task of hollowing out a quartz crystal or a mass of agate is no simple matter, even with the aid of modern tools; yet this task was accomplished at a very early time. It is said that the emperor Nero had two large goblets carved from crystal quartz and engraved with subjects from the "Iliad," which cost an enormous sum to produce. In a fit of fury, Nero dashed these works of art to fragments.

In the eighth century, the rock crystal deposits in the province of Mutsu, Japan, were first developed on a commercial scale. The Japanese generally worked the material into spheres of various sizes; the smaller ones were carried about in the hand in hot weather to cool the body, while the larger ones, possessing more mystical properties, were reserved for religious purposes.

The noted agate industry of the Idar-Oberstein center in Germany had its beginning about 1497 and has continued to the present day. For many years, the industry used agates gathered in the immediate territory; but as it became more difficult to secure the needed material near at home, agates were brought from other countries. Practically all the agates now cut in that district are obtained from several South American localities, where the deposits were first discovered by a German in 1576 but remained undeveloped until 1827, when the German fields became practically exhausted. While the industry was primarily developed in the Idar district to cut agates, it has subsequently turned to the working up of other soft gem minerals. Through the work of the Institute for Precious Stone Research, located at Idar, not only has the matter of coloring been successfully worked out, but also many semiprecious stones are being synthesized and worked up in the district.

AGATE BIRTHSTONE FOR JUNE

As agate is the birthstone for June, the gem has special favor among those born in that month. Moss agates appear to be particularly popular and are widely sold, mounted in rings of either silver or gold. Cut stones showing clear-cut or odd scenes are classed as "fancy" stones and often bring a high premium. A moss agate of this quality may bring as high a price as $100 or more, while an inferior example is generally not worth much more than the cost of cutting and selling. Owing to the fact that the black types of moss are more plentiful, these are the kinds generally seen in shops, but the fancy-colored varieties are rapidly coming into popularity. Agate is hard and tough, wears well when carried in a ring, and justly deserves its universal popularity. Its relatively low price makes it available to all.

THE BIBLICAL QUARTZ GEMS

In the Bible, there are numerous references to the quartz gems. Many of the stones are still held in religious reverence,

18

today. Only a few of the references are given here. Due acknowledgement is made, for much of the information given here, to Dr. Rolland Butler, a San Diego minister. The collection of Biblical gem stones and minerals made by Dr. Butler received the gold medal at the California International Exposition of 1935. The collection is on exhibition in Balboa Park Museum, San Diego.

The Biblical story of gem stones begins in the second chapter of the first book of the Bible, with the mention of bdellium (probably opal) and the onyx stone, in the Land of Havilah, just outside of the Garden of Eden. In Revelation, Chaps. XXI and XXII, we read a glorious description of the Holy City, the New Jerusalem, with walls of solid jasper and streets of gold. Between the first and last chapters of the Bible, a total of 1,704 references are made to gem stones and minerals, under 124 different Hebrew and Greek names. A number of these stones are minerals of the quartz family.

Seemingly, there were many gem-mineral localities in the Garden of Eden. The Holy Spirit, in describing the glory of this dominion, states: "Thou hast been in Eden, the garden of God; every precious stone was thy covering, the sardius (carnelian), topaz, diamond, beryl, onyx, jasper, sapphire, emerald, carbuncle (garnet and sard), and gold."

In the Bible we read a fascinating account of the directions given to the High Priest for a marvelous breastplate he must wear: "And thou shall set in it settings of stones, even four rows of stones; the first row shall be a sardius, a topaz and a carbuncle. And the second row shall be an emerald, a sapphire and a diamond; and the third row a ligure, an agate and an amethyst. And the fourth row a beryl, and an onyx and a jasper." Thus, of the twelve cut stones in the breastplate of the High Priest, at least half were of the quartz family, counting the two onyx gems which were attached to the chain of pure gold by which the large plate was suspended over the neck. In all probability, the quartz gems were in Biblical times the most plentiful of all gems, even as they are in our own time.

REPRESENTATIVE MINERALS OF QUARTZ FAMILY
Top row (from left): Chalcedony, quartz crystal group, and smoky quartz crystal.
Center: Group of amethyst crystals. Bottom: Geode, "eye" agate, and quartz enclosing rutile. (*Photograph, Ward's Establishment of Natural Science.*)

The Historical Lore of Quartz

The stones of the breastplate were all engraved with the names of the tribes of the Children of Israel, like the engravings of a signet. The significant feature about the breast-plate is the amazing fact that the individual gem stone chosen by God to represent the individual tribe bore within the very nature of that stone itself the nature of the tribe it represented. Thus, these twelve gems held considerable religious meaning at that time.

In the description of the city of New Jerusalem (Rev. XXI: 19–27), the Bible goes into the realm of gems and minerals, with those of the quartz family taking a conspicuous part. The foundations of the wall of the city were garnished with all manner of precious stones. The first foundation was jasper; the second, sapphire; the third, chalcedony; and so on down, including emerald, sardonyx, sardius, chrysoprase, jacinth, and amethyst. Again, the quartz minerals appear to be given a prominent part.

TABLE OF BIBLICAL QUARTZ GEMS

Scriptural References	Biblical Name	Modern
Isaiah 54:12	Agate	Agate
Revelation 21:20	Amethyst	Amethyst
Genesis 2:12	Bdellium	Opal
Revelation 21:19	Chalcedonius	Chalcedony
Revelation 21:20	Chrysoprasus	Chrysoprase
Revelation 21:20	Chrysoprasus	Citrine
Revelation 4:6	Crystal	Quartz Crystal
Deuteronomy 8:15	Flint	Flint
Revelation 21:11	Jasper	Jasper (Jade)
Exodus 28:19	Ligure	Opal (Zircon)
Genesis 2:12	Onyx	Onyx
Revelation 4:3	Sardine	Carnelian
Revelation 4:3	Sardius	Sard

The above Biblical references are not complete but include some of the principal ones, as given in the work of Dr. Rolland Butler.

CHAPTER III

The Way to Quartz

"One enjoys the mountains more after having come a long way o'er dreary plains to find them—the plains can only be fully appreciated when we consider them as the foundation of mountains."

Our secret ambition in discussing the broad subject of quartz is to build a word picture so realistic that the reader will never again look upon the mineral as a cold, inanimate object; but, that he may come, rather, to think of it as a lifelong friend and acquaintance; for, wherever one may roam throughout the wide world, he is apt to contact quartz on every hand.

Already, far more has been written about the subject than about any other mineral species, yet it is a question whether the facinating story of quartz will ever be completely told. With these few preliminary remarks, let us be off across the plains on our journey toward the "mountains of quartz." On our way we shall first pause to consider nature's workshop.

NATURE'S WORKSHOP

It is not our purpose to speculate freely upon the primordial condition of the earth. However, when considering any important mineral family representing a considerable portion of the earth's crust, we must go back a long way toward the beginning to select a suitable starting point. Sufficient time must be allotted to provide for the numerous and sometimes highly complicated chemical reactions which have entered into the production of the vast quartz world as it exists today.

It has been truly said that the bank of time is inexhaustible, and the geologist has drawn heavily upon it in attempting to solve nature's riddles. Somewhere, then, along the line of our retroactive thinking, we must stop and drive a peg, or put our finger on a certain spot and say, "For our present investigation we shall begin *here*." But, in so doing, we must be able to make correct assumptions, supported by strict reasoning and the best information available. To do this is not always an easy matter, and in preparation we must attempt to place ourselves in the proper mental attitude to view in correct perspective all the various phenomena which are involved in the natural processes.

We must early recognize the fact that the earth is actually a gigantic chemical laboratory, working with natural forces and materials, ceaselessly, and in devious manners, to accomplish her ultimate ends. Dealing with enormous quantities of raw materials, nature's processes are seldom hurried, and they are not always continuous. She is not particular or over-fastidious, but takes into her maw the gist of such material as may come along and makes of it whatever she may. She has no special orders to fill. If for some reason the inflow ceases, she just suspends operations until conditions become more favorable. There are no pay rolls to be met. If a quartz crystal was in the making, she simply begins over again where she left off, and probably a phantom crystal, or one containing several phantoms, may result. If in the interim some accident may have befallen the product of her previous endeavor, in some uncanny manner she goes about promptly to repair the damage to the original crystal before proceeding to build again.

We must also realize that Mother Nature has at her command all the essentials of the most modern laboratory, although perhaps they are not so evident to the untrained eye. These include innumerable chemical reagents in solution, both acid and alkali, as well as an abundance of ground water, the most important solvent and catalyst of all. She also employs organic agencies, and, in addition, tremendous natural temperatures and pressures, such as until quite recently man has never even been able to approach. Supported by the forces of vulcanism, nature works with such tremendous resources and masses as to utterly stagger the imagination. It is difficult to realize the amount of material which may be brought into solution and transported under high temperatures, and the extreme penetrating power of exceedingly high pressures, such as must always prevail deep within the bowels of the earth.

THE GENESIS OF QUARTZ

The elements, of which there are some ninety or more, have been very cleverly called nature's building blocks. They are the fundamental materials out of which everything is made, including all organic and inorganic chemical compounds. This, of course, means our entire mineral kingdom.

No one is aware how, when, or where these elements were first formed, as nature has not yet chosen to reveal that secret to mere man, and surely, this is not the proper place or time to discuss cosmology. Therefore, like the wise men of old, we must simply pass by such basic and fundamentally interesting questions as where the oxygen and silicon entering into the make-up of quartz first originated, by stating that they were "created in the beginning." Someone has facetiously said, that the universe is made up of "star dust," and perhaps no one has yet evolved a more reasonable or expressive explanation. In the beginning, this matter must have been very widely diffused throughout the universe and highly attenuated.

Somehow, in obedience to natural forces, great masses of that star-dust became segregated into regions of definite limit. One of these was eventually to become the nucleus of our present order. It was long thought that the birth of all elemental matter took place before it became segregated into solar aggregates. We must, however, now modify these older ideas somewhat, in the light of more recent discoveries respecting the slow disintegration or stepping down of certain types of elements known as the radioactive series. In general, though, we may yet safely state that the present pattern of the elements has probably endured since the beginning of time. They are the result of mathematical laws, and fundamental mathematical concepts do not change.

Came the dawn of our solar system. This important event occurred at a period so remote that no one may safely hazard a guess as to when it actually happened. Doubtless most of the material of our present solar system was first gathered into one great original central body. Gravity may account for that. Next, in some yet largely speculative manner, disruptive forces were at work, and numerous smaller masses of material became separated from the parent nucleus. Later, these condensed or concentrated to form our planetary system and the numerous other members of the sun's large family. Therefore, we may safely say that all the substance of the earth, including the quartz materials, came to us indirectly out of the great original universal mass of matter, and that all of it, excepting possibly a negligible amount of cosmic meteoric accretion, has been inherited directly by way of the sun. None can really doubt that the sun was actually the "mother" of the planets.

Spectroscopic evidence indicates all elements existing throughout space to be the same. Their state and density, however, must vary greatly according to their location. No less than forty of the total number of the elements have been positively identified in the sun's atmosphere, where, due to intense heat (7000°C. to 8000°C.) they must exist largely as white-hot gases. There is no evidence that the sun was ever materially cooler than at present, and it is entirely probable, then, that at the time the earth matter was wrested from it, it was actually hotter, and the silicon and oxygen which are now so intimately associated in the great quartz and silicate families of the earth were then entirely uncombined or un-related elements, each existing as gases in its own free or native state.

Eventually, a stage arrived in the history of our embryonic earth when it had sufficiently cooled to permit the chemical combination of certain elemental substances to form more or less stable compounds. These later became the primary materials out of which was slowly evolved our present complex and highly diversified mineral world. Just what first took place and in what chronological order the principal events occurred are obviously cosmological secrets concerning which we know little. In due course of time, however, a period must have arrived when conditions were favorable for the combination of the elements silicon and oxygen, on a superlatively grand scale. The reactions involving silicon and oxygen, in view of the great abundance of these elements, doubtless began early in the cooling process and must have continued progressively over an exceedingly long period of time; even today, in a feeble way, these processes must still be going on, as the two elements combine spontaneously at surprisingly low temperatures.

The fact must not be overlooked that, simultaneously with quartz building, hundreds of other important integrating reactions were taking place, and that the entire world-building process was one of utmost complexity. Contemplation of the great primeval tempest which must have prevailed upon the earth's surface overwhelms our intellect as much today as it did in times past when man first gave serious thought to the problems of creation. We cannot carry this line of thought further, however, until we have considered some of the chemical and physical properties of the building blocks out of which quartz is formed.

Quartz Building Blocks. We shall pause here long enough to examine more closely the nature of the two elements which enter into such very intimate chemical association in forming quartz, usually spoken of by chemists as silica. An element has been defined as a substance which is composed of nothing but itself. In other words, it cannot ordinarily be further divided or refined into any other substance. Each element has its own set of physical and chemical properties by means of which it may be readily identified, and so we are not surprised to learn that elements are individualistic and, like people, they may have personality. When they are dealing with elements, we constantly hear chemists speaking in terms of atoms. Some atoms, like helium, are lazy or inert and hold themselves aloof from chemical combinations, while others, like oxygen, are always busy and active uniting with atoms of other elements to form compounds.

An atom is the smallest physical portion into which any element can be divided and yet maintain all of its natural properties. It is represented by a symbol—either a capital or a two-letter abbreviation which stands for the element. Thus Si is the symbol for the element silicon, while O stands for oxygen. The atom has significance in many ways, as when elements unite in forming chemical compounds they always combine in either the ratio of their combining (atomic) weights, or of simple multiples of these weights.

The elements may be divided electrochemically into one of two groups; those which are electropositive or those which are electronegative. When forming chemical unions, an electropositive element must combine with one which is electronegative. Elements also possess different valances, which implies that they have different combining strengths; thus, a single atom of any quadrivalent element such as silicon, being electropositive may react with and hold in chemical combination two atoms of any electronegative bivalent atom, such as oxygen. The resultant binary chemical compound, silicon dioxide, known throughout the mineralogical world as quartz, therefore, carries the formula SiO_2, which represents not only the elements present but their correct atomic proportions. The smallest imaginable part of any chemical compound which may exist and yet possess all of the chemical and physical properties of a substance is called the molecule. It is expressed by the letters of the formula; thus, SiO_2 represents a single molecule of quartz. The *molecule*, therefore, bears the same analogous relationship to the compound that the *atom* does to the element.

Oxygen reveals its existence in the sun's atmosphere by the presence of a bright line in the blue (0.4642 micron) portion of the spectrum. It was first isolated as a terrestrial element by

Priestley in 1774. Its atomic number is 8, and its atomic weight is 16.0. It may be liquified at a temperature of $-182.7°C$., and solidified into oxygen ice at $-218°C$. In its ordinary gaseous state it is slightly heavier (1.1053) than air, and in its liquid state it is 1.13 heavier than water. Gaseous oxygen is colorless, odorless, and tasteless, although in its liquid and solid states it exhibits a pale-blue color. As a liquid or a solid it is slightly magnetic. It will combine with all elements except the inert gases of the atmosphere, and fluorine and bromine. The word comes from the Greek; a liberal translation is "acid former." This name reveals one of the most important chemical properties of oxygen, and may give the reason why the SiO_2 molecule behaves as an acidic radical when passing into combinations to form the multitude of silicate rocks and minerals with which we are all more or less familiar.

On the other hand, the word "silicon" comes from the Latin word "silex," meaning flint. It is identified by two prominent lines in the ultraviolet (0.2516 and 0.2881 micron) end of the spectrum. Silicon is never found free in nature on earth, but is always combined with some other element, most often with oxygen. For this reason, unless perchance one has procured a sample for his collection of elements, he will have to visit some museum or laboratory to view silicon. It is a nonmetallic element, which is grouped chemically with boron; but in its chemical affinities it bears a striking resemblance to carbon. It exists in three allotropic forms—an amorphous brown powder, a graphitoidal or semicrystalline form, and a crystalline variety. The amorphous form may be obtained by passing chloride of silicon over potassium heated in a bulbed test tube. When heated, it becomes darker and denser, is a conductor of electricity, and burns readily and brilliantly in air. When crystalized, it forms black needles which belong to the hexagonal system. These may be prepared by dissolving its amorphous form in molten zinc at a temperature slightly less than its boiling point. When cooled, the mass will contain crystalline silicon, which may be removed by dissolving the zinc in a solution of dilute hydrochloric (HCl), or other acids.

Silicon has a specific gravity of 2.42. Its atomic number is 14, and its atomic weight is 28.06. It melts at 1420°C., but its boiling point is about 3500°C. The amorphous form does not dissolve in any acid except hydrofluoric, but it dissolves readily in hot potassium hydroxide to form a silicate. The crystalline variety is very hard and is but little affected by hydrofluoric acid or potassium hydroxide, and cannot be burned. Silicon forms compounds with many elements, including fluorine, with which it will unite at ordinary temperatures. It will unite with oxygen at 400°C., with chlorine at 430°C., with bromine at 500°C., with sulphur at 600°C., with nitrogen at about 1000°C., and with carbon and boron only at the temperatures produced by the electric furnace. Next to oxygen, it is the most common element, being first isolated by Berzelius in 1823. It is the essential element in nearly all of the important rocks except the carbonates. As a soluble silica, it exists in all ocean, river, and ground waters, large deposits being formed from volcanic waters in the form of siliceous sinter. In the entire inorganic world, silicon is the predominant element almost to the same extent as carbon is in the organic realm.

Now that we seem to have been properly introduced to the elements entering into the make-up of quartz, let us consider further the reason why these two elements team up so readily, or, shall we say, putting the question a bit more scientifically, why the elements silicon and oxygen possess *such great chemical affinity for each other*. The matter of chemical affinity is one of atomic structure, which obviously is the controlling factor. It would be entirely impossible fully to consider this subject here; we must, therefore, assume the student's willingness to pursue this line of investigation independently if he wishes or chooses to learn more about it. However, it will not be out of place for us to make a simple, brief statement of the well-known essential facts surrounding the problem. Perhaps it will spur some reader on to greater interest and research.

Should anyone care to read further upon this vitally important subject of atomic structure, he would do well to consult Chap. IV, of George Letchworth English's admirable book, entitled "Getting Acquainted with Minerals." Here he will learn that an atom of any element, to be perfectly balanced or satiated, must possess eight electrons in its outermost shell. As the oxygen atom contains only six electrons in its outer shell, it lacks two electrons; while the atom of silicon, which contains only four electrons, lacks four of being completely balanced or satisfied. Inasmuch as each silicon atom has four electrons to lose, and each oxygen atom requires only two, each silicon atom can accommodate two oxygen atoms, and the chemical formula for the new compound thus formed is SiO_2. Using a rather homely illustration, we might liken the reaction to a regular "he" man's acquiring twin sisters for wives and living happily together ever afterward. This chemical union or reaction completes what appears to be an ideal or a perfect electronic arrangement; it cannot, therefore, be easily broken down. So we are constantly speaking of the quartz molecule (SiO_2) as being a very stable compound, and indeed, it must be admitted that our whole experience with the mineral quartz supports this assumption.

QUARTZ PREDOMINANT

Just why quartz should be one of the most predominant minerals is a question which has doubtless perplexed the minds of many students of mineralogy. We are told upon good authority that, in its various forms, free quartz composes approximately 12 per cent of the earth's outer shell. This is nearly one-eighth of the total substance. Consulting Frank Wigglesworth Clarke's incomparable reference work, "Data of Geochemistry" we find that this estimate is not merely guesswork, but the result of careful analysis made after an extensive and painstaking sampling of all the material of the outer lithosphere (the rock earth).

About the beginning of the present century, a number of scientists conducted an extensive investigation, attempting to ascertain the relative abundance of the elements, during which they brought together all available information and previous analyses bearing upon this subject. A. Harker accounted for

30

some 526 analyses from British localities, H. S. Washington some 1,811 analyses of material from all parts of the world, and Clarke made and checked nearly 2,500 analyses of material, also from widely scattered sources. The close correlation between the work of these men, operating independently, was astounding. The results left little doubt concerning the actual validity of their findings, and subsequent investigation has not materially altered their conclusions. Among other things, it was learned that the average composition of the igneous rocks taken alone was very nearly that of the average composition of the entire lithosphere. In fact, to include, as well, the materials of the hydrosphere (water) and the atmosphere did not perceptibly change the figures.

By examination of the following list it will be noted that the eight most common elements make up more than 98 per cent of the total material of the earth's crust—(based on standard assumption for the outer 10 miles of thickness).

Element	Symbol	Igneous Rocks, per cent	All Rocks, per cent
1. Oxygen	O	47.05	47.17
2. Silicon	Si	28.26	28.00
3. Aluminum	Al	7.98	7.84
4. Iron	Fe	4.47	4.44
5. Magnesium	Mg	2.34	2.27
6. Calcium	Ca	3.43	3.42
7. Sodium	Na	2.54	2.43
8. Potassium	K	2.50	2.49
Total		98.57	98.06

It seems unbelievable, though nevertheless true, that the two elements entering into the quartz molecule, make up 75 per cent of the surface material of the earth. Just why nature was so generous in allotting these two particular elements and apparently so stingy with others may always remain one of the mysteries. Perhaps there is a good enough reason if we could but fathom it. With these figures in mind, it is not hard to see where all the silica of the world comes from, when we remember that silicon and oxygen are per-

Quartz Family Minerals

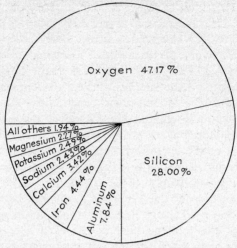

Percentage graph. The eight most common elements of the earth's crust.

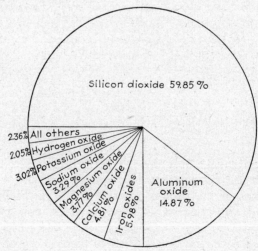

Percentage graph. The eight most common compounds of the earth's crust.

fectly compatible elements, combining at temperatures as low as 400°C.

Let us now examine what disposition nature has made of these elements. Understanding the unbounded activity of oxygen and its ability to combine readily with almost all other elements, we are not surprised to learn that, when temperatures upon the cooling earth became favorable, it went about uniting chemically with almost everything in sight, the resultant compounds being the various oxides. Considering the fact that nearly half (47 per cent) of the earth's substance is oxygen, there was enough of it to satisfy all of the remaining 53 per cent which was so constituted atomically that it could react with it, thereby forming not only the greater portion of the earth's solid substances but the water as well. After these requirements were met, there still remained enough free oxygen to form almost 21 per cent of the atmosphere (20.99 at sea level).

In her laboratory, as we have before intimated, nature works with the law of supply rather than with that of demand, yet, strangely enough, most of man's legitimate needs have been amply provided for in a manner which seems wholly providential. When we look to see what she has made, we find that the eight most important chemical compounds all are oxides of various kinds, silicon first and then the various metals (bases) in following rank:

Compound	Formula	Igneous Rocks, per cent	Lithosphere, per cent
1. Silicon dioxide	SiO_2	59.93	59.85
2. Aluminum oxide	Al_2O_3	14.97	14.87
3. { Ferric oxide	Fe_2O_3	2.58	2.63
{ Ferrous oxide	FeO	3.42	3.35
4. Magnesium oxide	MgO	3.85	3.77
5. Calcium oxide	CaO	4.78	4.81
6. Sodium oxide	Na_2O	3.40	3.29
7. Potassium oxide	K_2O	2.99	3.02
8. Hydrogen oxide	H_2O (water)	1.94	2.05
Total		97.86	97.64

Here again we observe that among the eight most common chemical combinations making up almost 98 per cent of the earth's outer crust, silica holds a predominating position at the top of the list, composing the amazing total of nearly 60 per cent of the whole amount. We have previously stated that free quartz, SiO_2, makes up only 12 per cent, so we must examine the picture still further to learn what may have become of the remaining 48 per cent. It is a law of chemistry that acids always react with bases (alkalies) to form salts, which are neutral in character, that is, neither acidic nor basic.

The nature of silica (SiO_2) is plainly acidic, while that of the metallic oxides of the eight most common natural compounds is basic, and thereby hangs a matter of momentous importance. Just as oxygen went about satisfying all demands made upon it by the oxide-forming elements, so the SiO_2 radical likewise went about in its turn to unite with these basic radicals to effect their complete neutralization, forming chemical mineral "salts," which are known as silicates. So abundant was the original quantity of silica in the beginning, that after all possible demands which nature made upon it had been supplied, there yet remained a great surplus uncombined with any other mineral or element. So numerous and important are the minerals of the great silicate family, that Crooks says they constitute nine-tenths of the mass of the earth's crust. As a rock-forming mineral par excellence, it becomes the chief builder of many great mountain ranges. Several hundred species of silicate minerals are known to exist, of which some are highly prized as gems. Others are useful as minerals from which are obtained valuable chemical and other commercial products. Most of the minerals of the silicate group possess complex chemical formulas—some of them highly complex:

Wollastonite	$CaSiO_3$
Orthoclase	$KAlSi_3O_8$
Hornblende	$Ca(MgFe)_3(SiO_3)_4 \cdot CaMg_2Al_2(SiO_4)_3$
Pholidolite	$5H_2O \cdot K_2O \cdot 12(Fe, Mg)O \cdot Al_2O_3 \cdot 13SiO_2$

We present the above series of formulas of typical silicates so that our readers may see and realize for themselves the manner in which silica has entered into and become locked up in the molecular structure of all such minerals. This accounts readily for the problem as to where all the vast quantity of the earth's silica may be stored.

There is yet another important reason for our emphasizing here the nature of the silicates and speaking of it in considerable detail. As will be shown later, from this great class of minerals is derived much of the supply of soluble silica from which have been produced the enormous quantities of secondary quartz in all of its numerous forms. A full consideration of these varieties and subvarieties is to form the central theme for later chapters of the book. Free quartz alone, being only slightly soluble in water, never could possibly have furnished the enormous amount of silica required to account for all the vast areas of silicification existing in the states of our own Pacific Northwest, to say nothing of other parts of the world, which have been accumulating almost since the beginning of time.

It will be noted, at the bottom of the list of the most common oxides of the earth's crust, that there is one which is neither acidic or basic. That is the oxide of hydrogen, better known as water—aqua pura. It is, without doubt, nature's most important mineral substance and chemical compound. Silica does not react chemically, either directly or indirectly, with water (the universal solvent) but it does dissolve (slightly) in it; then, under proper conditions, through concentration, it again becomes a solid mineral substance. In so doing, the silica (SiO_2) sometimes incorporates into its molecule an additional molecule of water (H_2O) to form an entirely new substance. While in some few ways it resembles quartz and chalcedony, in others it exhibits definite and considerable differences. Its formula is written thus, $SiO_2 \cdot H_2O$, representing a new mineral in which the molecule of water it holds is spoken of as being water of crystallization. This alludes only to the manner in which the water is incorporated into the molecular structure and not to the mineral itself, which is strictly amorphous and has no crystal forms. Mineralogists sometimes speak of it as hydrated silica, but to the gemmologist it is known as opal. More light will be thrown upon this phenomenon in the special chapter upon that gem.

THE CHARACTER OF QUARTZ

It will, perhaps, prove profitable for us at this time to examine further some of the reasons why the mineral quartz is so admirably qualified to fit into the major role nature has allotted to it in the great rock-building process of the earth, in which we meet it on every hand. We shall, however, touch only on those broad general properties which are applicable to all the numerous varieties of the mineral. Such special properties as belong to the individual varieties will not be mentioned here.

To begin with, all the varieties of quartz may be divided into two great classes: (1) the crystalline, and (2) the amorphous; those which possess definite internal molecular structure, and those which do not. Both forms possess certain properties in common. The first, and perhaps the most important, is their chemical and physical stability, as quartz is practically insoluble in acids, although it may be dissolved readily in certain alkaline solutions. This, with its physical hardness of seven (7), on the Moh's scale, is sufficient to enable it to withstand successfully most of the ordinary agencies of weathering. Thus the processes of disintegration and erosion are greatly retarded. Owing to the fact that its silicon atom already holds all of the oxygen it desires, quartz does not readily oxidize when exposed to the ordinary weathering agencies. It has one of the highest melting points of all the common minerals, 1600°C. Thus it is enabled to resist all ordinary temperatures existing upon the earth's surface. Only the internal heat of intense vulcanism can possibly reduce it to a molten condition.

The specific gravity of quartz varies with different sub-species, and also with different samples of the same variety. The purest quartz (rock crystal) has a specific gravity of 2.69, while other varieties range from 2.5 to 2.8, with a mean specific gravity of 2.65, which is that usually given in the texts. This rather wide range in gravity may be accounted for by varying quantities and types of included impurities, as well as by variations in its physical density or compactness. Porosity and microscopic vesicles of air or other occluded substances also have their effect upon the gravity. Quartz does not ordinarily exhibit cleavage, and most varieties break with a marked conchoidal (shell-like) fracture. This is one of its most distinguishing characteristics. One of the most unusual properties of quartz is its ability to give off empyreumatic or ozonic odors, when two pieces are struck together with a sharp blow. Its hardness is such as to enable it to strike sparks with steel— a property which has made possible one of its most important benefactions to mankind, the introduction of the common use of fire. This same property gave rise to the invention of the flint-lock gun, which marked the beginning of the modernization of firearms.

While the formula of the quartz molecule would indicate it to be definitely acidic, in its common forms and under ordinary conditions of temperature and pressure it is, on the contrary (perhaps due to the great physical stability of its molecule), usually passive so far as its chemical action is concerned. There is, however, at the base of the chalk formation at Farnham, England, a large bed of quartz that is actively acidic. If slaked lime is mixed with it in a thin paste and allowed to remain for a few weeks, a silicate of lime is formed, the action of which may be promoted by the addition of 2 or 3 per cent of carbonate of soda.

Quartz enters into and performs a variety of functions in the organic world; it forms the substance of the skeleton or framework of diatoms and the spicules of sponges. To the former are attributed whole massive formations of diatomite (infusorial earth), and both have contributed in no small manner to the growth and formation of cherts, flints, and related subspecies. Silica also gives firmness to the stalks of grasses and to the stems of trees. It is quartz on which we cut our fingers when we draw grass blades quickly through them. Quartz also forms the external coat of certain species of reeds, known as the "equisetums" and furnishes them with a surface sufficiently rough to serve admirably for rubbing, polishing, and scouring uses. Our great-great-grandmothers found nothing more to their liking for brightening up their choicest pewter ware— a purpose for which these reeds were very highly prized. In the stems of common grains, such as wheat and oats, there is so much that when stacks of the straw are burned large masses of highly siliceous cinders are sometimes formed about their margin.

It is assumed that our readers are already fairly familiar with tests commonly applied in sight identification of quartz, which is one of the easiest of minerals to determine in this way. In fact, a collector of any experience soon reaches the stage where he seems to recognize most of the forms of quartz almost intuitively. Every text and reference book contains material which need not be repeated here. However, by way of recapitulation, we shall state that any mineral which possesses a glassy to waxy lustre, which has average gravity when hefted, which breaks with a conchoidal to subconchoidal fracture, and which will scratch glass easily but cannot be scratched in turn by the sharp point of the blade of a good steel pocketknife, is most likely to be quartz.

QUARTZ—THE GEOLOGIC THERMOMETER

Over twenty years ago, Dr. Esper S. Larsen, of Harvard University, a noted petrographer, referred to quartz as a "geologic thermometer." Hence, a study of the origin and deposition of quartz has led to numerous important conclusions in the field of geology, mineralogy, and ore deposits. The many modifications of quartz occurring in nature can, with very few exceptions, now be prepared by simple laboratory methods. Various silica solutions, when treated with strong acids, undergo decomposition and yield gelatinous masses which, upon drying, become virtually identical with some of the natural forms of silica observed in the field.

Many laboratory experiments and investigations have been made regarding the artificial preparation of quartz, chalcedony, and the higher temperature forms of silica-opal, tridymite, and cristobalite. A solution of colloidal silica heated in a Papin digester will yield a crystalline quartz. Temperature, pressure, and the presence of other chemical reagents will exert their influence on the variety of quartz obtained. Exceptionally fine, doubly-terminated, clear crystals of quartz were obtained by one scientist, when magnesium ammonium chloride and sodium metasilicate and water were heated for three days in a steel bomb at 450°C.

In addition to the various wet methods by which quartz minerals can be produced in the laboratory, dry means have also been employed with equal success. Quartz may be transformed into tridymite by heat treatment, while simple fusion of crystal quartz yields only an amorphous, glasslike mass. Quartz glass has been transformed into crystallized quartz by heating it in the presence of alkaline chloride vapors to a temperature of 700°C. Above 800°C. and below 1000°C., tridymite is formed. However, the fact that various forms of quartz can be produced without the intervention of water does not necessarily mean that this method is largely utilized in nature; in all probability, water is generally an important factor in the great laboratory of the master architect.

It has also been proved that the different varieties of quartz are unstable at higher temperatures and will pass from one form to another. Experiments indicate that crystalline quartz is unstable at temperatures above 800°C. and that with favorable conditions it will pass into tridymite. Still higher temperatures (1200°C.) will frequently yield the highest temperature type of quartz—cristobalite.

Thus we see agate, chalcedony, and jasper deposited as low-temperature minerals, even at the temperature of percolating ground waters, crystal forms of quartz depositing at temperatures below 800°C., and tridymite and cristobalite still higher. Hence, a study of the form of quartz present in a rock or ore deposit yields information of considerable value and bearing on the nature of the deposition. While we have only touched on this important phase of the study of quartz, we can readily see the correctness of Dr. Larsen's assertion when he speaks of "quartz as the geological thermometer."

OPTICAL PROPERTIES OF QUARTZ

Optically speaking, quartz exists in two different modifications, which differ in their optical properties, and can be distinguished by the use of the petrographic (polarizing) microscope. The α (alpha) form of quartz exists only below 575°C.; above this temperature it passes into β (beta) quartz. Hence, at ordinary temperatures, all quartz is alpha quartz, but, if at any time it has been subjected to temperatures above the critical point, 575°C., this fact is recorded through a change in its optical properties and the manner in which "etch" figures appear when treated with hydrofluoric acid. In short, subjecting quartz to temperatures above 575°C., produces rearrangement of its molecular or atomic structure.

Quartz, in any rock, is generally considered to have formed at temperatures below 800°C., but its optical peculiarities will indicate whether crystallization took place above or below 575°C. Vein quartz and the huge crystals in pegmatite dikes generally form at lower temperatures, while the granitic quartz crystallizes at the higher points. Like crystal quartz, tridymite and cristobalite also exist in the alpha and beta modifications. Thus, optically, we recognize six forms of quartz. With the various known temperature factors, quartz well deserves very careful study on the part of the student for the light it is able to throw on the past history of the earth and the numerous factors to be considered concerning its formation.

As examined with the petrographic microscope, the various forms of quartz differ markedly. Dr. Larsen states in his book (*U. S. Geological Survey Bulletin* 848) that chalcedony is so finely crystallized (being intricately twinned), as to render studies of its optical properties difficult. He assigns a mean refractive index of 1.537 to chalcedony. Crystal quartz is always hexagonal, with refractive indices of 1.553 and 1.544. On the other hand, cristobalite may appear either isometric in crystallization, with a refractive index of 1.486, or tetragonal, with

40

slightly different indices. Tridymite may also exhibit anomalous refractive phenomena. The amorphous forms of quartz do not show dichrotic or twin colors when examined by the dichroscope, or with polarized light of the petrographic microscope. The colored varieties of crystal quartz, such as amethyst and citrine, show a distinct, although not strong, dichroism.

There are numerous rarer forms of quartz whose chief distinguishing properties are essentially optical, such as *Lussatite*, which has a structure like chalcedony, but the former is optically positive and has an index of refraction similar to opal. Lussatite may be a form of tridymite. Other rare forms are *Quartzine* and *Lutecite*, with optical properties also differing from those of "normal" quartz. *Asmanite* is the name given to a form of silica found in the *Breitenback* iron meteorite, in very minute grains, and is thought to be identical with tridymite. *Melanophlogite* occurs in minute cubes and spherical aggregates, found with calcite and celestite implanted upon an incrustation of opaline silica over the sulphur crystals of Girgenti, Sicily. It consists of SiO_2, with 5 to 7 per cent of SO_3 (Dana). However, Crook gives its formula as $SiO_2 \cdot O_3$, with Xl form *regular;* hardness, 6.5; specific gravity, 2.0; and describes it as being brown in color and in use for ornamental purposes.

ON THE COLOR OF QUARTZ

It will be noted that in our entire discussion or preview of the quartz family, the question of color and its causes has been studiously avoided. This is due to the fact that the entire subject of color, especially in regard to the crystalline varieties, seems at present to be so much "up in the air," that to make a positive, definite, or final statement of the matter would be neither possible nor desirable. There are several divergent opinions current, and one scarcely knows what to believe.

The older school of thought related color definitely to one of three causes:

1. Minute (even microscopic) included particles.

2. Something staining or impregnating the quartz, but not a part of it.

3. The natural chemical constituents of the quartz.

The number of elements to which we can turn as a possible cause of color in quartz is really quite small as compared with the total. The first three in the following table are the most important:

1. Iron (Fe). Ferrous, green; ferric, red, brown to black.
2. Chromium (Cr.) Chromic, green; acidic oxide, yellow to red.
3. Manganese (Mn). Manganous, pink; manganic, violet and black.
4. Titanium (Ti). Titanic, blue to violet.
5. Copper (Cu). Cuprous, red; cupric, blue to green.
6. Cobalt (Co). Red.
7. Nickel (Ni). Green.
8. Carbonaceous (organic) matter. Brown to black.

It was formerly taught that the color of most minerals could be accounted for by minute quantities of some one of the above list of color-producing elements, but as analytical methods became more and more refined and not even a trace of the expected mineral could ever be found in even the most deeply colored quartz, mineralogists finally came to the conclusion that in most quartz minerals they must look elsewhere for a satisfactory solution of the color phenomena.

Various other theories have been advanced; but the one most favored at the present time, is that color is an optical property and therefore of physical rather than chemical significance. The phenomenon, it is thought by some, is definitely related to radium, cosmic, or ultraviolet ray emana- tions. This is discussed fully under the topic, Amethyst. The question is at present far from being definitely settled, and the time seems ripe for some mineralogist to distinguish himself by following this matter through to its final conclusion, or in other words, to reduce theory to accepted facts.

CHAPTER IV

The Matter of Crystallization

HOW QUARTZ CRYSTALS FORM

Before proceeding to a more formal discussion of the crystalline varieties of quartz, a review of the more significant and commonly accepted facts concerning the true character and meaning of crystallization will prove helpful. We feel such preliminary exploratory investigation to be essential, as it will furnish our readers with a backlog of information, enabling them not only better to comprehend but also more fully to enjoy much of the material that is to be presented on the crystalline and other varieties of quartz in subsequent chapters.

To begin with, we shall touch upon some simple ideas concerning the physical aspect of the question. (1) All matter normally exists in one of three states—a solid, a liquid, or a gas. The condition in which any substance, either elemental or compound, is ordinarily found is called the normal state; thus, oxygen is normally a gas, while, on the other hand, silicon is a solid. (2) Any substance, regardless of its normal condition, may be changed physically into either of its other two states by altering its temperature or its pressure, or both.

The matter of crystallization, it is true, presents numerous perplexing problems, and while the average collector in the field soon learns, after some experience, to recognize by the nature of the adjacent rocks or soil the places where quartz crystals are most likely to be found, yet his actual ideas concerning their origin and manner of development are often vague and indefinite. Even mineralogists themselves do not

43

always agree upon all phases of the phenomenon of crystallization, but there are, nevertheless, many firmly established facts
and principles which we shall now attempt to present in
such a way that even a novice may readily understand and
appreciate them. To begin with, we shall review briefly the
various manners and conditions under which crystallization
of quartz may take place, and then continue later with a
somewhat more detailed discussion of crystallographic forms.

Sublimation. The first, and probably the most elementary
method, is that of sublimation. This also is by far the rarest, or
most uncommon, manner. It has long been known that certain
elements and compounds, such as iodine, arsenic, and sulphur,
as their temperature is increased, pass directly from the solid
state into a gaseous one, without going through the usual
intervening molten or liquid condition as do the great majority
of substances. Conversely, under rare or exceptional circumstances, upon the lowering of the temperature, the reversal
of this phenomenon occurs, and the gas, reaching its critical
temperature, will also crystallize or resolidify directly, without
passing through the usual intervening molten condition.
Sublimation seems to be one of the exceptions or curiosities
among natural phenomena, and to some it may at first appear
quite inconsistent with natural laws.

In the case of quartz, with its exceedingly high point of
fusion, this can happen in nature only under instances of
extreme vulcanism. That it does actually occur at times there
has been ample observational proof. That the intense internal
heat of the earth is further capable of dissociating the elements
of various mineral compounds, permitting them to reform
their chemical alignment, building strange and new minerals
about the vents of volcanoes, has also long been observed.
Indeed, almost all of these natural processes, involving among
others the mineral quartz, have now been duplicated by man
in modern physical laboratories (see reports, Data of Geochemistry Laboratory). It is known that this mode of crystallization may account for, or at least play some important part in,
the formation of certain of its less common varieties, known

to mineralogists as "high-temperature quartz," but since this manner of crystallization is doubtless the exception rather than the rule, we shall pursue our policy of giving more space to other, commoner methods, leaving this phase of the discussion to be taken up later under the subject of tridymite.

Fusion. The second method of crystallization occurs upon a slow cooling from a molten state. This is known as the pyrogenetic (heat-origin) method. In the case of quartz, the cooling must have taken place first at the time of the original congealing of the earth's outer crust. So long ago did this event occur, however, and so much of profound geological importance has happened since, that it is generally agreed that little or none of this original quartz (or, in its strictest sense, superprimary quartz) may now be actually found at any place upon the face of the globe. At many subsequent periods since that time, much of the earth's original crust, if not the whole, must have been remelted—most of it perhaps several times—either under the intense heat of vulcanism or upon the release of enormous internal pressures, to which all rock materials must be subjected at no very great distances beneath the earth's surface.

Whenever and wherever this remelting occurs, of course, all the material, of whatever nature, that may have existed within the area of fusion, becomes incorporated and mixed thoroughly into one great molten mass, known as the magma. The character of this magma is strictly heterogeneous, and in it all individual minerals lose their identity. While it is under this condition, there is also ample opportunity for a chemical rearrangement of elements and radicals, to form new chemical substances or minerals. We shall see later what takes place again upon its resolidification.

Under ordinary conditions (pressure), we may expect pure quartz or silica to become fused or melted to a viscous or semifluid state, at a temperature around 1600°C., and to become completely liquefied at 1700°C. When the material is impure or mixed with certain minerals acting as a fluxing agency, liquefaction may occur even at considerably lower tempera-

tures. Molten quartz has a density of 2.2 as compared with 2.65 in its solid state. This lighter density may have a tendency to segregate the quartz toward the top of the molten mass. This is an important consideration, as it helps us to account for the exceeding abundance of silica present in the upper or outermost layers of the earth's crust, as compared with the amount existing at much greater depth.

Upon further increase of the temperature, the quartz constituents of the magma may also become volatilized (converted to their gaseous state), at temperatures around 3600°C., and then even the resultant gaseous compound (SiO_2) must itself also break down, or become dissociated into its primary elements—oxygen and silicon—at temperatures which are actually much less than those prevailing upon the surface of the sun. Since this is as far as we can go in the direction of high temperature, let us now see what takes place when the order of these processes is reversed.

Conversely, as high temperatures gradually recede and cooling progresses, some of the gaseous atoms will once more unite (react) to form new SiO_2 molecules, which in turn will at the proper moment either sublime or condense into a liquid, finally congealing into their solid state. When their congealing temperature (which may be somewhat lower than the true melting point) is finally reached, one of two things may actually occur as this plunge from the liquid into the solid state takes place. (1) If the cooling be slow and other conditions be favorable, the individual molecules will arrange themselves in an orderly manner, row upon row, etc., into a definite structural pattern according to their own crystal character, gradually building up solids of symmetrical form, obeying nature's unalterable mathematical laws in their construction. It would seem almost as if they were following certain plans or blueprints prepared in the beginning of time by an inscrutable intellect. These symmetrical solids are called crystals, and the process of their formation is called crystallization. More will be said later upon the external and internal structure of crystals.

On the other hand, (2) if the cooling process be rapid or other conditions be unfavorable, no such evidence of special structure or form will obtain, and the solid mineral in this instance is said to be uncrystalline or amorphous (without form). Time is a necessary and important element in the formation of crystal structure. It is as though workmen engaged in the construction of a building were receiving material by truck. Given time, the unloaders upon receiving the bricks or blocks from the trucks will stack and arrange them neatly in piles of regular rows, whose linear dimensions would depend upon the amount of material, the space, and the circumstances under which it was corded. The angular dimensions of the pile, however, would be controlled by the shape and dimensions of the individual or component block. This illustration may logically represent our present accepted notion of the crystal structure of minerals.

Now let us see what might happen if the twelve o'clock whistle should blow at about the moment the truck arrived. The driver would quickly pull the endgate, dump the materials in a heap on the ground, and drive away. The substance in both of the two piles would be exactly the same, both physically and dimensionally, and their other properties and character would also be alike, yet it must be evident to all that the external and internal structure of the piles would not even remotely resemble each other. The former of the two would exhibit orderly structure as evidenced by the presence of cleavage and crystal form, while the other would be characterized by the absence of such properties (amorphous).

Igneous Quartz. The petrological significance of the two underlying principles above illustrated is as follows. Rocks which have been formed by the cooling of a molten magma are properly called the igneous (fire-formed) rocks, although they are sometimes spoken of as the "crystalline rocks," which in the strictest sense might be a misnomer. The igneous rock system is divided into two great classes, controlled by the nature of their cooling process: those which were cooled slowly beneath the surface, called the "intrusive" igneous

rocks, and those which were cooled rapidly on or near the surface, called "extrusive." The intrusive rocks are, as a rule, truly crystalline in character, while the extrusive ones, like obsidian, are amorphous. The reason for this must be evident to all who would give the matter careful consideration.

At this point we must digress, to explain a matter which as a rule sorely perplexes those who are studying the nature of crystalline rocks for the first time. Upon close examination of their crystalline structure, it will be observed that the many particles or crystals of the various minerals involved, such as feldspar, mica, and quartz (if the rocks be granitic), all appear to be compactly interwoven or even overlapping, each seeming to encroach upon the space occupied by the other. Further examination will reveal that there exists a definite pattern or order connected with the phenomenon, which would indicate that this arrangement is not all a matter of chance, but that the different masses were formed or crystallized according to some definite plan or system. As a matter of fact, that is exactly what has happened. Different minerals have individual congealing temperatures, each in turn crystallizing out of the slowly cooling magma at the moment its own appropriate temperature is arrived at, thus contributing to an orderly sequence of crystal growth which gives individual character to the various types of igneous rocks.

This is known as the law of paragenesis, and will account for such strange facts and observations as a perfect plate of mica apparently shot through with long crystals of tourmaline, and then the whole, perhaps, surrounded by compact masses of white, milky quartz. When viewed in the proper light, with the facts and principles above stated kept in mind, the matter is relieved of much of its mystery. In fact, all strange and peculiar natural phenomena invariably have a plausible explanation for anyone who has the training and inclination to seek their solution and possesses the patience required for careful research.

One of the prerequisites for the formation of perfect crystal growth is the presence of free or unoccupied openings in the

rocks, in which they may form unhampered. Obviously, this is not possible when masses of minerals are crowded together in insufficient space; consequently, those which form earliest are more nearly perfect, and those forming last, being compelled to occupy such intervening space as may remain and not having the opportunity to complete their crystal pattern, are most imperfect so far as their outward form is concerned. They are, nevertheless, crystalline in character and structure just as truly as are those with forms most beautiful and complete.

That much of the massive quartz formed through the agency of fusion is typically crystalline in character may be readily demonstrated in numerous ways. First, if such material is strongly heated, and then plunged quickly into cold water, its rapid contraction will cause it to fracture or cleave in definite planes which are parallel with or related to the crystallographic structure. This will not be true of amorphous quartz. An unusual variety known as "Lamellar" quartz has been found at Overbrooke and Howard House, Delaware County, Pennsylvania. It has also been called "cleavable" quartz, very good specimens in loose boulders of both the milky and the clear variety being found. Second, if the numerous tests (such as for hardness, density, cohesion, tenacity, elasticity, and thermal conductivity) applied to the material, reveal indications of perceptible variations in the nature of the physical properties of a crystalline substance as opposed to an amorphous one, it will be shown that these differences occur in close relation to the direction of the crystal axis, cleavage planes, and crystal faces. Third, if it is also noted that there is a marked difference in the optical properties of the crystalline and noncrystalline varieties of quartz, as is revealed by the ability to transmit light of the several wave lengths, also ultraviolet and X rays, in different directions through its structure, as well as by the manner of transmitting them, the crystalline material will present definite modifications as indicated by refraction and X-ray patterns which the amorphous form will not show. It is by this means that much of our knowledge is

gained concerning the true nature of the internal structure of crystals.

Solution. The third, and probably the most common and important, mode by means of which quartz crystals are formed, is their crystallization out of solution. One may ask, "By what inference do we draw this conclusion?" The answer is unmistakable; it is to be read on every hand. The nature and association of deposits of crystalline quartz make it self-evident. The presence of calcite, zeolites, and other minerals which are destroyed by even moderately high temperatures; the existence of coloring matters which disappear on gentle heating, in the quartz or the crystals themselves; the occurrence of corrosion figures—all these point unswervingly to the fact that quartz crystallization does occur at low temperatures and out of a water solution.

In the course of considering this form of crystal growth there are many things which must be borne in mind, such as the source of the silica and the manner in which it is brought into solution; the nature of the solution itself; the method and causes of precipitation and crystal formation; and, finally, the nature and origin of the cavities or places of deposition. All these things have direct bearing upon the question itself; we shall, therefore, take up discussion of them singly, each in its turn.

Just what is the source of the immense amount of silica which has been brought into solution and redeposited as crystalline quartz? Free quartz itself is insoluble to a high degree in most liquids, although it can be brought readily into solution in the presence of certain alkalies (potassium), especially when they are in a strongly heated condition. While such solvents are not uncommon in nature, they are not especially widespread in their distribution—most certainly, not to an extent comparable to the prodigal way in which quartz is scattered over the face of the earth; therefore, we must look for other and more likely sources to account for the enormous deposits which undoubtedly owe their origin to the soluble silicas.

The rocks exposed at the surface of the earth are continually undergoing alteration; or, as it is commonly expressed, are being attacked by the numerous agencies of weathering. Besides simple mechanical disintegration, a chemical change is taking place in nature's workshop, in which certain of their more complicated mineral constituents are constantly being broken down. It is a matter of quite common observation that feldspars are altered into clay and that the silicates and their derivatives are the most abundant and common of all the rocks in the earth's crust. This process is known as kaolinization, since kaolin (clay) is the by-product. The following comparatively simple case may be taken as the type of alteration for all other minerals with comparable chemical formulas.

$$2KAlSi_3O_8 + 2H_2O + CO_2 \rightarrow H_4Al_3Si_2O_9 + K_2CO_3 + 4SiO_2$$

Interpreted, this says: Orthoclase, when acted upon by water and carbon dioxide (carbonic acid), yields kaolin, potassium carbonate, and free silica.

The source of the carbon dioxide is twofold. (1) It exists at all times in the atmosphere, being the result of the oxidation of all carbonaceous matter; and (2) it is also released upon the decay of organic substances, both entering into the above reaction through the agency of ground water. Of the products, the kaolin is almost completely insoluble in water and remains behind as clay; the potassium carbonate dissolves in water; and the silicon dioxide, which is released from the reaction in a colloidal state, enters into an intimate relation with water differing somewhat from a true solution. A colloid is a substance which is only apparently dissolved in water, being really in a fine state of suspension, and which may be removed from the solution by dialysis; that is, it may be filtered out by means of animal membrane. While in this condition, the silica (SiO_2) colloid is often spoken of as silica gel. This name is doubtless derived from its appearance when in highly concentrated condition.

It must be remembered that this type of mineral disintegration is taking place not only on the earth's surface, although, to be sure it is most active there, but under normal conditions it may and does occur several hundred feet beneath the earth's surface—under exceptional cases, as much as or possibly more than half a mile down into the rocks. Accordingly, as the water slowly finds its way down through the feldspathic rocks, it picks up more and more colloidal silica as it descends. The farther downward it goes, the greater become the temperature and the pressure to which it is subjected. This, in turn, increases its carrying capacity. Finally, it eventually becomes so thoroughly saturated with the substance that it can absorb or carry no more. It is in this condition and by this means that the siliceous material may be transported to a considerable distance from its place of origin.

It is true also, that, in their downward movement, ground waters eventually reach a stage, down deep within the very "bowels" of the earth, where they must come in contact with the forces and agencies of vulcanism. By these associations their nature and even their properties are greatly changed, as they mingle with and dilute the *magmatic waters* derived from the cooling igneous magma. The work that they perform will be discussed more fully in later chapters in treating the subject of "areas of extensive silicification."

In studying the nature of solutions, we must soon learn that the *solute* dissolved in the *solvent* gives us the *solution*. With this definition of terms, we are prepared to carry our discussion further. When any liquid (solvent) has dissolved as much of any given solid (solute) as it can hold in solution, it is said to be *saturated*. Now, if such a solution is kept under constant conditions of temperature and pressure, amount of liquid and amount of foreign matter present in solution, it will neither take up additional solute nor deposit any of the solid that is in the solution. However, such perfectly stable conditions could never exist anywhere on the earth for any great length of time, as one of the first laws of nature is the law of change. That nothing is very permanent, especially respecting those natural solutions which are continually coursing their way through the earth's crust, is a foregone conclusion. Consequently, whenever those conditions are changed, even ever so slightly, the solution becomes unbalanced and will tend either to dissolve more solid or to become supersaturated, depositing some of its dissolved substance out of the solution. The solid thus separated is said to be precipitated.

It is always interesting to speculate on the nature of the physical change which takes place when a substance which has previously existed as a solid goes into a molten condition or into a solution. It has been established that the electrons of all atoms exist in a state of continual and extreme agitation. The extent or rate of this disturbance is affected by the temperature. As the temperature increases, the electronic activity likewise increases, causing the atoms to fly farther apart; and, conversely, as the temperature is decreased they become more and more quiescent and consequently draw closer together, until a stage is finally reached where cohesion is permitted and the substance again becomes solid. This accounts for the fact that the phenomena of contraction and expansion are controlled by temperature.

Now, when a substance goes into solution, its atoms are similarly moved farther apart, but in a slightly different manner. When any substance is dissolved, the individual atoms of the solute are held uniformly farther apart by the atoms of the solvent—to what distance, depends entirely upon the concentration of the solution. The greater the concentration, the closer the molecules are brought together, until a state is reached where they can no longer be held separated and so fly together, forming a solid substance.

In both instances, when solidification takes place, the atoms of the original substance, upon precipitation or solidification from a molten or dissolved condition, are permitted, if the process be sufficiently slow, literally to flow together, and, row upon row, layer upon layer, to draw themselves into whatever natural pattern their physical predilection will permit. Thus is crystallization brought about. In a solution, a decrease in pressure acts in much the same manner as would a decrease in temperature, bringing about precipitation and crystallization of the excess quantity of the solute present under the altered condition. Thus, ground water moving about from one level to another under hydrostatic pressure is compelled to precipitate and leave behind such material as it can no longer carry.

Another factor which operates similarly, although from slightly different causes, is the matter of the evaporation of a portion of the solvent. As the solvent evaporates, upon exposure to the atmosphere in caverns and crevices or upon the surface, or under an increase in temperature of the solution, its volume gradually decreases, thus increasing the concentration of the silica in the solution. As the concentrating process proceeds, sooner or later the saturation point must be reached. Then but one thing can happen: since the solvent can no longer carry all of its silica in its dissolved state, some of it must be thrown down, and that brings about a separation or crystallization of the solute. There are also cases where precipitation is hastened by the introduction of some natural foreign substance or impurity into the solution, which diminishes or partly destroys its solvency, bringing about a chemical precipitation.

CRYSTAL HABITAT

An important factor in the building of any crystal structure is free space or cavities in the rocks where it may grow in its own good time, unobstructed and unmolested by the crowding of other solidifying materials. This statement would be equally true concerning the deposition of the forms of amorphous quartz. Such openings may be created in numerous ways, for example:

a. In the cooling of the molten magma, especially when, on or near the surface, it is relieved of its pressure and consequently of its water vapor and other free gases, many small bubbles of these gases become entrapped in the molten mass, so that they cannot reach the surface and escape into the atmosphere. In such event, the material often becomes puffed up into a frothy mass, filled with openings ranging from those of microscopic size to spaces of several inches or even larger. These openings are known as vesicles, and the rock material so constituted is said to be vesicular. That nature, on occasion, fills these cavities with both crystalline and amorphous forms of quartz and other minerals is a well-known fact. When so filled, such rocks are said to take on an amygdaloidal structure. Due to their mode of formation, the inner walls of these vesicles are almost always smooth, curved, and regular, the smaller ones sometimes being almost globular in shape. This is of utmost importance, as it, of course, has its own positive influence upon the specific outline or shape of those minerals which are formed therein, not infrequently giving distinct character to chalcedonies, agates, and other forms of quartz.

b. Another type of opening within the mass of igneous rocks which is of almost like importance, is the result of an entirely different cause. These spaces are known as "miarolitic cavities" and are due to a shrinkage of the magma which takes place, after partial solidification has occurred, upon further and complete cooling of the mass. These are cavities differing distinctly from the gas-formed vesicles. As a rule, they are decidedly irregular in character and of varying size, ranging from small openings to those of cavernous proportions. They may be easily recognized by their irregular, often lenticular, shape, and from the fact that in the cooling of the crystalline rocks containing them, partly formed or at times almost complete crystals may protrude into the cavities, exposing to view terminal, pyramidal, and other crystal faces lining their interior. More often these crystals may be quite small or drusy in character. It may also be noted that unless they are subsequently loaded by the work of ground water, they have no distinct inner lining of chalcedony or other coating minerals.

These miarolitic openings, which may be minute, perhaps even microscopic, in size, account for the porosity of the many varieties of igneous rocks. This condition gives such rocks the ability to absorb much silica-bearing moisture; and thus, by capillary action, the constant upward movement or creeping of large quantities of ground water through the rocks may be explained. Among other things, this may account also for the ready decay and crumbling of certain types of igneous rocks to a surprising degree, when they are exposed to the agencies of weathering for only a relatively short time. This circumstance serves continually to bring fresh supplies of the silicate minerals to the surface, where they in turn may weather and liberate their new quota of free colloidal silica, later to be employed by nature upon a large scale in her widespread processes of silicification.

c. Perhaps the most important way in which contraction of the cooling magma may be accommodated is by jointing. This produces innumerable cracks and fissures, which run in various directions through the rock mass, separating it into more or less regular-shaped blocks, which fit together like masonry in a wall. Sometimes these blocks are large and the partings wide, while at other times the jointing may be on a small scale and the separating cracks of only paper thickness; but regardless of their size and thickness, they always become the courses or channels of circulating ground waters, and the silica which is in solution therein is more often deposited within the cracks, serving as a cementing agency, thereby healing nature's wounds.

d. Another type of fissure extending through the rocks is brought about by major stresses in the earth's crust, classed as diastrophism. This brings about what is called faulting of the rocks, producing cracks which may be irregular or smooth, and due to a shifting of the earth's material, they may in places cause fault fissures, openings of considerable width and size. In the healing process, these may become either partially or wholly filled with quartz minerals and form excellent habitats for crystal growth, as they often extend to great depths into the "bowels" of the earth. Completely filled, they form major veins, sometimes of great economic importance, as they frequently become highly mineralized and so are a source of immense wealth. These should not be confused with dikes and sills, which are of volcanic origin—the result of molten magmas being literally pushed or squeezed through the rocks by the action of enormous pressures connected with the forces of vulcanism.

e. Yet another very important kind of cavity in the rocks, in which quartz crystals may conveniently form, is caused by solution. Percolating ground waters are never pure, but are always charged with some natural reagent, either acid or alkali, which aids in the development of cracks, channels, caverns, or other types of openings in the rocks through the effect of its dissolving force. These waters have not only the power to dissolve rocks but also the ability to carry away in solution that which has been dissolved, thereby making room for the subsequent deposits of quartz and other minerals. All rain water, in passing through the atmosphere, quickly picks up or absorbs a certain amount of atmospheric carbon dioxide which makes it weakly acidic, so when strata of carbonate rocks (limestone) are reached, it immediately reacts to bring into solution a sufficient amount of $CaCO_3$ to neutralize completely its acidity.

Many of our most important and interesting forms of quartz are found deposited in the sedimentary rocks of all ages, and therefore they are worthy of our careful consideration. Many of the geode formations in the sedimentary rocks, it is thought, may be accounted for in this manner. Rocks of this class may also possess irregular openings, called vugs, comparable to miarolitic cavities of igneous rocks. These are also frequently lined with beautiful and interesting formations of quartz. They are, in part at least, considered to be the result of a shrinkage in the original rock-building materials, caused by drying or a loss of moisture during the process of their formation. Sometimes such shrinkage results in a checking or cracking, not unlike mud's cracking when it dries. When these cracks are subsequently filled with deposits of quartz or other minerals, unique examples of interesting so-called "boxwork" (septaria) are formed.

RECAPITULATION OUTLINE

By way of recapitulation in closing, let us briefly outline the entire matter of crystallization, before proceeding with our discussion of the way in which quartz crystals are actually formed and the manner in which they are affected by their environment.

1. Crystal growth may take place upon
   a. Sublimation of material from a gaseous state
   b. Solidification of molten magma
   c. Precipitation of dissolved or colloidal material out of a supersaturated solution.

(Of these three methods, the last is by far the most important.)

2. The source of the crystallizing silica is
   a. Free quartz being dissolved in hot alkaline waters
   b. The breaking down of silicate minerals, especially feldspars, during which reaction much soluble colloidal silica is released.

3. Quartz crystals are deposited in cavities in the rocks, which are created in the following manner
   a. Vesicular, formed by gas bubbles in the molten magma
   b. Miarolitic, due to shrinkage upon cooling
   c. Joint cracks, caused by a general shrinkage on cooling
   d. Faulting planes due to diastrophism
   e. Cavities, channels, etc. formed by ground water solution.

CHAPTER V

The Quartz Crystal

It will be recalled that in the preceding chapter we noted how, upon the weathering or breaking down of the silicate rocks, soluble colloidal silica is liberated. This silica is picked up and incorporated into the percolating ground waters in ever-increasing amounts, until eventually they become thoroughly saturated. The solution of colloidal silica is very sensitive to changing conditions and, in obedience to the principles previously related, it readily becomes supersaturated, thereupon tending to deposit that part of its solute which it can no longer carry. In the process of deposition, the many divergent varieties of quartz are brought about as the direct result of environmental influences. It seems that a thorough understanding of such causes and effects should prove most vital to every true mineral lover.

CONDITIONS REQUISITE TO FORM CRYSTALLINE QUARTZ

Perhaps the first observation we should make concerns the variety, hyalite (colorless opal), and its transitional forms passing into crystalline quartz, for from them we learn something of the controlling factors of crystallization. This mineral (hydrolite) is frequently found lining fissures through which silica-charged waters have been descending. At first it would seem as though there could be no limit to the depth at which hyalite might form. One important factor, however, must not be overlooked; that is pressure. Everyone knows that, owing to the weight of the overlying column of water, pressure increases rapidly as we descend below the surface. It has been

59

proved experimentally that to increase the pressure greatly increases the solubility of colloidal silica in water, and therefore, it follows directly that the tendency for opal to separate from the solution becomes less and less as we proceed downward. There is, however, another property of colloidal silica which comes into play—its instability.

Like many other similar substances, the colloidal form of silicon dioxide possesses, especially at rather elevated temperatures, a strong tendency to revert to the crystalloidal form, which is quite insoluble in water. This will separate out from a highly supersaturated solution, as fast as it is produced, and we call the resulting substance crystallized quartz. The three conditions requisite, then, for the formation of crystalline quartz are: (1) water saturated with colloidal silica derived from the belt of weathering rocks; (2) a fairly high pressure to keep the colloidal silica, as such, in solution; and, finally (3) a moderately high temperature to promote the change of the colloidal silica into the crystalloidal form.

CAUSES OF DIFFERENCES IN SYMMETRY OF CRYSTALS

Nuclei. Our story, however, does not end here, as there yet remains to be considered the cause of the great number of varieties in which the crystalline forms of quartz are known to be found. The conversion of sandstone into quartzite is a typical example of the actual process of crystal growth. Whenever a silica solution filters through a bed of common sand, the whole becomes cemented together to form sandstone. The well-rounded grains of sand, being largely quartz, furnish ideal nuclei about which crystal growth may easily take place. Every grain of sand will, therefore, if the process be continued sufficiently long, grow into a crystal, and the loose formation changes, as the pore spaces are completely filled up, into a closely consolidated quartzite. All stages of the process may be observed by the examination of their sections under the microscope.

Now, precisely the same thing on a larger scale occurs when the solution enters rock cavities and fissures. Crystallization takes place about any nuclei which happen to be present. The crystals formed in such openings may grow to large size, but they are more often unsymmetrical, distorted, striated, and bounded by "rare planes or faces." This may be accounted for in several ways. To begin with, the crystal nuclei are almost always particles of the wall rock, which, as is to be expected, would be quite irregular in shape, and thus the crystal growth gets off to a poor start, so far as its symmetry is concerned. Furthermore, since the inbearing solution is always in continual, more or less rapid movement, the crystals must adapt their sides to conform, after a fashion, to the shape of the nucleus as modified by the direction of flow, instead of each standing out boldly in the expected normal or regular manner. In such event, shall we say, the shape (not form) of the crystal may be quite accidental.

Foreign Matter. A second, and perhaps even more important, consideration influencing the symmetry of crystals is the presence of foreign matter in the silica solution. Common laboratory experience teaches us that the introduction of minute amounts of impurities of various kinds will profoundly alter the shape of a crystal that is forming in a solution. Just why or how the introduction of any slight impurity into a saturated solution will change the form of the crystal which is produced, yet not interfere with its crystallization entirely, is a question which has never been satisfactorily explained, although there are several more or less tenable theories concerning it. That we are reasonably safe in assuming that the extensive development of "rare planes" on quartz crystals is directly associated with the presence of impurities, there is ample evidence, which may be summarized as follows.

Filtering Process. Such impurities would naturally be more likely to be present in fissures which connect directly with the surface of the earth, than in cavities to enter which the silica-bearing solutions would be compelled to pass through pore spaces in the rocks. These would serve as a filtering medium, separating and holding back much of the foreign material which might have continued on with the solution and found its way into the crystal structure itself. Knowing this, we should naturally expect to find that crystals whose growth takes place in fissures would present a definitely greater number of irregular and "rare planes" than those occurring in closed cavities. The field experience of every ardent mineral collector, we are sure, will bear out the truth of this expectation, and usually, one need not go far away from home to verify these facts.

CHANGES DURING FILTRATION

Smoky Color. It was formerly taught that the smoky color so common in this class of crystals followed as the direct, logical consequence of the descent of the silica solution through fissures. It was stated that the carbon dioxide which brought about the disintegration of the feldspar, giving rise to the entire series of phenomena which we are considering, came in part from the decomposition of vegetable matter upon the surface of the ground. It must be remembered, too, that as the result of this process, carbon dioxide was by no means the only important product. There were liberated, also, many complex organic compounds which, especially in the presence of potassium carbonate, one of the other principal by-products of the reaction, would be dissolved in the water and carried downward, thus accounting for the smoky color.

While this explanation has now been almost entirely supplanted by the *Wild theory* (discussed thoroughly elsewhere in the book), which attempts to account for *smoky color* by X-ray and other forms of emanations, it is surely worthy of mention from the historical standpoint, as well as for the reason that there are yet many sound mineralogists who adhere to it firmly.

Now, if, as above stated, the solution passes through pore spaces in the rocks, as would be expected, a great part of such compounds will be filtered out and decomposed before penetrating very far. But if, on the other hand, it enters comparatively roomy cracks or fissures, where the descent is rapid, there is ample opportunity for the introduction of such organic compounds into the zone where quartz crystallization is taking place and the carbonaceous matter may become entrapped in the growing crystals, not only producing the smoky appearance but also accounting for the presence of bubbles or minute inclusions of gaseous or liquid carbonic acid. These will be discussed at the appropriate time under the topic of liquid inclusions. It is for this reason that smoky crystals are more likely to present "rare planes" or perhaps, conversely, that highly modified crystals are likely to show signs of being smoky.

Inclusions, Cappings, and Etchings. Frequently the presence of inclusions, cappings, and etchings figures upon such fissure-formed crystals is definitely attributable to the same cause, because it is in these fissures that water is freely descending and that silt, asbestos, chlorite, or what not, would naturally be stirred up to fall or lodge upon the growing crystal, only to be subsequently covered or coated over by later layers, and thereby become incorporated into the actual body of the crystal itself. On occasion, the chemical character of the solutions may vary so drastically as to create these "capping" layers and etchings upon crystal faces, and at times the passing solution may even change to a solvent. Then, instead of deposition of materials continuing, portions of the growing crystals may be actually dissolved away, leaving cavernous and hopper-faced crystals. In like manner, we may account for glazes of various types which are sometimes found as external coatings upon many of the individual specimens seen in representative collections of quartz crystals.

ZONES OF CRYSTAL FORMATION

Another matter of intense interest is the vertical zone in which quartz crystals may form. All rocks beneath the earth's surface, lying between certain limits, are necessarily completely saturated with ground water. The upper limit is dependent, of course, upon the sheet-water level and usually varies between 10 and 100 feet below the surface, according to the season and the amount of rainfall. The lower limit is fixed by the temperature above which water changes to vapor and can no longer be held in a liquid state, regardless of the super-incumbent pressure upon it. This temperature is given as 365°C., and in general (outside of areas of vulcanism) exists only at depths of several miles. So, for all practical purposes, we may assume the rocks which we may study to be within these limits. Within this zone, water must at times fill all cavities in the rocks, and being in continual motion or circulation, though perhaps exceedingly slow at times, it attains results which, in the end are considerable, distinct, and definite. Eventually, we should expect to find all such cavities completely filled with deposits of quartz and other minerals. Whenever they are not, it may safely be assumed that sufficient time, only, has been lacking to accomplish these ends.

Even after considerable filtration, upon its having passed through the porous rocks, there must yet remain in the solution a considerable quantity of almost impurity-free soluble silica. It is when this material chances to enter suitable cavities, where the crystal may develop quietly, slowly, and gradually, that we may expect to find (if they are not molested by contact with other adjacent growths) our finest and most perfectly developed quartz crystals, possessing all the rare qualities of symmetry and beauty of which the mineral quartz is capable. Even here, it is true, there may be possible also many variations in form, habit, and distribution of crystal faces, for while many of the foreign salts will be removed by filtration and chemical reaction with the minerals with which they came in contact on their slow journey through the rocks, there will always remain the chance that other impurities may escape removal, and yet new mineral chemicals may be dissolved, and therefore be present when such crystallization takes place. It is to be regretted that all too little is known concerning the different and specific influences of individual impurities, and from a practical standpoint, so far as actual proof is concerned, the entire question is largely one vast field of fantastic speculation.

The Quartz Crystal

CHARACTERISTICS OF DIFFERENT VARIETIES

We may say, however, that there are certain well-known facts which have been gained from actual observation. For example, amethyst nearly always occurs in short, prismatic crystals with characteristic pyramidal terminations; the absence of prismatic faces is usually connected with the presence of mineral hematite; rock crystal usually presents long, well-defined prism faces; and pink or rose quartz forms crystals upon only the rarest occasions. The actual causes of all these and many other peculiarities of crystals remain almost as much of a mystery today as when these questions were first seriously pondered over by our earliest mineralogists and crystallographers; but the time may possibly come, in the not-too-distant future, when the causes of all such phenomena may be common knowledge and the great variety of forms may be prepared at will in the modern laboratory in the electric furnace or by other methods; then, too, the factors of their control may become well-known and calculable.

The actual form of the quartz crystal, with which all are visually so familiar, is in reality but poorly understood by the vast majority of mineral collectors. Even well-trained mineralogists are at times bewildered by the vast number of forms encountered. Most of those who have shown any curiosity upon the subject and consulted texts on crystallography in an attempt to satisfy this desire for facts, have soon become perplexed, trying to make "horse sense" out of the maze of formulas and technical terms given, and have quite likely become discouraged, possibly giving up the matter regretfully as being "far too deep for comprehension." We shall, therefore, in so far as possible, strive to avoid a technical or academic discussion of the subject. Such a study can readily be consulted in almost any text or reference book, should the reader desire. Our remarks in this direction shall be confined, therefore, to such ideas and facts as any layman can readily understand.

PROGRESS IN STUDY OF CRYSTALS

It will be remembered that in earlier chapters we observed that all solid matter exists in one of two forms: namely, (1) crystalline, whose shape is limited in fixed directions, rather than by "fixed forms"; and (2) amorphous, which is entirely without definite form or shape. The consideration of symmetrical solids and crystal forms was one of the first studies to engage the attention of the early mathematicians and naturalists, and, in view of their number, general distribution, and attractive qualities, it is not surprising to learn that the quartz crystals were among the very first to be seriously examined and analyzed by man in his slow progress toward our present mineralogical attainment. In fact, it can truthfully be said that the quartz crystal has received more attention than any other mineral form.

It furnished the renowned Danish geologist, Steno (1669), the material with which to establish the *Law of the constancy of the crystal angle*, which proved to be the very foundation of the great science of modern crystallography. The law is stated thus: *However much a crystal of any mineral may vary in size or shape, its corresponding interfacial angles are the same value, provided they are measured under the same conditions* (Bayley). As early as 1783, Romé de Lisle seriously discussed this crystal in his "Cristallographie, ou description des formes propres à tous les corps du règne minéral." The abbé Hauy, made further progress in his notable work, "Tableau comparatif des résultats de la cristallographie et de l'analyse chimique," published in Paris in 1809.

Thereafter, steady progress was made and, while the systematic classification of crystals was a slow and laborious process, after endless comparisons of angle measurements, mineralogists came to the conclusion that all crystals could be arranged into six groups or systems (consult English), with respect to the angular and proportional relation of their crystallographic axis. It is to be taken for granted that the reader is more or less familiar with primary differences between

66

the tetrahedral (four-faced) and the hexagonal (six-faced) prism, especially with reference to their axial relations. While such knowledge will be helpful, yet a complete understanding of the many details presented by the world of crystals is by no means essential to a fair degree of comprehension and enjoyment of facts which are now to be touched upon concerning the mathematical form of the quartz crystal.

STUDY OF SPECIFIC QUARTZ CRYSTALS

To describe the salient features of the quartz crystal, in so simple a language as to be helpful to laymen or those untrained in the science of crystallography, seems a difficult matter, especially when one realizes that entire volumes have been written upon this most intricate subject alone. Nevertheless, we shall attempt to discuss just a few of the more obvious points of interest which might come under the observation of any collector handling quartz crystals and pondering over the nature of their singularly beautiful structure.

Preparation. In order fully to appreciate and understand the following, he should select one of his more perfect rock crystals, of medium size, as well as several which present rare faces and distortions, and conduct his own experimental investigation as we proceed with our explanation. To do this properly, he should first equip himself with pencil, plain paper, ruler, compass, protractor, and a simple goniometer, or some other convenient means of securing the measurement of angles. In measuring interfacial angles care should be exercised to see that the reading is taken perpendicularly to their line of intersection, as this angle only will be the correct one.

By way of a preliminary excursion into the realm of the angles and geometrical patterns involved in the quartz crystal, let us first take a compass and draw a circle (one and one-half inches, radius) on a plain piece of paper, then inscribe therein a perfect hexagon (six-sided figure) by stepping off six points around the perimeter of the circle with the points of the compass set at the distance of the radius and then joining these points with straight lines. On measuring the angle between any two adjacent sides of the hexagon so drawn, we shall find every such angle to be exactly 120°. The geometrical proof of this, with which we are not at present concerned, is simple. Furthermore, the lines joining the mid points of each of the three sets of opposite parallel sides are all equal, intersecting each other in a single point at the center. Lines so drawn represent the three "horizontal" axes of the orthodox hexagonal quartz prism, and the fourth axis, which is perpendicular to their plane at their point of intersection, bears the ratio, 1.099:1:1:1, to the three which are equal. Another set of

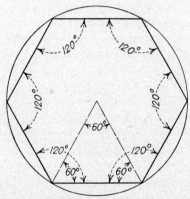

The geometric pattern of the regular hexagon wherein the angle 120° is developed.

three similar lines (axes) might be drawn by joining the vertices of the series of opposite interfacial angles.

Angles. Now, if we set the goniometer to coincide with the angle of 120°, and carefully measure the lateral interfacial angles of a number of quartz crystals, we shall find each of them to be exactly 120°. Further examination will reveal, however, that while in the quartz prism the opposite faces are always parallel, they are seldom if ever equal, and there-fore a cross section of the prism does not present the pattern of a regular or perfect hexagon. Indeed, they may be quite unequal, some being wide while others are very narrow. This observation may create considerable perplexity as to how such a thing can be possible, when under no circumstances does their angle vary from 120°. Light may be thrown upon the matter, if with the ruler lines are drawn on the diagram parallel to each of the three sets of opposite parallel faces, some being closer and others farther removed from the center. We now have the pattern of sections of a distorted quartz prism, and yet, by applying the protractor, we shall find the angles of intersection to be always 120°. This also can be confirmed by geometrical proof, if the reader desires to work it out.

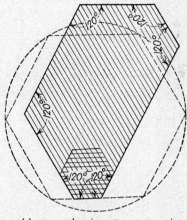

Pattern of the distorted hexagon, showing type cross section of the quartz prism.

Prism Faces. An examination of the prism faces will reveal them to be rectangular in outline, their lateral edges forming right angles with the base of the corresponding pyramidal face. One of the distinguishing characters of quartz is the presence of horizontal, parallel striations (scratchlike lines) which occur upon the faces of the prism. These lines, which are usually fine, although sometimes grooved, show distinctly when turned at the correct angle to the light. They are always perpendicular to the edge of the prism and according to English, striations upon crystal faces represent a sort of conflict waged between two nearly balanced forces—one which wishes to produce a crystal of a certain type, and one which strives toward another type, the result being an arrangement of minute, sometimes microscopic, faces, called an "oscillatory combination." The horizontal striations on the quartz crystals show plainly the oscillation between the prism and the terminal rhombahedron. While crystals of other mineral species frequently present striations, they are more often parallel to the prism edges.

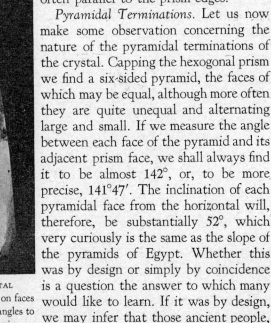

QUARTZ CRYSTAL
Showing striations on faces of crystal, at right angles to the long C crystal axis.

Pyramidal Terminations. Let us now make some observation concerning the nature of the pyramidal terminations of the crystal. Capping the hexogonal prism we find a six-sided pyramid, the faces of which may be equal, although more often they are quite unequal and alternating large and small. If we measure the angle between each face of the pyramid and its adjacent prism face, we shall always find it to be almost 142°, or, to be more precise, 141°47′. The inclination of each pyramidal face from the horizontal will, therefore, be substantially 52°, which very curiously is the same as the slope of the pyramids of Egypt. Whether this was by design or simply by coincidence is a question the answer to which many would like to learn. If it was by design, we may infer that those ancient people, like moderns, were intrigued by the beauty and form of the quartz crystal, studied it, and perhaps attached thereto some religious significance or symbolism. Thus, the whole conception of pyramidal design and construction may have been conveyed to the human intellect through the observation of nature working with crystals.

Angle at Apex. The angle between alternating faces at the apex of the pyramid, will be found to be 94°14′. To the eye this will appear to be almost a right angle; therefore, when three alternate faces are largely developed at the expense of their neighbors, the crystal may take on a cubical aspect, frequently appearing so different that it would scarcely be suspected of belonging to the mineral quartz. When the pyramidal faces are of equal size, they occur as acute isosceles triangles with base angles of 70°, and with an angle of 40° at the apex. The legs of the triangle will be 1.5 times the length of its base. In examining "drusy" quartz with the microscope, it will be well to bear these facts in mind, for they will aid greatly in identification as the tiny crystal faces are reflected in the light, bringing the angles into full view.

PRIMARY FORM AND VARIATIONS

Primary Form. It may come as a complete surprise to many, after all this discussion of the hexagonal prism with pyramidal termination, to learn that its primary form, which as a matter of fact is but rarely seen, is not that of the hexagonal prism, but that of the rhomboid, and that crystallogically it is classified in the rhombohedral-trapezohedral group of the hexagonal system. Their symmetry, therefore, is trigonal holoaxial, which is to say, they do not possess a center or plane of symmetry, but if revolved around their *c* axis, their planes occupy similar positions three times during one complete revolution.

English says, "This is true of many other rhombohedral minerals, all of which occur with their parts in threes instead of sixes, but in such instances the expert crystallographer is able by certain tests, to detect the fact that the apparent hexagonal pyramids are really combinations of two rhombohedrons, while the apparent hexagonal prisms are combinations of two three-sided prisms. The terminal faces are, therefore, called rhombohedrons and not pyramids, and are quite different from simple hexagonal forms."

Unusual Forms. On this account, quartz crystals may frequently occur in many odd and unusual forms, ranging from tabular hexagonal prisms, without even a semblance of pyramidal terminations, to the opposite extremes in which the pyramidal faces *r* and *z* are so enlarged at the expense of the prism faces that the latter may be wholly absent. Most quartz crystals are distorted to a certain degree, some of them extremely so; but if we remember that the "law of the constancy of crystal angles," is immutable, and that similar angles are always uniform, regardless of however much the crystals may be flattened or lengthened, we shall have at hand the clue for a simple way out of the perplexities experienced when we encounter one of these crystal "freaks."

Rare and exotic faces, in addition to the regular faces of the quartz crystal, are not uncommon. At each of the three alternating faces, and separating the pyramid from the prism, there may sometimes occur a small rhomboidal face, and

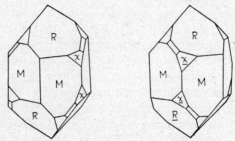

Left: A right-handed quartz crystal.
Right: A left-handed quartz crystal.

occasionally between the latter and the prism face there may also be a small trapezoidal face. If this trapezoidal face should occur at the right-hand corner of the prism face, then the crystal is called a right-handed crystal, and should it occur at the opposite corner, we have a left-handed crystal. One such crystal may be the exact counterpart of the other, except that each is the mirror reflection of the other, and that, like the two shells of a bivalve, they cannot be made exactly to coincide with each other.

Twinning. The crystals of many minerals have an occasional habit of intergrowth, and as a result of this phenomenon it may appear as if two crystals were striving to occupy the same space at the same time. This propensity of crystals is called "twinning." In such an event, each may remain in undisputed possession of certain of its individual parts, while apparently

t͟here are other parts which may be shared in common by both
crystals. Quartz is no exception to this rule. We quote from
Dr. A. R. Crook, who has written one of the most helpful
books touching upon this subject:

"Twinning in quartz crystals is common, according to three
laws: first, two crystals of the same sort, both right-handed

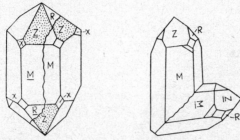

Left: Right-handed "Interpenetrant Twins."
Right: Quartz crystal twinned on (112̄2). A "Bourg de Oisans Twin."

or left-handed, may be united, parallel to the c axis in interpenetrant twins. Thus x (plane) may appear at each corner and
R and z in the same plane. However, since R is usually smooth

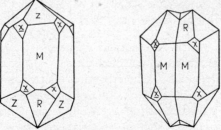

Left: "Brazil Twins," interpenetrant right and left-handed twinned crystals.
Right: "Brazil Twins," two right-handed juxtaposed crystals.

and bright, while z is pitted or coated, they may be distinguished from each other. The boundaries of the two interlacing
crystals show a zigzag pattern. Second, right-handed and
left-handed crystals interpenetrate parallel to the c axis and at
the same time parallel the diagonal prism (112̄0). In this case

twinning is betrayed by the *x* and *z* faces. This is called the 'Brazil twin.' The accompanying figure shows two juxtaposed Brazil twins. Third, Bourg de Oisans in Dauphiny (France) has long been noted for fine quartz crystals twinned in the manner shown on page 73. Recently, Japan has furnished the museums of the world with a large number of these twins. They are united parallel to the diagonal pyramid (11$\bar{2}$2) so that the *c* axis and the line of union form a zigzag."

Other Kinds of Intergrowth. Intergrowths of quartz crystals produce many strange, almost wierd effects which, when well understood, will account for many of the eccentric and exotic forms to be found in every collection of any importance. For instance, "twisted quartz," while seeming to consist of a single warped crystal, is in reality composed of many individuals, each turned through a small angle so as to produce a spiral effect. When intergrowths of right- and left-handed quartz break with a wavy surface, "ripple-fracture" is produced, which is sometimes mistaken for fracture other than the expected form (conchoidal).

Airy's spiral. Characteristic of right-handed amethyst Crystal. (*After Crook.*)

Color Distribution. In amethystine quartz crystals, it will be observed that the color is quite often uneven or irregularly distributed, with alternating layers of opaque whitish material, violet or purple transparent material, and brownish layers. When it is examined under the microscope, this will be seen to be caused by alternating layers of right- and left-handed lamellae. The mingling of the right and left layers produces convergent light lines, which are known as "Airy's spirals," after the English astronomer, Sir. George Biddell Airy, who discovered the right- and left-handed crystal and its principles, while studying optics, at Cambridge.

The Quartz Crystal

COMMON PROPERTIES OF CRYSTALS STUDIED IN QUARTZ

Obviously, it is impossible to do more than touch on the matter of optics associated with the quartz crystal. This alone could easily be the topic for an entire chapter. For the study of the optical and many other common properties of crystals, quartz is unexcelled. It illustrates splendidly not only the geometrical, but the optical, electrical, thermal, and chemical

TWIN QUARTZ CRYSTAL
(Kai, Japan.)

features of crystals, as well. Crook says: "The connection between geometrical and electrical properties may be illustrated as follows: The three horizontal axes are polar (i.e., not symmetrical around the center) for one end of each axis emerges through the prism edge that is truncated by the planes s and x, and the other through a prism lacking these planes. Since the horizontal axes are polar, they exhibit pyro-electric polarity."

Finely powdered red lead and sulphur are sifted through a piece of cloth, and thus become electrified by friction. The red lead is positive, the sulphur negative. When they touch the heated quartz crystal, the *s* and *x* faces become negatively electrified on cooling, *i.e.*, attract the red lead, thereby giving an illuminating bit of information concerning the nature and structure of the crystal and its polarity. By employing caustic alkalies or hydrofluoric acid, one may observe the different effects upon the various planes, and thus the right-handed and the left-handed nature of the crystals may be revealed. The etchings which are formed are related to each other like the right hand and the left and hence they are said to be "entantiomorphous."

No laboratory study of the quartz would be complete without examination of the quartz under the polarizing microscope, and one of its characteristic properties, when studied in that manner, is the power of colorless transparent crystals to impress circular polarization upon a ray of plane—polarized light. They also exhibit double refraction when the object is observed through two faces which are not parallel to each other. One of the very strangest properties of the quartz crystal is its behavior in respect to the transmission of heat. At ordinary temperatures, it is a very poor conductor of heat, but "at exceedingly low temperatures quartz becomes as good a conductor of heat as copper is at ordinary temperatures," it was revealed at one of the most recent meetings of an important national science conference.

While we have only begun to relate the many strange and sometimes wonderful properties of the quartz crystal, limitation of space demands that we must now take up the consideration of its various and more definite forms.

CHAPTER VI

The Crystalline Forms of Quartz

ROCK CRYSTAL

Owing to its wide dissemination in nature and the unsur-
passed beauty of its crystalline forms, quartz has been admired
by man since remote antiquity. To quote from John de Trevisa,
1398: "Crystall is a bryght stone and clere wyth watry colour.
Men trowe that snowe or yse is made hard in space of many
yeres; therfore the Grekys yaue (gave) this name therto."

In 1592, Robert Green, the poet wrote:

"The precious stone silex is full of secret vertue."

Thinking man has always been intrigued with the marvelous
symmetry of rock crystal, and the earliest scholarly investigations of the *solid forms* were inspired by observations made
upon this mineral species. Steno (1669), the great Danish
physician, theologian, and geologist, got from it the clue by
means of which he established his law of the constancy of a
crystal angle, which is recognized by everyone as the foundation
or starting point of modern crystallography.

Its superabundance, the great profusion of its forms, and
its key position in the mineral kingdom serve to distinguish
it as the most studied mineral of all. The story of quartz
permeates all mineralogical and geological literature. As early
as 1855, its crystallography was fully investigated by Des
Cloizeaus, who prepared and published, in Paris, his classical
"*Mémoire sur la cristallisation et la structure intérieure du
Quartz.*"

To the present day rock crystal continues not only to
captivate and hold the interest of all mineral lovers but

also to play an important role in modern science and in the many industries carried on in our exceedingly complex civilization. It is truly the king of minerals. The ancient Greeks thought rock crystals to be ice so thoroughly frozen as to have permanently lost the power of melting, and hence named it "krustallos," which is translated "ice." Perhaps its association with extreme cold, in the high altitudes of the Alps, where many of the finest specimens are to be found, lent credence to this strange belief. Even yet, many people speak of "crystal," when they refer to quartz. The name "quartz" is an old German mining term introduced into mineralogical literature by Agricola in 1529. Its crystalline varieties were formerly spoken of as "vitreous quartz" on account of their glassy luster.

Quartz crystals vary greatly in size. There are those which can be observed only through a microscope, while at the opposite extreme there are others which are actually huge. Quartz crystals of remarkable size have been found in the Alps, Brazil, Japan, and Madagascar. In the last-named place, it is said, a crystal 25 feet in circumference was found. A very large crystal, $6\frac{1}{2}$ feet long and $1\frac{1}{2}$ feet in diameter, weighing 2,913 pounds, was taken out of a cavity at Grafton, New Hampshire. In the museum at Milan, is a rock crystal $3\frac{1}{4}$ feet long by $5\frac{1}{2}$ feet in circumference, weighing 870 pounds; and from a huge pocket discovered at Buckfield, Maine, a crystal was taken which was 3 feet long and 2 feet in diameter, weighing 500 pounds. Very large crystals are for the most part of translucent, milky-white color.

Rock crystals of smaller dimensions are found in great profusion in so many places throughout the world that we shall attempt to mention only a few of the most noted localities. At Berner, Oberland, in Switzerland, is a famous cave from which more than 500 tons of quartz crystals have been removed. Crook says that "there is hardly a state in the Union in which fine quartz crystals have not been found." Maine is a prolific source, and at Buckfield a cavity was broken into, some 20 feet long and 9 feet wide, from which thousands of crystals were taken. The geodes of the "Keokuk" beds of Iowa,

Missouri, and Illinois probably contain, in the aggregate, the largest single source of quartz crystals in America, but since they are never large and are always found lining the interiors of small cavities, from which they may be separated only with difficulty, they are not so well known or widely distributed among collectors as are those of certain other localities.

Without doubt, the two best-known rock-crystal regions in America are in the vicinity of Little Rock, Arkansas, and in Herkimer County, New York. The latter locality furnishes crystals which are remarkably clear and limpid, with natural faces which sparkle with the brilliance of cut gems. These are often cut into beautiful beads and other ornaments, or even so as to resemble diamonds. They have been sold sometimes to the unwary under the names of "Herkimer diamonds," "Alaskan diamonds," or "Rhinestones." Mr. A. B. Crim, a resident of Middleville, New York, spent the greater part of his life making a marvelous collection of the Herkimer crystals. Working in the virgin field while the choicest specimens were still available, his was without doubt one of the finest collec-tions of quartz crystals ever assembled. It contained over 14,000 individual specimens, and attracted extraordinary attention at the World's Columbian Exposition, at Chicago in 1893, where it was exhibited.

There were included in this remarkable assemblage, many thousands of single crystals, also twins and triplets; groups, both smoky and clear; crystal inclusions within crystals; car-bon inclusions, calcite inclusions, and numerous examples of liquid inclusion. There were also hundreds of crystals in the limestone matrix, exhibited to illustrate the manner in which the Herkimer crystals develop. Of outstanding interest was a tube which contained perfect quartz crystals so minute that over 100,000 were required to weigh an ounce. Doubly terminated examples were represented by the thousands. We have been unable to learn what final disposition was made of this splendid collection, but in all probability it has long since been broken up and scattered to numerous private collections and museums. At least, we are safe in saying that it would be impossible for it ever to be duplicated.

The region about Little Rock, Arkansas, has for more than half a century furnished countless thousands of quartz crystals annually as souvenirs for the tourists who visit the Springs. While the Little Rock crystals are of first quality, for sheer brilliance and beauty they hardly compare with those of the Herkimer deposits, which are among the finest in the world. The rock crystals of Arkansas, especially in Garland and Montgomery counties, are found lining cavities of variable

QUARTZ CRYSTALS

Group of clear, well-terminated quartz crystals from Hot Springs, Arkansas. This locality produces some of the finest found in America. (*Photograph, George L. English.*)

size. One such cavity was so huge that more than thirty tons were taken from it. At many places in this region rock crystals are mined by farmers during their spare time and then sold in season to visitors upon the streets of Hot Springs. There is scarcely a collection in the United States, of any consequence, that does not contain at least a suite of these beautiful Arkansas crystals. The discovery of pockets or veins of crystalline quartz almost anywhere while mining or quarrying operations are being carried on is not unusual, but most of these deposits are of small extent and local in character, so their yield is generally small and they are soon worked out.

Often, however, many excellent specimens are obtained in this manner.

No work on quartz would be complete that did not at least mention the wonderful deposits of Brazil. There occurs not only one of the most extensive, but also one of the finest deposits of rock crystal or transparent quartz known to be anywhere. These deposits occur in the vicinity of the town of Crystalina, in the southeastern corner of the state of Goyaz. The crystals are obtained from a strip of subsoil gravel that is known to extend for at least 65 miles. The mining methods still employed are primitive, though a company organized in the United States is planning to open a tract, employing modern methods and machinery. (*Bulletin, Pan American Union*, Vol. LXXI, 1937, p. 543.) Brazilian crystals are exported principally to manufacturing jewelers in the United States, Japan, and Germany. These crystals are of two kinds, transparent and colored. The colored varieties include many yellow crystals, known as "false topaz." In size they may vary from mere specks to crystals weighing in some instances up to 150 pounds. Brazilian amethysts, which are known by every collector of minerals for their exceeding beauty, sometimes occur in slabs of great size, but more often in small pockets or geodes.

Crystal in Art. From time immemorial, rock crystal and other varieties of quartz have been employed as material for some of the finest, most elaborate, and most valuable works of art. Many fine specimens dating back to the ancient Mycenaean era of Greek history are known to exist. The Romans made wine jugs, cups, vases, and other articles from large quartz crystals, and two rare and beautiful drinking cups made of flawless crystal, worth about $3,000 in our money, were owned by Nero. Certainly, one of the very finest Roman pieces ever carved from a single quartz crystal was an urn, $9\frac{1}{2}$ inches in diameter and 9 inches high, which now reposes among the French national jewels. Lenses of rock crystal were used to concentrate the rays of the sun to procure heat for cauterizing wounds and to light fires—especially sacrificial fires. Farrington quotes the following lines, adapted from an early Roman writer, referring to the latter custom:

Take in thy pious hand the Crystal bright,
Translucent image of the Eternal Light;
Pleased with its luster, every power divine
Shall grant thy vows presented at their shrine;
But how to prove the virtue of the stone,
A certain mode I will to thee make known;
To kindle without fire the sacred blaze,
This wondrous gem on splintered pine-wood place,
Forthwith, reflecting the bright orb of day,
Upon the wood it shoots a slender ray
Caught by the unctuous fuel this will raise
First smoke, then sparkles, then a mighty blaze:
Such we the fire of ancient Vesta name,
Loved by the immortals all, a holy flame;
No other fire with such grateful fumes;
The fated victim on their hearths consumes;
Yet though of flame the cause, strange to be told,
The stone snatched from the blaze is icy cold.

Quite out of keeping with the forms into which we usually expect quartz crystal to be carved and polished, is the image of a human skull, found in Mexico, which is of very ancient origin. It is most realistically cut, and was without doubt held as an object of great reverence by these peoples, who endowed it with some not-too-well-understood religious significance, for in the Aztec ruins of Mexico several highly decorated human crania have been found completely covered with a mosaic of turquoise.

Possibly, nowhere did the art of quartz engraving reach higher perfection than in old Russia, where the industry was founded under the royal patronage by Empress Catherine, at Ekaterinburg. Here, literally thousands of art objects were carved from quartz, in a great variety of forms and for many utilities. Among their most wonderful productions are vases of fruits of various kinds which are, indeed, most admirable counterfeits of nature. These include grapes of amethyst, cherries of onyx, raspberries of rhodonite, mulberries of yellow chalcedony, currants of white rock crystal, and green leaves of serpentine. Probably the best example of Russian workmanship in America is a seal showing Atlas holding the world, exhibited in the American Museum of National History in New York. The Chinese artisans have for centuries carved beautiful small objects of art out of transparent quartz—vases, snuff bottles, ink boxes, incense burners, pendants, and figurines. All these objects, except ink boxes, were produced also in smoky quartz, amethyst, and rose quartz.

However, none of the art objects into which quartz has been fashioned attract more attention than the beautiful crystal balls of pure transparent quartz. These date back far into antiquity. At the dawn of history the Hindus used "reading balls," and both Greek and Roman seers employed them for the same purpose. Even today, crystal gazing is a popular pastime among many civilized as well as uncivilized people of the world; smaller balls are much in demand for this and other purposes. Perfect spheres over six inches in diameter, however, are so rare and beautiful, when flawless, that they find a ready place in the most valuable art collections of the world; if perfect, they may command almost fabulous prices.

In the first place, the construction of one of them requires a large block of flawless quartz crystal, which of itself is of no mean intrinsic value; and, in the second place, the process of reducing it into perfect spherical shape often takes months of patient, painstaking effort upon the part of the lapidary. Even modern methods have not greatly reduced this effort in turning out balls of larger diameter. So difficult it is said to be to obtain a piece of perfect quartz that will yield a ball more than three inches in diameter that such spheres increase in value enormously as the diameter exceeds this length. While the Japanese have been especially adept in fashioning these art objects, not all that are offered for sale are from this source, by any means. Most of them are said to be actually made in France and in Germany, from material which has been obtained in Brazil and Madagascar.

The old method of manufacture, used by the Japanese was exceedingly laborious. They began by chipping the rock into a roughly spherical shape with hammer and chisel, afterward rendering it round and perfectly smooth by rolling it with water and sand in an iron trough, then polishing the ball with emery and giving it the final finish by rubbing it with rouge by hand. In Europe the modern lapidary holds the revolving ball in a cup against the grooved edge of a sandstone wheel which revolves in water at about one hundred times a minute. By this method, it is said, in a week or two a crystal sphere can be made which formerly might have taken even years to produce by the more primitive means.

At the Centennial Exposition at Philadelphia in 1876, a sphere of flawless rock crystal, 7 inches in diameter, was exhibited, standing in splendor alone on a dais, with several cases about it well filled with all kinds of ornaments carved from transparent quartz. It was said at that time that an American traveling in Japan had paid $2,500 for a perfect 4-inch sphere. The 7-inch sphere must have been a foreign exhibit, for at the time of the World's Columbian Exposition in Chicago, in 1893, it was said the largest crystal ball in the United States was slightly more than 6½ inches in diameter, and was valued at $10,000. It came originally from Japan. This was ½ inch smaller than one in the "Green Vaults" at Dresden. At present, the largest flawless sphere in this country is in the United States National Museum, Washington, D. C. It is 12⅞ inches in diameter, and weighs 107 pounds. The value of such a ball is problematical, but it must be close to a quarter of a million dollars. The late Dr. Kunz, who was one of our foremost authorities, has stated that the most outstanding example for size known in recent times is a ball 30 inches in diameter made from Burmese material and finished in Japan.

At one time it was fashionable in ancient Rome for ladies to carry spheres of quartz in their hands, for the sake of their refreshing coolness. In the same manner, Japanese embroiderers keep their hands free from perspiration by use of crystal balls. Jewelers and connoisseurs may often be seen testing beads and other objects supposed to be made of genuine crystal, by touching them to the cheek. Real quartz has a characteristic cool feeling which is not possessed by articles made of glass. It is said that quartz is so poor a conductor of heat that a crystal three inches long may be held at one end with the fingers while the other end is heated to a white heat in the oxygen flame. Glass imitations of crystal balls may be detected in a very simple way. Glass always contains small round bubbles which can be seen with the aid of a strong hand lens, while pure quartz does not have such bubbles. Another test for quartz which is conclusive is that of its refraction. Glass is in no wise double-refracting, while prisms of quartz, although but feebly so, will show two distinct images of very fine lines or dots when they are examined through two non-parallel faces.

TRIDYMITE

Tridymite is a rare form of quartz. The hexagonal crystals are usually very small, thin, and tabular. Its name is derived from a peculiar habit of frequently crystallizing in groups of threes. It resembles quartz in every way except in the matter of its lower specific gravity and refractive index. It occurs chiefly as amygdules in acidic igneous rocks. It is classed as high-temperature quartz and can readily be produced in the laboratory by fusing quartz. As the temperature rises, quartz ceases to be quartz and becomes tridymite long before the quartz fuses. There are temperatures above which the several types of quartz cannot form. Silica crystallizes only below 800°C. Tridymite was discovered by G. Von Rath in the trachyte of San Cristobel, in Mexico; later, it was found to be quite generally distributed.

CRISTOBALITE

Another high-temperature quartz, companion to tridymite, is cristobalite, which occurs in the form of white octahedrons enclosed in amygdules in acidic igneous rocks. Good specimens of this form of quartz are not widely distributed. In the rhyolitic obsidians found along the road from Little Lake to Coso Hot Springs, Inyo County, California, large cavities in the igneous rock are filled with christobalite up to two inches in diameter. These examples are widely used as cabinet specimens and pass under the popular name of christobalite "eggs."

AMETHYST

Amethyst is that variety of crystalline quartz which shows various shades of purple or violet color. Its physical characteristics, other than its color, differ but little from those of quartz. However, since amethyst is composed of alternate layers of right-handed and left-handed quartz, and shows Airy's spirals, it breaks with a rippled fracture, instead of the conchoidal fracture most characteristic of quartz. Indeed, so distinctive is this fracture that some of our later mineralogists have proposed that the name "amethyst" be applied to all quartz showing the same kind of structure, regardless of the color. Amethyst is distinctly dichroic and somewhat doubly refractive. Amethysts are usually cut step, while the finer specimens are cut brilliant. The name "amethyst" owes its root to the Greek word *amethustos*, meaning "not drunken," and was construed to indicate the stone as a remedy for drunkenness.

Judging from its widespread use, the amethyst must have been a popular stone among the ancients. In the burial crypts and ruins of the ancient Egyptians and Babylonians, intaglio seals and ornaments of amethyst are not uncommon. Beads of amethyst have been unearthed from ancient Anglo-Saxon graves in England. During the Middle Ages, amethyst was often worn as an amulet, for it was thought that the stone had the power to preserve the wearer from bodily harm in battle. Many a Crusader, it is said, wore an amethyst attached to his rosary.

We note that the amethyst has always been held in high esteem by royalty. The famous amethyst that adorns the

British crown was once worn by Edward the Confessor, who became the king of England in 1042. This is, in all probability, the oldest of the English crown jewels. In the Eighteenth century, the amethyst was held to be nearly as valuable as the diamond. As an instance of this, the superb amethyst necklace made for Queen Charlotte of England was valued at $10,000. It is doubtful if a similar one today would bring even one-tenth of that sum, the drop in value being largely due to the discovery of the extensive deposits of amethysts in Brazil and Uruguay.

Among churchmen, the amethyst is regarded as a sacred stone and is used freely in ornamenting the altar and its accessories. At West Bend, Iowa, tens of thousands of amethystine crystals and polished agates have been used in the construction of a beautiful grotto and Via Sacra. Without doubt, here may be seen one of the largest, finest and most valuable collections of quartz crystals and polished agates in America. The "fishermen's ring," the ring of authority of the Pope, and the rings given to the Cardinals upon their investiture, are set with amethysts.

Amethysts occur usually as druses lining the inner walls of cavities or veins in granite or other igneous rocks. However, in Brazil and Uruguay they occur lining many of the hollow agate geodes. The West Bend grotto has a Brazilian amethystine geode 24 by 30 inches in size, valued at $5,000, and said to be the largest in America. The amethyst, to be suitable for gem purposes, must be of a deep, uniform color; otherwise the stone will appear almost colorless or gray when viewed by artificial light. Large crystals suitable for gem purposes are relatively rare, because the color is so unevenly diffused throughout the crystal. Usually the color is noticeably concentrated in the apex of the pyramid of the crystal, fading gradually into the milky variety of quartz below. Moreover, amethyst crystals rarely show prisms of any length, such as those in quartz crystals, the prisms being more or less hidden in the druse, where they are badly misshapen. Double-terminate crystals are also among the rarities. One such from the silver mines at Guanajuata in Mexico was once reported by William

Niven to be nine inches long; however, the subsequent history of this unusual crystal seems not to have been recorded. It is interesting to note that the faces of the pyramids are often arranged in parallel position, so that when the specimen is turned in the light the same face of every crystal reflects the light in the same plane. The only satisfactory explanation for this peculiar phenomenon that has ever been suggested is that

QUARTZ, VARIETY AMETHYST
Jefferson County, Montana.

it is due to the electrical polarity of the individual molecules, which causes them to align themselves in regular order with reference to some electric or magnetic axis upon the crystallization of the silica gel.

The color of the amethyst is another of the mineralogical problems that have given rise to much study and investigation. Formerly, it was confidently stated that manganese oxide was the coloring agent responsible for the violet color, but the fact that chemists have been unable to find traces of that metal in the crystals injected some doubt into the matter. It was then suggested that the manganese was present in so minute a quantity that it could not be detected by ordinary methods of analysis. This led Dr. George O. Wild, of the Institute for Precious Stone Research, at Idar, Germany, to attack the problem with the spectroscope. His results were negative also.

However, experiments carried on with radium and X-ray tubes produced some strange results. It was found that when colorless quartz was subjected to the rays, a smoky color resulted. Also, when natural amethysts were discolorized by heating, and then subjected to radiations, the original color was restored but with a superimposed smoky hue. This smoky color could be driven away by reheating, and the amethystine color restored.

In the next instance, colorless quartz was fused to silica glass, in which form it loses its crystalline structure and becomes a true amorphous quartz. Upon being subjected to radiation, it was found to take on an amethystine color. This question immediately arose: Why does the crystalline material become smoky, while the same substance, when deprived of its internal crystalline structure, takes on a violet hue? Dr. Wild suggests that perhaps the difference in the internal structure of the material might have an important bearing upon the color problem. Mineralogists have long recognized that from an optical standpoint there are two varieties of quartzes—those that rotate the plane of light to the right, and those that rotate it to the left. The case of amethyst is most peculiar, for it belongs to neither group. Microscopic studies of thin sections show that it consists of alternating right- and left-turning lamellae, and that the color apparently lies along the contact zones of these lamellae. Some investigators have hoped to show that the color is due to the concentration of molecules of different minerals along these contacts, but so far their investigations have been far from convincing.

The matter is at present somewhat in abeyance, but the consensus of opinion seems to favor the radium theory. The late

Dr. William Holden, who a few years ago wrote so much in the *American Mineralogist* on the cause of color in smoky quartz and amethyst, was a strong champion of this theory. X-rays are found to produce a like result. The finding of most amethysts in igneous rocks, where radium-bearing minerals are the most common, is a strong bit of evidence in favor of the theory. Holden believed that the emanations produced some molecular arrangements that were responsible for the appearance of the color, no inclusion of foreign material being necessary.

Any consideration of the color of the amethyst would not be complete without a word concerning the amethystine glass found in exposed places where it has been subjected to sunlight for a period of years. The longer the exposure of the glass, the deeper the color. Since some of the best examples of this phenomenon are found in desert places, some have argued that the heat of the sun was responsible for the appearance of the color; however, the extreme temperature of such places could scarcely exceed 140°F., and it is not at all likely that so low a temperature would be effective. The most probable explanation is that the ultraviolet (actinic) rays of sunlight have produced a chemical change in the manganese impurities in the glass, thus producing the color. The acceptance of this idea on the part of some has led them to assume that the color of all amethystine quartz has had a similar origin. However, the fact that practically all amethyst comes from cavities and vein linings deep within the earth's crust, where sunlight could not penetrate, refutes the idea.

For centuries, much fine amethyst for the European lapidaries was taken from the granites of the Ekaterinburg district of Russia, but at present most of the supply comes from Brazil and Uruguay. Many localities in India and Ceylon yield amethysts of gem quality. That region may be considered as the main source of supply of these stones used by the ancients. Recently a discovery of good amethysts near Pretoria, South Africa, has been reported, and several tons of material have been sent to England. Many fine stones have been found along the shore of the picturesque Basin of Minas, made famous by Longfellow's poem, "Evangeline." The best time to look for amethysts there is in the spring, after the frosts of winter have thrown down new material upon the talus slopes at the foot of the cliffs. It is said that several large stones from that region were taken back to France by the Sieur de Monts and given to the king, who caused the largest to be cut and placed in the crown of France.

In the United States, amethysts of good quality have been found in a number of localities, notably, in Llano and Burnet Counties, Texas; in the Yellowstone National Park; in Delaware and Chester Counties, Pennsylvania; in Haywood County, North Carolina; and in Oxford County, Maine. The last-named locality has furnished some of the very finest amethysts known, but in limited quantity. Formerly, one of the best known regions for amethysts in America was Thunder Bay, on the north shore of Lake Superior. Large slabs of strikingly beautiful amethysts removed from the walls of veins and cavities in that locality now appear in many of our finest collections. That area is now reported practically worked out.

One of the more recently revealed amethyst-producing areas in our country has been opened up in Jefferson County, Montana, east of Butte, in the Homestake Mining district. The best amethyst deposits are located on the west fork of Rader Creek. The amethysts and large groups and single crystals of quartz are found in a dike, which outcrops over a considerable distance. Some commercial mining of amethyst has been carried on there; excellent specimen material and gem-quality crystals have been found. Other localities in Jefferson County have produced amethyst crystals of considerable size.

Even though amethysts are quite common and low in price, they have been artificially produced, and a number of varieties are on the market. The cheaper imitations are ordinarily just glass, while the better types are either quartz or fused corundum, colored with manganese or iron compounds. When amethysts of large size and deep, even color are offered for sale at a low price, it is best to make a careful examination before purchasing. Any cut amethyst of ten or more carats in weight would likely show unevenness in the distribution of the color, and any stone of that size in which the color is evenly distributed should be looked upon with suspicion.

When amethysts are heated in a certain manner, they generally take on a yellow hue. It is said that many of the cairngorm and citrine stones used in jewelry are now obtained in this way.

SMOKY QUARTZ

Smoky quartz is a variety of crystal quartz characterized by a smoky-yellow to dark smoky-brown color; all gradations, from those with a mere tinge of color to some so dense as to be practically opaque, are found. The nearly black variety has been named *morion*. The color may be unevenly distributed in the same crystal, showing darker areas in places. The color of most smoky quartz can be altered by proper heat treatment. Among various varieties of quartz made in this manner are Spanish topaz and citrine quartz. However, amethyst also is used for the production of citrine quartz.

For years the color of smoky quartz was charged to the presence of carbonaceous and organic matter, but the experiments conducted by Dr. George O. Wild, at Idar, Germany, have disproved the organic matter theory. It is now thought that the smoky color is due to colorless crystals' having been exposed for long periods of time to radium emanations from the surrounding rock. This is substantiated by the fact that X rays in heavy doses will change some colorless quartz to smoky; these rays carry the gamma rays also present in radium emanations. Further, it has been noted in the Swiss Alps, that crystals found at various elevations vary in color. Experts can quite accurately estimate the elevation at which a crystal was found. It is known that the radioactivity of the rocks in the Swiss Alps varies at different elevations; hence the crystals are exposed to different radiations. Seemingly, not all colorless quartz will respond to X-ray or radium emanations, for colorless quartz is found in quantity at various localities in the Swiss Alps. Why some crystals should respond to treatment and others not is still a matter of scientific doubt.

The most notable find of smoky quartz on record was made in the Canton Uri, Switzerland, in 1868, when about 3,000 pounds of excellent crystals were taken from a single cavity in the rock. Fortunately, the best of these were preserved in the Berne Museum. An interesting account of the discovery of this remarkable pocket appeared in "The Subterranean World," by Dr. George Hartwig, which is given in part below.

In 1867 a party of tourists descending from the solitudes of Galenstock discovered, in a band of white quartz traversing a precipitous rock wall about 100 feet above the Tiefen Glacier, some dark spots, which the guide declared to be cavities in which crystals of quartz would be found. No search was made at the time, but later the guide, Peter Sulzer, revisited the spot, and after climbing with considerable difficulty, reached the cavity and collected a number of excellent crystals.

Later, the locality was again visited, and a more decisive attempt made to penetrate farther into the cavity by blasting out the narrow entrance. Bad weather, with wind and hail, made exploration difficult; the hardy adventurers were obliged to pass a miserable night huddled close together in a narrow cavity. The following morning they were able to widen the entrance to a larger cave, which was found to penetrate to a considerable depth into the mountain. The cave was filled nearly up to its roof with a mound consisting of pieces of granite and quartz mixed with chlorite sand; but here and there, embedded in the waste, glistened large faces of smoky crystals, which indicated that the toil had not been fruitless. Originally, the crystals had grown from the sides and roof of the cavern. Who can tell the ages that were required for their growth, or the mysterious circumstances that favored deposition? Then, at an equally unknown time, the concussion of an earthquake, or perhaps their own weight, had detached them from the rock to which they had grown and clung.

After the first explorers had collected about a ton of crystals, the whole able-bodied population of Guttenen, provided with tools, ropes, and baskets, came forth to carry down more crystals. Thousands of splendid crystals were obtained, some of them weighing from 50 to 100 pounds or more, in single crystals and in large groups. One lot of the finest crystals was sold to the Berne Museum for 8,000 francs. One of the largest crystals, which has been named "The King," stands 32 inches high, is 3 feet in circumference, and weighs 255 pounds. A similar one, named "The Grandfather," is slightly heavier in weight. Many other fine crystals were sold to various museums and private collectors for from 6 to 7 francs per pound, so that Sulzer's discovery will long be gratefully remembered in the annals of the village of Guttenen.

Probably the best-known American locality for smoky quartz is the Pike's Peak region in Colorado, where a coarse pegmatite contains numerous veins and pockets filled with crystals, along with amazonite and other gem minerals. Kunz mentioned one huge crystal, four feet long, found there. Such large masses furnish excellent gem-cutting material; and stones (faceted) weighing as much as a pound or more have been cut from large crystals. Other noteworthy localities are Alexander County, North Carolina, and Auburn County, Maine, the latter locality yielding exceptionally large crystals. One is recorded as nearly two feet long and remarkably smoky and clear. Crystals from the Maine locality have been cut into balls and faceted stones. Smoky quartz crystals are most likely to be found associated with granites and pegmatite dikes. It is a well-known fact that pegmatite dikes, originating as granitic intrusions from great depths, are likely to carry radioactive minerals. Moreover, these formations frequently hold a greater than normal (for rocks) percentage of radium, hence it is to be expected that smoky quartz will appear, in accordance with the theory given for the cause of color in smoky quartz.

Smoky quartz is often mentioned as "cairngorm stone," from its occurrence at Cairngorm, in northern Scotland. There it has a sentimental and historic interest, and because of its use as a decorative ornament for the weapons and picturesque dress of the Highlanders, it may be regarded as the national gem of Scotland. In Scotland, smoky quartz is found in the granites, and as water-worn pebbles in stream gravels. Before cutting, heat treatment is applied to the Scottish smoky quartz, to give it the pleasing yellow-brown (citrine) color.

Smoky quartz has the physical and chemical properties of ordinary rock crystal, with the exception of difference in color. The gem is frequently cut in standard round, brilliant styles, but step and table styles are also pleasing and popular. Because of the great masses available, it can be worked into large spheres, seals, brooches, and numerous other ornamental shapes. Its crystal forms are identical with those of colorless quartz. Japan has produced some remarkable smoky crystals over a period of many years, and these are sometimes worked by the Oriental artisans into carved objects of art.

CITRINE

Citrine is a light golden-yellow or reddish-yellow variety of crystalline quartz which probably owes its color to a slight trace of ferric iron. The gem, very popular during the Victorian period of the last century, was erroneously called "topaz." Even today there is an excellent demand for stones of good quality, as they wear well and present an unusually distinctive color. Practically all the yellowish, reddish-yellow, and brown stones of commerce, frequently sold under the name of "topaz," are in reality quartz—either heat-treated, fused quartz or the natural mineral.

Some types of smoky and brown-colored quartz will, when heated properly, change to a yellow, reddish, or pale citrine quartz. Pale or inferior-colored amethyst also is used to produce a yellow-colored quartz. "Spanish topaz" and "Saxon topaz" are jewelers' names given to the deep reddish or orange-colored types. The heat treatment of quartz to produce the citrine varieties is now largely carried on at the European cutting centers, where modern thermostat-controlled ovens and furnaces are used. Technical studies indicate that quartz, like some of the other species of gems, has what is termed a "critical" temperature, where the change in color takes place almost instantly. Temperatures which are too low or too high may not produce the change or may destroy the color after it has been attained.

It is stated by J. C. Kleiner, in Vol. III of the *Mineral Collector*, that the Russian peasants of the province of Perm, where smoky quartz crystals are found, are accustomed to alter them to a deep-yellow color by baking the crystals in loaves of bread. If the color is not sufficiently changed by the first baking, the treatment is repeated until the desired color is attained or the stone given up as hopeless. No matter what form of heat treatment is employed, be it the kitchen-oven variety or the modern thermostat-controlled muffle, only a relatively small percentage of the material will change to a satisfactory commercial color and escape breakage or other damage; some resist all treatment and remain wholly unaltered. Sometimes, a crystal will shatter with explosive violence, under heat treatment. This is probably due to the presence of minute cavities filled with liquid carbon dioxide or water; or the material may be under the strain of crystallization.

In all probability, a number of the cheaper types of citrine quartz are cut from some form of fused glass having a very high percentage of quartz. These gems give about the same specific gravity as the natural gem and will have a similar hardness. They may even show a very feeble dichroism. Optical tests, however, will reveal their true nature.

Good gem crystals with a distinct yellow, or "citrine," color are not found in many localities in this country. One area in New Mexico has yielded some very fine groups of citrine quartz crystals. Much of the commercial supply of the natural gem comes from Brazil. The yellow, reddish-brown, and similar colors in quartz are thought to be due to iron, in the form of ferric salts. It is possible that the heat-treatment change depends upon the presence of minute amounts of iron as an impurity, the heat converting this iron into a ferrous state, with the accompanying color change.

SAGENITE

This form of crystalline quartz has long been known and, because of its peculiar structure, held in great esteem for ornamental purposes. It was formerly known under a variety of names, such as, *flèches d'amour*, or Cupid's darts, Venus or Thetis hair-stone, the needle stone, etc. Some specimens show the hairlike crystals crossing one another roughly at right angles, giving a netlike appearance to the stone; from this the name "sagenite" has been derived from the Greek word for a net. Sagenite is usually named from the included mineral; thus, if rutile is present, it is called rutilated quartz, or, if tourmaline be the included mineral, it is known as tourmalinated quartz, etc.

Since quartz is usually nearly the last mineral to crystallize or separate out during the process of solidification of a rock magma, it may include within its crystals all other minerals which have crystallized previously or at the same time with it. Of the minerals so included, rutile is the most common, but tourmaline, hornblende, epidote, actinolite, goethite, and many others occur. Indeed, the number of minerals so included becomes impressive when tabulated by one giving some thought to the matter. Peter Zodac, writing in *Rocks and Minerals Magazine* for February, 1937, calls attention to some forty different substances that have been noted in quartz, and concedes that the list may not be exhaustive. This would make a fruitful phase of the study of quartz, as new varieties are being found from time to time. One of the latest additions to this already long list of included minerals comes from the Sillimanite mines near Laws, California, where small amounts of massive quartz, colored by the inclusion of dumortierite, have been found. This is probably the first recorded occurrence of that peculiar combination of minerals.

The lengths of the included crystals are at times surprising. Some as much as six inches long have been reported in crystals from Madagascar. The number of hairlike crystals noted in a single quartz crystal varies from a few isolated long crystals to a multitude of short ones, often much crowded together. For cutting purposes, pieces of the latter variety are much preferred. Some of the most striking effects are obtained when the included mineral is rutile, that is, sufficiently transparent to be of a blood-red color, by either direct or transmitted light. Another beautiful effect is produced when the crystal is of a light, golden-brown color. Such stones when cut flat cabochon,

SAGENITIC QUARTZ CRYSTALS

With inclusions of acicular crystals of rutile (left). Green actinolite within quartz (right).

seem to have a golden glow with sparkles of light caused by the included crystals.

The origin of these elongated crystals has always been a bothersome point to the beginner in the study of minerals, but in reality it is not difficult to explain. English, in his recent book, "Getting Acquainted with Minerals," describes what he terms "stretched-out crystals." He says, "We must bear in mind that, theoretically, the angles between their faces are constant, and, indeed, this constancy of angles is one of the essential characteristics of crystals. It seems all the more remarkable, therefore, to find freak crystals, which, at first sight, seem to be so different from the typical forms as to make them more like forms in some other system."

Possibly, the most wonderful of the "stretched-out crystals" are the cubes of cuprite (chalcotrichite) from Morenci, Arizona, which have been elongated into hairlike forms by expanding all in one direction. To English this represented a battle between the crystallizing forces, the one striving to pull the cubes out into hairs, overcoming the natural forces that were trying to form perfect cubes. In reality, the formation is a pile of cubes one on top of another.

Sagenitic quartz is obtained in many places, both here and abroad. The island of Madagascar has long held the lead in the production of this type of quartz. Considerable material is now being produced in Brazil. Most of it is shipped to Germany for working up into jewelry and ornaments. In Japan are found crystals of quartz with hairlike inclusions and scales or masses of chlorite. Many of these are prepared for market by simply polishing the crystal faces. They make beautiful cabinet pieces. A pale, amethystine variety, called onegite, from Lake Onega, in Russia, where it was first found, is penetrated by needles of goethite. This is cut generally as love charms in the form of hearts, and is sold as "Cupid's darts." For a long time it was thought that Russia was the only place where this peculiar mineral could be found, but some years ago considerable quanti-ties were found at Florissant, Colorado, where it was at first described as a new species. By transmitted light the crystals show a very attractive blood-red color.

The most remarkable specimens of rutilated quartz ever found in this country were taken from the glacial drift near Hanover, New Hampshire, nearly a century ago. Two of these probably equal in beauty any sagenites known. One of them was preserved in the collection of George Vaux in Philadelphia. This piece consists of a large crystal of a smoky-brown color, five and a half by six inches in dimensions. The acicular needle-like crystals of rutile, which are long and well distributed throughout the mass, show a rich red color when viewed by direct light. The second finest specimen belonged to Prof.

Oliver Hubbard, of Dartmouth College; it is six inches long and three inches wide. Kunz figures this specimen in his book, "Gems and Precious Stones of North America." A study of the characteristics of these two specimens suggests that they are fragments of a much larger mass; however, diligent search has failed to reveal their place of origin or additional specimens.

Sagenitic structure occurs also in chalcedony and agate, notably in Oregon and other localities in the Western states, where agates are found in profusion. The acicular and similar growths noted in the cryptocrystalline forms of quartz are described under a separate heading.

AVENTURINE

Aventurine is a form of crystalline quartz that contains inclusions, not in the form of fibers, but as scales of some bright mineral, such as mica or flakes of hematite, which present a spangled appearance when turned in the light. The included flakes may vary in size, being either coarse or fine. The best stones show spangles of a medium size, which are more or less evenly distributed. Cut cabochon-style, such stones present a pleasing effect, especially by artificial light. Also, the quartz base may be of several colors—brown, red, yellow, or black, rarely bluish or greenish. The variety most generally cut for gem purposes is of a reddish-yellow color and has a coppery sheen. Sometimes, small, well-developed crystals are prepared for watch charms by smoothing and polishing the several faces and supplying a suitable mounting.

The classic area for the production of aventurine is in the Ural and Altai Mountains of the U.S.S.R. In the Altai Mountains, not far from Kolivan, pieces of aventurine have been secured of such size that they have been cut into vases and dishes. One of the finest of these is preserved in the Museum of Practical Geology in London. Of it Farrington says: "This vase was presented by Nicholas I to Sir Roderick Murchison in recognition of his services in investigating the geology of the Russian empire." India has long been noted for its production of this stone, though not in a quantity comparable with the mines of the U.S.S.R. Small amounts have been found, besides, in several places in Europe, but not very good in quality. This applies also to the United States.

Goldstone is an artificial product imitating yellow or red aventurine. It is said that a French (or maybe an Italian) glassmaker accidentally spilled some brass filings into his glass pot, and the results were so pleasing that the artificial stone met with immediate favor. Even at present, goldstone, as well as many other glass imitations of gems, are exported in astonishing quantities from Gablong in Czechoslovakia. So extensive is the industry that more than 12,000 people are employed in the various processes necessary for the making and preparation of the tons of glass gems annually disposed of through our popular ten-cent stores.

ASTERIATED QUARTZ

Asteriated or "star quartz," a term which we now find rather infrequently mentioned in modern mineralogical literature, was formerly listed in most catalogues of quartz varieties. As the name implies ("aster" meaning star), this variety is associated with any form of crystalline quartz where the star-shaped figure or pattern manifests itself in any way. Since the phenomenon is definitely related to the matter of crystal structure, we should expect the six-point star pattern to prevail, and that assumption is indeed correct.

This structural variation asserts itself in at least two distinctly different ways. First, in certain geodes, particularly of the "Keokuk" beds, there is found radiate crystalline quartz of very definite character, with flattish pyramidal terminations emerging upon the inner surface of the geodes, presenting marked estellate patterns, suggesting evidences of twinning. These figures, being unique in the quartz world, present very pleasing and surprising effects. Those examined by the author usually have had a marked yellowish tinge or cast and they sometimes have a thin outer coating of blue-gray chalcedony.

Asteriated quartz of a different type occurs as a constituent of a granite vein, in pieces seldom larger than small eggs, in the neighborhood of the Gatineau, Canada. This stone is perfectly transparent, and by reflected light exhibits a star of six rays. A few pieces even showed the same effect when viewed by ordinary, direct light. Many years ago Ottawa lapidaries sold a number of these specimens polished, at from four to ten dollars each, according to their quality. Asteriated rose quartz of a rare form, which exhibits striking starlike patterns on cut and polished faces, has been recently reported from the feldspar quarries at Bedford, New York.

It is said that some varieties of quartz may also exhibit percussion figures of estellate pattern, when they are struck a sharp, pointed blow under proper conditions.

FERRUGINOUS QUARTZ

As the name indicates, these are crystals of quartz which either are closely associated with iron (ferrum), or have the appearance of being so. They often look as if they were coated or dusted with rust. When they are examined carefully, however, it will be observed that this coating is not merely superficial, but seems, rather, to impregnate the entire crystal, making it practically opaque. At times, the amount of included impurity is so great as to cause the crystal to take a form greatly distorted or misshapen. In the author's collection are crystal specimens which are much flattened and elongated, appearing as though they had passed under a heavy roller while in a semifused condition. This, of course, is not the case. They are merely extreme examples of the influence or effect of the presence of impurities upon crystal structure.

This form of quartz is not uncommon, occurring in most localities where deposits of iron ore exist. So uncomely are the individual specimens, however, that they are usually overlooked or discarded by the finder as being without interest or, at least, undeserving of a place in any collection of beautiful quartz minerals. Not all ferruginous crystals, however, are of this type, for at Seven Rivers, New Mexico, small, doubly terminated crystals are found, averaging half an inch in length, which have a uniform red-brown color and are quite perfect. The larger crystals from the same locality, averaging one and a half inches in length, are of a dirty brown color, but with faces as bright and perfect as are the smaller ones.

These crystals sometimes assume a cubical aspect, and, in the iron deposits of St. Lawrence and Jefferson counties in New York, it is said that quartz crystals are also found in dodeca-hedral form. We are not informed whether in their case this is the primary form or perhaps a pseudomorph after pyrite or some other mineral.

CHAPTER VII

Massive Forms of Quartz

Of the making of classifications, as of the making of books there is no end. Organization in science is just as essential as in a business institution. In either case, no definite progress could be made without the aid that comes from a preconceived plan. It is a well-known fact, that while business administration follows certain fully tested lines or procedures, in minor details they may all differ one from another. In the discussion of the various members of the prolific quartz family, the authors have endeavored to follow, in a general way, the classification handed down to us by the numerous writers in this field of mineralogy who have gone before. However, in minor detail, we have deemed it to be our prerogative to deviate wherever, by that means, the story of quartz would move along more smoothly. Therefore, the grouping together of the several minerals in this chapter, which at first might seem to be very unorthodox, or even unrelated, will be found to be based especially upon the characteristic of mass.

MILKY QUARTZ

Milky quartz is a translucent to opaque variety of massive quartz which is very widespread in occurrence. It is nature's great healing agent, most vein-filling in igneous and metamorphic rocks being composed of it.

The color of milky quartz is an anomaly, as it is due not to any pigment but to the presence of vast numbers of cavities, which usually contain water or liquefied carbon dioxide, thus greatly impairing the transparency of the crystals. In *Minerals*,

Massive Forms of Quartz

Vol. I, No. 4, Dr. H. Hensoldt writes concerning the color of milky quartz thus:

In terrestrial minerals enclosures of fluids are common. If we prepare a thin section from one of the quartz pebbles to be found in any river bed and examine it under a microscope, we observe the field crowded with dustlike particles like a cloud. If we increase the magnification, these dots enlarge in proportion to the power employed until each expands into a cell or cavity, in the interior of which a round object is seen moving about. These objects are cavities filled with liquid, and the moving object is a bubble which is perpetually in motion. In the largest cavities the motion is barely perceptible, but in the smaller ones it is lively, the bubble darting from one side of the cell to the other. Now what causes the white appearance of milky quartz? Some coloring principle? Nothing of the kind; the white color is due to millions of fluid enclosures. The cavities do not enclose a white fluid; the white color is merely an optical phenomenon due to the reflection of the light by the myriad walls of the cavities. We have the same thing in snow, which is not white by virtue of color; if we melt it, we get the clear water of which it is composed.

The bubble movement has nothing to do with Brownian motion. . . . But the bubble movement in our fluid cavities is due to the ever-varying temperature of the atmosphere. The temperature which surrounds us is never constant, though we cannot with our coarse instruments perceive small differences. If we focus a high-power objective on the level of the thermometer column we can see it constantly shifting. The same effect can be shown with a spirit level. If a spirit level is placed on a table, so that the bubble is in the center, the holding of a hand in the air a foot from the tube suffices to cause a disturbance. The warmth of the hand drives the bubble from its position, which it will resume when equilibrium is restored.

Concerning the presence of liquids in cavities in quartz, Dr. Hensoldt goes on to say:

The liquid imprisoned in the cavities of quartz and other minerals is generally water. Sometimes it is strongly charged with sodium chloride, and in the cavities of granites, notably those of Cornwall, we frequently observe cubic salt crystals floating in the liquid. This would indicate a saturated solution which once doubtless filled the cavity, but in the course of ages some of the water evaporated through the rock, or a lowering of the temperature took place, so that the salt was precipitated. Occasionally the liquids are hydrocarbons, oily, petroleum-like substance.

The German investigators, Vogelsang and Geissler, discovered that in many rocks the imprisoned liquid was carbon dioxide in the liquefied state. This was checked by warming the thin sections by means of an electric wire coiled around the slide, and watching the temperature on a stage thermometer. It was noted that the bubble suddenly disappeared when a temperature of 30°C. was reached, but returned again as soon as the temperature dropped below this point. Between 30° and 31°C. lies the critical point of carbon dioxide—that is, above this point, carbon dioxide cannot exist in a liquid state, however great the pressure to which it is subjected. Had the bubbles been filled with water, they would not have shown any change at this temperature. To verify this, Dr. Hensoldt subjected to a boiling temperature certain quartz crystals which he knew contained water bubbles, without detecting any effect upon the bubbles.

Carbon dioxide is a gas which can be reduced to a liquid only by pressure of not less than 65 atmospheres: equivalent to a column of water 2,000 feet high, or a rock stratum 700 feet thick. Wherever we find liquid carbon dioxide in terrestrial rocks, we may take it for granted that the formation of those rocks took place deep in the earth's crust under a gigantic weight of superimposed rocks. Cavities containing carbon dioxide often occur in basalts and other basic lavas, which are known to have been derived from deep-seated magmas, where, besides the weight of tremendous rock masses above, we have the compressing force of elastic vapor held in confinement; while in acid lavas, of which there is evidence that they are formed at no such depths, the presence of liquefied carbon dioxide is rare. The fact that the quartz of granites contains such cavities may be taken as evidence that they have been formed deep within the earth and under enormous pressure. No such cavities are to be found in sedimentary strata.

Massive Forms of Quartz

One of the largest pockets of quartz crystals ever discovered in this country was found at Buckfield, Maine. It was about 20 feet long, 9 feet wide, and from 5 to 8 feet in height. It was entirely lined with large quartz crystals, most of them ranging from a foot to 18 inches in length. The most striking crystal of them all was doubly terminated, three feet high and two feet in diameter, and weighed nearly 600 pounds. Almost all of the crystals from this find were of a translucent milky color.

It would be a useless task to attempt to mention the many deposits of milky quartz that exist in this country. Many of them occur in the form of broad bands, filling veins and fissures in both igneous and metamorphic rock. Such vein fillings are of extreme importance as carriers of the precious metals, especially gold.

Canada seems to be particularly well supplied with this variety of quartz, some beds being of great extent and thickness. One of the largest of these deposits occurs on Wells Island, in the St. Lawrence River. The quartz at that point is massive, milky-white to transparent in color, and suitable for commercial purposes. Large quantities of the stone are quarried and prepared for market. Other islands of the Thousand Islands group have similar large veins of milky quartz.

Existing as constituents of many igneous rocks, massive crystalline quartz occurs in many distinctive shades, aside from the pure-white or milky variety. The color variations most frequently met with are: reddish, pale to deep, of a shade distinctly different from that of rose quartz; yellowish, pale to a yellow-brown, of a translucent variety which is of entirely different character from the yellow jaspers; and a bluish-gray quartz, which is also frequently associated with vein minerals, especially those bearing gold. As these granitic rocks break down and weather away, the quartz portion, being more resistant, will persist in the sand and gravel beds as pebbles, which are often very common and sometimes make cabinet specimens sufficiently attractive to be deserving of a place in any collection of quartz minerals.

Boulders of milky quartz are not uncommon in the glacial drift of our Northern states. No doubt, the material was derived by the ice from the extensive Archaean complex of Canada. In the absence of flint, the Indians used this material in the fabrication of spear and arrow heads, etc. In the very complete collection of Indian relics of Judge George Bedford of Morris, Illinois, may be seen many objects worked from this material. One piece, in particular, is a mortar about eight inches in diameter, very symmetrical in shape. The outer surface shows partial polishing, probably by rubbing. The depth of the object is over three inches, and one wonders by what means the aboriginal artisan accomplished this exceptionally difficult piece of work.

Commercially, for abrasive purposes, crushed vein quartz is preferred to sand or crushed sandstone, because it has sharp angles. For this reason it is chosen for paints and as a wood filler, because the sharp particles adhere to the surface of the wood more closely than those with rounded edges.

ROSE QUARTZ

This is a rose-red or pinkish variety of massive quartz, the color of which is attributed to the inclusion of a small amount of the salts of titanium or manganese. Rose quartz in crystal form is exceedingly rare. What are probably the only crystals of rose quartz in existence are to be seen in the collections of the Boston Society of Natural History and in the Mineralogical Museum at Harvard University. The Boston collection has three specimens—one from Paris, Maine, pale in color, and two from Newry, Maine, which are smaller crystals but of a much deeper color. In the Harvard collection may be seen a single specimen, which is a part of one of the above-mentioned Boston specimens. The reported occurrence of rose quartz in crystal form at Grand Rapids, Wood County, Wisconsin, never, to the writer's knowledge, has been confirmed.

One of the largest deposits of high-grade rose quartz in this country, if not in the world, is located in the Black Hills, about eight miles from Custer, South Dakota. The quartz is of a beautiful rose color and is found in large segregations of irregular shape in a pegmatite. It is believed to represent late crystallization during the cooling and consolidation of the magmatic solution, at a temperature somewhat below that at which milky quartz crystallizes. There are all gradations of color, from milky white through pale pink to deep rose red. This latter color is fugitive and on long exposure to bright sunlight fades and becomes pale; but it is said that if the specimen is placed in a dark, humid place for some time the color recovers its former brightness. Why this is so poses another interesting question for some mineralogist to solve.

The best grade of rose quartz is worked up into jewelry, chiefly necklaces and settings for rings and pins. From the next-best grade of material, vases, trays, paperweights, and other ornaments are cut and then polished. Strange as it may seem, almost all this lapidary work is done in Germany, and the resulting articles are then returned to be sold to tourists and others in this country. The cheaper grades of the rose quartz are used for monumental work, facings for fireplaces, tops of water fountains, and many other purposes. Crushed to small pieces, it is meeting ever-increasing popularity in "pebble-dash finish" for stucco construction work. The results are pleasing.

In the Field Museum in Chicago may be seen a beautiful carving of rose quartz in the form of a bowl, some eighteen inches in diameter and standing six inches in height. The walls of this piece have been worked down to a thickness of less than one-half inch, so that when the light shines through them it gives a delightful appearance to the dish. This is probably the finest large piece of lapidary work ever executed in this material.

Rose quartz occurs in several other places in our country, notably at Exeter, Tulare County, California, also at Stow, Albany, and Paris, Maine, and at Southbury, Connecticut. The Maine localities formerly constituted our chief source of this stone, which was often obtainable in pieces four or five inches square, free from flaws, and of a deep rose-red color.

That these pieces were worked up beautifully is attested by the numerous spheres, small dishes, etc., that may be seen in both public and private collections throughout the country.

Some rose quartz occurs in numerous other places in the Appalachian Mountains, especially in Stokes and Ashe counties, North Carolina. In Colorado it has been reported in several localities, notably near the head of Roaring Fork, in Pitkin County, near Clear Creek, and on Bear Creek. It occurs also at Tuscarora, Moray, and Silver Peak, in Nevada. Very small quantities of a translucent pink-milky variety of rose quartz is found in some localities in Maine. This is often very high-grade gem material. Any type of rose quartz, including the milky variety, may show asterism, if the stone happens to be properly oriented on the steep cabochon surface.

QUARTZ SAND

It may not surprise the reader to learn that the great Swedish scientist Linnaeus was misled by the erroneous notion which prevailed during his time that crystal quartz was simply water so thoroughly frozen that it could not be melted. In one of his writings, Linnaeus states that sands, as well as other related siliceous materials, had their origin in raindrops which had grown together and solidified. This peculiar idea prevailed unquestioned until 1777, when Gmelin published a German translation of the works of Linnaeus, in which he corrected the matter from the then-known difference in the composition of the two substances.

Sand is mineral matter in more or less uniform grains that have resulted for the most part from the disintegration of igneous and metamorphic rocks, though all kinds of rocks will contribute to the accumulation. There are many varieties of sand, named according to the mineral which predominates in their composition, as quartz sand, magnetite sand, etc. In texture, sand may range from grains just large enough to be seen with the unaided eye, up to those too small to be readily picked up by hand. Ordinary sand, however, resembles granulated sugar in fineness. When first formed, the particles are sharp and angular, but after being blown about by the wind, or worked over and over by the waves or running water, they become subangular or even rounded. Also, the older the sand, the more complete the separation of the quartz grains from the particles of other minerals that may have been originally present.

Siliceous sand, owing to the resistance of the individual grains, is by far the commonest of the sands. Such sand is composed of fine, incoherent grains of quartz, with some impurities, such as magnetite, etc. Even quartz sands differ considerably, according to their mode of origin. River sands and those directly due to the disintegration of rocks through atmospheric agencies usually show angular grains, while desert and wind-blown sands are, for the most part, fine-grained, much rounded and pitted by abrasion. Beach sands, which are constantly being agitated by the surge and ebb of the waves, also are somewhat rounded by attrition. A little practice with a magnifier soon enables anyone to differentiate with considerable certainty these sands, with respect to their mode of origin.

There are many seemingly mysterious occurrences in the realm of nature; some, indeed, have never been satisfactorily explained and remain as items to whet the interest of future investigators. Along certain sandy beaches, a little way back from the water's edge and paralleling it, there occurs a strip of sand which, when scuffed with the feet or disturbed by dragging a stick over it, gives off a peculiar sound. These are known as "singing sands" or "musical sands." The sound produced by several people scuffing their feet as they walk over the beach is weird and difficult to define. It can be distinctly heard for some distance. The phenomenon has always courted an explanation, and, as is to be expected, several theories have been offered, but with little in common among them. According to some, the sound is due to the friction of one sand grain against another; others, possibly better acquainted with sand near an ocean shore, think it due to a thin layer of salt deposited on the sand grains, which causes them to rasp over each other when disturbed. Obviously, this explanation would not hold at all for sands accumulated in regions of fresh-water lakes, like those along the south shore of Lake Michigan.

Probably the best explanation of all those offered is, after all, the simplest. This ascribes the phenomenon to a certain moisture content of the sand. According to G. F. Shepherd, this seems to be the most reasonable explanation, because it is to be noted that the singing sands always occur where the sand is not thoroughly saturated nor yet too dry. The capillarity of the water film upon the sand grains, it seems, must be just sufficient to bind them so that they will rub against one another when disturbed. When the sand is saturated, the grains are held apart, and when dry, they are not held together at all, so no sound is produced when they are stirred.

Besides the type of musical sands that sometimes occurs along sandy shorelines, we find in certain desert areas an altogether different variety of this strange phenomenon. At any rate, the cause of the sounds appears to be an altogether different set of physical conditions. These "singing sands" of the deserts have been responsible for the rise of strange tales and queer superstitions. They have figured in travelers' tales for over a thousand years. Marco Polo, the Venetian traveler of the thirteenth century, writing the account of his journey across the Great Gobi desert on his way to the land of the Great Kahn, said "Sometimes you shall hear the sounds of musical instruments, and still more commonly the sound of drums." Needless to say, this traveler gave no explanation for the strange sounds— rather, leaving the reader to infer that they were the manifestation of the spirits that inhabited the sandy wastes.

The Arabian desert affords several instances of "singing sands," which produce weird sounds that intermittently break into the desert silence. According to Hawks, in his recent "Book of Natural Wonders," "The music varies, from the thin, high-pitched twanging of harp-strings to the rumble of distant drums." Few, indeed, are those who, having heard these strange sounds, have not had their curiosity aroused as to the source.

Many scientists have made exhaustive studies of the phenomenon, with somewhat conflicting results, owing to varying field conditions.

One of the most frequently visited and described of the areas of "singing sands" is the famous Jebel Nakus, or Hill of the Bell, located in the Sinai Peninsula, on the eastern shore of the Red Sea. Prof. E. H. Palmer visited the region in 1869 and gave a very full description of what he saw and heard there. He found the hill to be about 380 feet high and composed of very fine, dry sand. He noted that the sand lay at an angle of about 30°, so that it was very easily set in motion from any point along the slope "with a sluggish, viscous motion, and it is then that the sound begins, at first a low vibratory moan, but gradually swelling out into a roar like thunder, and as gradually dying away again until the sand has ceased to roll." He further observed that the heated surface was much more sensitive to sound than the cooler layers beneath. Altogether, he concluded from his observations that the phenomenon was purely local and superficial, due in some manner to the combined effects of heat and friction, with the possibility that some electrical influence was also at work.

"Singing sands" have been reported from other places in Arabia, but none comparable to Jebel Nakus. In the Libyan Desert, musical sands have been found on the west side of the Nile Valley. In the western Sahara, they have been discovered between Timbuktu and Morocco, and also in South Africa, on the west of the Langberg Mountain, in Griqualand. In the Western Hemisphere, we find in Chile the Rumbling Mountain, which is an object of curiosity to the traveler, and of fear to the simple-minded Indians.

In the United States, "singing sands" occur in Churchill County, Nevada, where there is a sand dune four miles long which, according to Hawks, "gives out a sound that has been likened to humming of telegraph wires." In the dune area of Southern California musical dunes have been responsible for the legend that a monastery lies buried under the dune sands.

The so-called "barking sands," described by W. A. Bryan, in his "Natural History of Hawaii," are located on the Island of Kauai, and "consist of a series of wind-blown sand hills . . . along the shore at Nahili. The bank is nearly 60 feet high, and the front wall is quite steep. The white sand, which is composed of coral, shells, and particles of lava, has the peculiar property, when very dry, of emitting a sound when two handfuls are clapped together, that, to the imaginative mind, seems to resemble the barking of a dog." Bryan reports that "the sound varies with the degree of heat, the dryness of the sand, and the amount of friction employed." Several attempts to explain this natural phenomenon have left much of the mystery unsolved. However, the dry sand doubtless has a resonant quality that is the basis of the peculiar manifestation, which disappears when the sand is wet.

The primary cause of all these extraordinary phenomena is the movement of the sand grains, either by the wind or by any other cause. Other factors in the production of the sounds appear to be somewhat conjectural. Hawks seems to think that the reason why all sand does not sing is that the individual grains lack some peculiar natural quality or conformation. He says, in support of his theory: "Experiments have shown that sand only sings when the grains are of a certain size, uniformity, and shape."

Sand is a much more useful and valuable commodity than we are in the habit of thinking. Fortunate, indeed, are the circumstances that supply that commodity in such immense quantities over a widespread area. Few are the localities that are not supplied with enough sand for at least their immediate needs. In this day of concrete and cement work, sand is indispensable, and the amount used by man in his various building operations in a single year is simply prodigious.

Sand for commercial purposes is usually classified according to its uses as: building sand, used for cement, mortar, and plastering; molding sand, used in foundries for iron and other metal castings. Silica sand is also in demand for refractory purposes about blast furnaces and other metallurgical operations, such as ladle and cupola linings. Engine sand is a hard, sharp sand, graded to a definite size for sanding the rails of railways. Most of this sand, as well as the sand for abrasive purposes, is obtained from silica mines, where a coarse-grained sandstone is quarried, crushed, screened, and washed, in preparation for its uses. Abrasive sand is used extensively in the sawing and smoothing of granite, marble, and other building stones. A small quantity is employed in the specialized making of sandpaper. Considerable abrasive sand is used in the plate-glass industry, in the first grinding of the crude plate to remove the irregularities before the final grinding and polishing operations. Sharp quartz sand is used in sand-blasting castings, cleaning the outer walls of stone buildings, frosting glass, etc.

The foremost of all its uses depends on the fact that clean quartz sand is the basic material in the manufacture of high-grade glass. This industry alone consumes an enormous quantity annually. For this purpose, sand is usually screened and washed, since the presence of any impurities, especially iron, seriously affects the quality of the glass. Filtration sand is used in the sand beds of large filter systems for the clarification of municipal water supplies. Some sand is used in the manufacture of fireproofing material, safe filling, soundproofing, and wood filler, in paper making, and in the manufacture of sand-lime bricks.

In the pulverized state, it is extremely useful in the manufacture of scouring soaps and washing powders, grinding and polishing powders, glazes in the ceramic industry, such alloys as ferrosilicon, and as a mineral filter. Lastly, thousands of tons of silica sand are annually transformed into the extremely useful substance "water glass," or sodium silicate, which is mentioned more in detail elsewhere.

SANDSTONE

A sandstone is a rock composed of grains of quartz or other minerals held together by some cementing material. It is a member of the sedimentary rock system, which may readily be divided into three great groups, namely: shale, sandstone, and limestone. A rough estimate based on thickness classifies some 80 per cent as shale, about 15 per cent as sandstone, and only 5 per cent of the whole as limestone.

The cementing in sandstone is not nearly so complete as in the case of quartzite, as is shown when a sandstone is broken; the fracture takes place in the cement, leaving the grains entire. This causes a broken surface to assume a surgy appearance. Sandstones vary greatly in regard to the cementing material. Sometimes percolating water deposits silica in the interstitial spaces and thus produces our hardest and most resistant sandstone. Perhaps the most common of the bonding substances is calcium carbonate, which is present in all underground water to a greater or less degree. Quite frequently the cementing material is iron oxide, which infilters in between the sand grains, forming a reddish or brownish-colored stone. Red sandstones of a very striking color occur over a considerable area in Oklahoma and the adjoining states, where they are called the "Red Beds."

Occasionally we find other cements, such as dolomite, clay, siderite, or hematite. However, sandstone may be almost entirely devoid of cementing material, in which case the compacting action of pressure is largely responsible for any induration that the stone may exhibit. Usually, such a stone— the St. Peter sandstone, for instance—is very friable and readily breaks down into a mass of incoherent sand. Such sandstones are, however, often very pure, consisting almost entirely of well-rounded quartz grains.

Sandstones commonly exhibit stratification bedding planes. Cross-bedding, a shoal-water feature of sedimentation, is also frequently present, as are rill and wave marks. Nothing can be more fascinating than the points of raindrops engraved as fossils upon the sand of some ancient bar or beach—"fossil showers," if you please, to beguile our stunted imagination. Most peculiar of all the features are the occasional tracks of prehistoric animals that walked across the sandy seashore before it had turned into stone. The Connecticut River valley has long held the distinction of furnishing the best series of dinosaur tracks anywhere in the world. As a rule, fossil remains are not common in sandstone; usually, all that remains of the organic form is an impression, or mold.

Nearly all sandstone is very porous, the amount of porosity depending upon the size of the sand grains and the amount of cementing material present in the interstitial spaces. It has been computed from laboratory experiments that the ratio of the volume of the pore space to that of the rock varies from 5 to nearly 30 per cent. Because of its porosity, sandstone is considered our best water-bearing stratum, and serves, too, as the reservoir rock for most of our enormous supplies of petroleum and natural gas. Also, some sandstones contain minerals, which were either accumulated along with the sand or were concentrated in it later, such as the carnotite ores of western Colorado.

Itacolumite, or flexible sandstone, occurs in several places in our Southern states; the most notable locality is at Linville Mountain, Burke County, North Carolina. The finding of diamonds associated with flexible sandstone in Brazil led to numerous expensive and fruitless efforts to obtain them from the North Carolina stone, as well. The ordinary way of explaining the flexibility of the sandstone is by assuming that it contains talc or mica distributed through it in such a way that when force is applied the grains will move over one another considerably before rupturing will take place.

Few objects in a mineral collection attract attention more quickly than a group of sand crystals. The grotesque arrangement of the crystals and their unusual outward appearance always elicit comment from the observer. They were once mistaken for pseudomorphs after calcite, but the studies of O'Harra, Barbour, and Wanless have shown them to be sand-calcite crystals, made of about 60 per cent of very fine, much-worn sand, and about 40 per cent of calcium carbonate. According to O'Harra, "The sand occurs as an inclusion, while the latter, the mineralizing agent, is the crystal proper." The acute hexagonal, pyramidal shape "is due to the tendency of lime salts to crystallize according to the laws governing calcite as far as the interference on the part of the sand grains will allow." They may be found in sizes varying from a quarter of an inch up to fifteen inches in length. The crystals occur as singles, groups, and solid masses in any quantity desired. Their origin is thought to be in a bed of sand connected in some way with springs, the water of which was highly saturated with calcium carbonate, perhaps resembling a bed of quicksand.

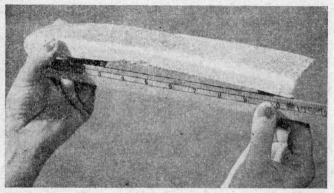

FLEXIBLE SANDSTONE

A sandstone that can be bent by hand pressure. Composed largely of grains of cemented quartz. Stokes County, North Carolina. (*Photograph, courtesy Ward's Establishment of Natural Science.*)

The best locality for sand-lime crystals in the United States is on the Pine Ridge Indian Reservation, about twenty-eight miles south of Interior, South Dakota. Rattlesnake Butte (Devil's Hill), on which they are found, is a low sandstone ridge in the open prairies and is infested with rattlesnakes, hence its new name.

Many sandstones contain concretions of all sizes up to many feet in diameter. In the Dakota Sandstones of Kansas are sandstone balls, twenty feet in diameter (see *National Geographic Magazine*, August, 1937, p. 163). At times these are set free by weathering and remain covering the ground long after the sandstone that enclosed them has disappeared.

118

Usually, the cementing material responsible for these rounded structures is iron pyrite, which, during the process of oxidation, disintegrates and, spreading out from the center, causes the sand grains to be more firmly bonded than those not so influenced. An extensive area covered with thousands of such concretions may be seen near Minneapolis, Kansas.

Sandstone is everywhere used for construction purposes. The fact that it is easily worked to any desired shape, coupled with the fact that it can be obtained in pieces of large size,

SILICEOUS SAND CRYSTALS
Quartz sand cemented by calcite. Rattlesnake Butte, South Dakota.

has made the stone very popular. Also, it is well known that sandstone is one of the stones most resistant to fire, and this fact has had considerable influence in the selection of it for building purposes. The famous "brown-stone fronts" of the aristocratic homes in the days of the "gay nineties," were constructed of an attractive brown sandstone obtained from the quarries of Connecticut, Wisconsin, and other states.

As an abrasive, sandstone has long been in use. Before the discovery and widespread use of silicon carbide and other artificial abrasives, the old hand-turned grindstone, of unpleasant memory, was an adjunct of every shop, factory, and farm. At present, most of the sandstone abrasive industry is concerned with the production of pulp wheels, used by the paper factories. Large quantities of sandstone are ground for glass making; in this way a purer material is obtained.

Perhaps the most unusual use to which sandstone was ever put, was as a material for fine arts. In the cliffs of St. Peter sandstone located at Iowa's Pike's Peak, a few miles south of McGregor, Iowa, may be found more than forty delicate shades of colored sand, which are known widely as the "pictured rocks." About fifty years ago, a deaf-mute by the name of Andrew Clemens, made pictures in glass display jars with colored sand, which were of unbelievable beauty and craftmanship. Some of these exquisite gems now have an art value exceeding $10,000.

QUARTZITE

Quartzite is simply a sandstone that has been subjected to the agencies of metamorphism until it has become a very hard, resistant rock, by the complete filling of the intergranular spaces, silica cementing the grains so firmly that the rock will break as readily through the grains as around them. This change may be brought about in one of two principal ways. Silica may be deposited from solution in sufficient quantity to fill completely the intergranular spaces and thus change the sandstone into a homogeneous mass. Or, intense heat and great pressure may deform and compress the sand grains into a consolidated mass. In some instances, intense metamorphic processes convert the sandstone into a dense, flintlike rock, which shows no traces of the original grains, and which breaks with a smooth, conchoidal fracture.

Quartzite is seldom composed of pure silica, because the sand from which it was originally derived included particles of minerals other than those of quartz, such as mica, iron, feldspars, and some others in varying amounts. These impurities of the original sandstone will appear in the resulting quartzite, usually affecting the color—that is, if the sandstone has an iron cement, the resulting quartzite will be brown, red, or yellow, dependent upon the amount of oxidation that the iron has undergone. The color varies from pure white (which, of course, represents a clean quartz sandstone) to gray, brown, red, and even black.

Several varieties of quartzite are recognized and named from the mineral, other than quartz, that is most prominent in their composition: feldspathic quartzite, etc. Metamorphism plays strange pranks with our minerals; for instance, a sandstone containing clay becomes a quartzite containing mica, and it is interesting to note that by slow gradations quartzite blends into quartz schists and mica schists.

Quartzite may also result from the metamorphism of a conglomerate. Several examples can be cited. Let it suffice to call attention to the basal conglomerate of the Cambrian age that outcrops in many places in the Upper Mississippi Valley, notably at New Ulm, Minnesota, and at Devil's Lake, Wisconsin. In nearly every instance where this conglomerate is found, the pebbles are so firmly cemented that they will fracture rather than loosen from the matrix.

Probably, what may be considered as one of the best known of such formations is the "Jasper conglomerate," concerning which much has been written, because in the Great Lakes region it is known to exist only in one locality. Glacially distributed boulders of this rock have proved very useful in determining the direction of ice movement during the Ice Age. Kunz has described it and its location as follows:

Jasper conglomerate occurs in mountain masses, along with the quartzite masses of the Huronian series, for miles in the country north of the Bruce Mines, on Lake Superior north of Goular's Bay, on St. Mary's River about four miles west of Campment d'Ours, on the east shore of Lake George, and on Lake Huron, Ontario. It is a rock consisting of a matrix of white quartzite, in which are pebbles, often several inches across, of a red, yellow, green, or black jasper, and smoky or other colored chalcedony, which forms a remarkably striking contrast with the pure white matrix. . . . It occurs in thick bands extending for miles, and in boulders, scattered along the shores of the lakes and rivers. Within half a mile of the northern extremity of Goular's Bay, Ontario, is a ridge containing several varieties. It is susceptible of a high polish, and has been made into a great variety of ornamental objects.

The distribution of quartzite is necessarily restricted to regions where the deforming and metamorphosing influences of intensive mountain-making movements have been at work. In such areas, the most highly metamorphosed rocks occur, and, along with others that have undergone either physical or chemical change, we find the quartzites.

Many fine types of this rock exist in this country and in Canada. Probably one of the best known of these is the Sioux Falls quartzite, locally known as the "Sioux Falls jasper." This stone takes a high mirrorlike polish, and can be supplied in a variety of pleasing colors, such as chocolate, cinnamon brown, brownish red, peachblow, and yellowish. For many years, extensive operations in quarrying and dressing this stone have been carried on in that locality, and the dressed product has been widely distributed for special ornamental purposes. For instance, in the transept of the Cathedral of St. John the Divine, in New York, at the base of the inner veneer has been placed a two-foot strip of this stone, in order that the Biblical injunction concerning the Holy City might be observed, namely: "The first foundation was jasper." It is also cut into pillars, pilasters, mantelpieces, table tops, and a great variety of smaller ornamental objects.

In central Wisconsin, in the vicinity of Baraboo, a quartzite occurs, to which Van Hise has ascribed the same age (Huronian) as that given to the quartzite appearing at Sioux Falls, South Dakota. However, in this instance, the iron content being much lower, the bright-red color so attractive in the quartzite at Sioux Falls is not so noticeable, except in a few localized areas. Much of this rock is quarried for commercial purposes. In times past, because of its wear-resisting qualities, enormous quantities were used for paving blocks, but the cement paving has almost eliminated that demand. Some small amount is used for building purposes, with both pleasing and lasting effect. The Adler Planetarium in Chicago is constructed of this quartzite. Large quantities of this stone are also used in the refractories (fire-brick) industry.

Some quartzite is so pure that in the crushed form it furnishes the silica of commerce, which has become practically indispensable in the manufacture of a great variety of useful products, one of which is silicate of soda. This compound is produced by the fusion of silica sand and an alkali, like sodium hydroxide. When the fused mass is cool, it looks like glass, but, totally unlike that substance, it is readily soluble in water, hence its common name "water glass."

From a relatively small amount used some sixty years ago in the making of laundry soap and in the time-honored household method of preserving eggs, the production of water glass has mounted steadily until at present the annual consumption is well over a half million tons. To enumerate all the various uses to which this versatile substance is put would be wearisome to the reader; let it suffice to say that, directly or indirectly, this product touches practically every major manufacturing industry in our country, and it might be added that scientific research is continually discovering new uses for the substance.

CHAPTER VIII

The Intermediary Forms of Quartz

FLINT

Flint is an opaque variety of nearly pure, amorphous quartz, usually presenting various dull colors. The coloring material of flint is thought by some to be organic, since it disappears almost entirely when a fragment is heated to redness. Flint is slightly transparent on the thin edges of flakes and at times has a glassy luster. It is also brittle, and with a hammer a fragment may be reduced to a mass of angular particles. Superficially, flint appears to be a homogeneous substance, but in reality it is composed of an intimate mixture of quartz and opal. This may be considered to be the secret of its peculiar fracture. When a piece of flint is struck in a certain way, flakes having a convex, undulating surface, are detached. This is known as a conchoidal (shell-like) fracture, and constitutes the chief characteristic of the mineral.

Flint occurs in the form of nodules and concretions of more or less irregular shape, in chalk or marly limestones. These nodules may vary in size from that of a pea to considerable dimensions. Sometimes layers of chert are confused with flint, which has a very different origin.

We know that the deposition of silica from colloidal solution may take place by the simple processes of concentration and evaporation, and also by the action of organic life. Of this latter method we have several outstanding examples, such as the work of the algae at the Hot Springs of Yellowstone National Park. It is also possible that deposits of silica may result from chemical reactions that are too complicated to discuss here. However, this has a direct bearing upon the origin of flint nodules.

In the first instance, the siliceous material of the flint was enclosed in the rocks of the earth's crust, whence it was taken into solution by hot alkaline waters, and eventually delivered to the sea. From the sea water the silica was extracted by the sponges, radiolaria, diatoms, etc., and incorporated into their skeletal parts. Upon the death of these animals, the silica thus accumulated remained in the muds and oozes of the ocean floor until again it was taken into solution and chemically deposited around certain centers where conditions were favorable. Such spicules of sponges and tests of radiolaria, etc., as were present at or near the center of deposition were incorporated into the nodule. For this reason, the microscopic examination of a thin section of flint will usually show a variety of these spicules and tests present. Flints from different localities often show that they were formed from the remains of a variety of silica-bearing organisms; some, indeed, show only the spicules of sponges, while others are composed almost entirely of the frustules of diatoms or radiolaria. These simply mirror the life conditions of the sea bottom at the time of their accumulation.

The ease with which flint could be fashioned early led to its use by primitive peoples, the world over, and even today some of the aborigines of Australia and the islands of the East Indies use flint implements that differ but little from those fashioned thousands of years ago. The American Indians of both continents, prior to the advent of the European invaders, used flint extensively for arrow points, spearheads, knives, and other useful objects. Truly the ancient arrow maker must have been a very industrious individual to have turned out the tons upon tons of worked flints that are to be seen in our museums and private collections.

With some practice, flint may be worked to any desired shape by well-directed strokes with a stone or a bone. The final touches can be effected by pressure applied in a direction slightly across the edge of the piece. Numerous archaeologists and students of Indian relics have by patient experimentation mastered the mysterious art of flint flaking, and have produced arrowheads hard to differentiate from those of Indian make. At the point of impact a slightly elevated conical mark is produced, known to archaeologists as a "bulb of percussion." These bulbs are taken as evidence of intentional percussion and often identify flints worked by man from those merely split by weathering.

ARROWHEADS OF COMMON OPAL AND AGATE

The aborigines of the Americas made wide use of the quartz minerals for tools and weapons. Artifacts of many types are found in all parts of America.

Flint is widespread in its occurrence, the world over, but for historical, archaeological, and mineralogical purposes, the classic area for the study of this mineral is the chalk formations of England and France. The chalk rock of England extends from Flamborough Head on the east coast to west of Dover on the south, a distance of 250 miles. It also reappears on the opposite side of the English Channel in France. In all places where the chalk is exposed along the coast, flint nodules weather out and collect in the debris at the foot of the cliff.

A specialized industry in the shaping of flints has long existed at Brandon, Suffolk, England. In fact, P. O. Lennon, writing in *Sands, Clays and Minerals* calls it "the oldest industry," which undoubtedly it is, having been carried on there uninterrupted since prehistoric times. Brandon is a veritable little village of flint, with flint roads, a flint war memorial, and flint houses. Nearby are the mines from which the flint is extracted in a very primitive fashion, that possibly differs but little from the methods employed by the Paleolithic miners of thousands of years ago. The best flint is obtained at a depth of about forty feet and is raised to the surface in baskets. From the mines it is brought to Brandon by the cartload.

Formerly, about thirty men were employed in "knapping" the flints, but both the art and the industry have become almost extinct, as the demand for gun flints is now restricted to the semisavage countries of South America and Africa, where ammunition for modern firearms is unobtainable. Also, before the universal adoption of matches, Brandon supplied much of the flint used in the old tinderbox. Flint being harder than steel, when the two were struck together with a glancing blow, sparks were shot off, which, when caught in the tinder could be blown into a blaze. During the Boer War in South Africa, each soldier of the British army had a "strike-a-light" as part of his equipment.

It may possibly come as a surprise to some that a rock as hard as flint shows evidence of weathering. Fresh nodules of flint or chert usually possess a white coating, which, to the uninitiated, might be mistaken for some of the matrix cemented to the outside of the mass. A close study, however, soon shows it to be composed of a different material from that of the matrix. Essentially this is tripolite. Stone artifacts made by prehistoric man sometimes show an incipient stage of disintegration in the form of a thin white crust, or "patina," as it is called. The thickness of this crust, in a general way, is indicative of the length of time weathering has proceeded upon the stone.

The "pebbles" used in tube mills in the United States for grinding ores, cement, and other hard materials, where a minimum of iron impurities is desired, are mainly flint nodules obtained from the beach near San Diego, California. The tubes in which the grinding is effected are lined with quartzite blocks to protect them from abrasion. Before the World War the pebbles were all imported; now domestic production nearly equals our demand. Imports are mainly from France, Denmark, and Belgium. The Danish pebbles come from Greenland, and the pebbles from France are obtained along the northern coast of that country.

Hornstone. In little use today, this term is practically obsolete. Formerly it was applied to flint or chert that was brittle, fracturing in a splintery rather than a conchoidal fracture. Hornstone was usually more translucent than ordinary flint, owing to the inclusion of chalcedony. The term is superfluous, and its use should therefore be discontinued.

CHERT

Chert is one of the amorphous quartz minerals the definition of which is still in the process of formulation. Much confusion has been injected into the matter because, up to a comparatively recent time, writers have been disposing of the subject by simply stating that chert was "an impure form of flint." Field investigations and laboratory studies of the extensive chert deposits of the North Central states, have shown that they, while possessing many of the outward appearances of flint, have a quite different mode of origin, and should be considered as a separate variety of the quartz family. In fact, much that is considered to be flint is in reality chert.

Cherts usually occur associated with limestones or dolomites, though there are occasional exceptions. The occurrence of fossils within the chert beds points to the fact that they were originally beds of limestone that have been changed by the process of replacement. This may be seen very plainly in the case of the Boone Chert of Missouri and adjacent states, in which fossils are quite numerous. In some places, in addition to the replacement of the lime carbonate by silica, there has been a deposition of chalcedonic silica from colloidal solution, solidifying the mass into a series of flintlike layers. Such deposits present the peculiar anomaly of "fossils in flint." Extensive deposits of this nature occur in the Flint Hills that extend, in an almost unbroken line, from Oklahoma across Kansas and into Nebraska. The cherts of the Niagara dolomite and some other formations show evidence of their secondary origin by being concentrated along bedding planes by silica-bearing waters.

One noteworthy locality for the study of chert is Flint Ridge, which is located in Licking and Muskingum counties, in Ohio. The ridge is about eight miles long, and from a few rods to nearly a mile in width. Portions of the top of the ridge are comparatively level and are underlain by the layers of cherty rock that varies from a few inches up to ten feet in thickness. The top of the ridge is literally pock-marked with the Indian diggings, some as much as thirty feet in depth. All about the ridge the ground is covered with chips, broken and discarded spalls, and irregular fragments of the chert. This seems to indicate that the roughly fashioned stones were carried away by the Indians for finishing elsewhere. Possibly the ridge was considered as neutral ground, much the same as were the Pipestone Quarries of western Minnesota.

At Flint Ridge and from several other localities in Ohio this cellular, fossiliferous chert was quarried and fashioned into millstones. The industry began in 1807 and continued to be very profitable for many years, a pair of four-foot stones selling for $150. Previous to the opening of this industry in the West, buhrstones were imported from France and hauled over the mountains by oxen at great expense. The Ohio-made stones were distributed all over the Upper Mississippi Valley region. The cellular structure was quite necessary to the right performance of the stone. If the stones were too flat they would not draw the grain properly and were likely to become caked with the crushed grain, in which case it was necessary to raise the upper stone and clean them. The best stones had about as much cell space as solid surface.

While most flint and chert is of a dull or drab color, which renders them unsuited for gem-stone cutting, the chert of Flint Ridge is a notable exception, presenting very attractive color patterns when worked up by the lapidary.

In the Mississippian limestones at the southern edge of Mt. Pleasant, Iowa, are found deposits of chert which are most

DISPLAY OF QUARTZ MINERALS

Public exhibit of cut and polished specimens by members of Oregon Agate and Mineral Society. Huge quartz crystal geode in background is four feet in diameter. Display includes over 200 specimens of Oregon material. (*Photograph by Gus Brockmann.*)

beautifully banded, with colors grading through dark blue, grays, reds, and browns, on up to ivory, creams, and almost pure white. Such material would work up beautifully if cut and polished.

NOVACULITE

Novaculite is now considered to be a variety of chert, though there are some elements in its origin that differ considerably from those exhibited by true chert. In the Arkansas region, novaculite is a fine, compact, sandstonelike rock, occurring especially in Garland and Hot Springs counties. In its greatest development it has a thickness of about 900 feet. The massive novaculite is usually dense, gritty, fine-grained, homogeneous, highly siliceous, translucent on thin edges, and has a marked conchoidal fracture. Though much of it is white, in some there are shades of red, gray, green, yellow, brown, and even black. It occurs associated with shales, into which it grades through opaque flinty layers. It is thought to represent a localized deposit of very fine-grained siliceous sediment that was later solidified by the infiltration of colloidal silica.

It takes a fine polish, and Kunz mentions it as suitable for cutting into small ornamental objects, though not much of it has been used for this purpose. In spite of the development of artificial abrasives, novaculite continues to be in demand for whetstones. The Hot Springs area, besides supplying domestic needs, ships a considerable quantity of finished stones to England and Germany.

SILICEOUS SINTER

Siliceous sinter is formed of material obtained by percolating ground water from the decomposition of silica containing minerals and rocks, and usually appears as a more or less consolidated deposit from hot springs. In appearance its color is commonly white or gray; or occasionally, when the oxides of iron are present, the color may be brown or reddish. The structure of the stone varies somewhat according to the circumstances attending its deposition, some occurring close-grained and in heavy masses, where it was deposited at an even rate for some considerable time. Other deposits, especially those of geyser origin, are found to be more of a shelly nature or even friable. Some deposits even occur in the form of a fine powder. A fibrous variety probably owes its peculiar structure to having been deposited by vegetable agencies. Mineralogically, siliceous sinter is classed among the opals, because it is composed of hydrated silica, with occasional impurities.

Water is nature's universal solvent. Pure or nearly pure water is a poor solvent, but in the natural state no pure water has ever been discovered. Chemically pure H_2O is a laboratory curiosity. All the water that we are acquainted with, therefore, holds in solution some mineral matter or gas, or both, making it either acidic or alkaline in its chemical nature, as the case may be. Whatever its character may be, the solution becomes active in dissolving mineral substances from the rocks. To be sure, these solutions are very weak and their chemical action is correspondingly slow; but the supply, being constantly replenished, assures the unceasing prosecution of the work, which, when carried on over an indefinite period of years, produces noticeable results.

It is a well-known fact that hot water will carry much more mineral matter in solution than will cold water. Just how much influence pressure plays in the process is not entirely understood, since the work takes place deep within the earth's crust, where its actions cannot be seen, but pressure is believed to be a very important factor in solution. In our Yellowstone National Park great terraces and flats of a hard, white geyserite occur in the Firehole Basin, and extend down that river for miles. All the material of these deposits has been brought to the surface from deep within the earth's crust by the waters of innumerable hot springs and geysers. Analysis of the waters of some springs in the Park shows them to contain nearly 3 grams of mineral matter per kilogram, most of which is silica. Some idea of the amount of water coming to the surface there may be gathered from the fact that Excelsior Cauldron pours out 4,400 gallons of hot water per minute, while Old Faithful throws into the air about 3,000 barrels of water at each eruption, repeating the performance some 8,000 times each year. Considering these facts, then, it is not difficult for us to comprehend how these geysers and hot springs have built up the structures that we see about their orifices.

The deposition of the silica from these solutions may be due to the influence of several factors, such as loss of heat, relief of pressure, evaporation of water, chemical reactions, or the action of certain forms of algae (Cyanophyceae) which nature has especially adapted to live in the hot water of the pools

132

and streams. In this latter case, Weed found that "the silica forms a gelatinous layer upon the algal growths, and this, after death of the algae, gradually hardens to sinter." The beautiful colors for which these deposits are justly famous are due to the minute plants, which spread bright-colored layers over the surface of the deposits that are kept wet, but as soon as the flow of water ceases, the algae die and the rock becomes a dull white or gray in color.

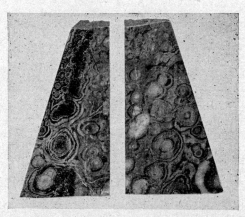

JASPER—VARIETY ORBICULAR

Book ends cut from large masses of jasper. Circular areas are composed of red jasper and white quartz, matrix red jasper. (*From collection of William B. Pitts.*)

Deposits similar to those in the Yellowstone Park are to be seen in the geyser regions of Iceland and New Zealand. The latter region is very large—150 miles long by 20 miles wide—and contains many imposing features, including up to a few years ago the very largest geyser in the world, the Great Waimangu, which on occasion would throw mud and water to a height of 1,500 feet.

According to F. W. Clarke, "The sinters represent only the simplest form of deposit from geysers and hot springs. A great variety of intermediate substances, mixtures of silica, of hydroxides, of carbonates, of sulphates, or arsenates, and even of sulphur have been observed." In this regard, the siliceous deposits now forming about Steamboat Springs, Nevada, indicate that along with the silica appreciable amounts of cinnabar, lead, copper, arsenic, and antimony, gold, and silver are present, as are traces of several other minerals. All this gives us a hint as to the methods employed by Dame Nature in concentrating the vast mineral wealth of our country.

TRIPOLITE

Tripolite is a siliceous mineral, the definition of which has undergone considerable change since it was first proposed, and concerning which some confusion still exists. The first tripolite was studied by Ehrenberg, the German microscopist, who pronounced it as composed almost entirely of diatom frustules. On this basis, Dana was led to give the name to a number of minerals of like characteristics, such as infusorial earth, diatomite, etc. More recent investigation of the original deposits fails to substantiate Ehrenberg's claims as to their depositional character, but rather shows them to be the siliceous residue from the disintegration of some silica-bearing formation, possibly a limestone.

According to Prof. W. S. Bayley, of the University of Illinois, tripolite is a mixture of quartz and opal produced by the weathering and disintegration of some cherty formation, or perhaps a siliceous limestone. In appearance it is a white to pink, fine-grained material always occurring in association with limestones. It is found in layers from a few inches to several feet in thickness and seldom is so consolidated that it cannot be readily mined with pick and shovel.

While tripolite occurs in numerous places, most of the deposits are either too small to insure profitable mining operations or are so situated that the transportation problem prohibits their exploitation at the present time. Our best known deposits of this material are located at Stella and Seneca, Missouri, and across the Mississippi River in Alexander and Union counties, Illinois, also in Ottawa County, Oklahoma, and in Tennessee.

Microscopically, the Missouri tripolite seems to be composed of spongy-appearing clusters of doubly refracting quartz, and because of this some think it is the decomposition product from a deposit of novaculite. On the other hand, the Illinois tripolite appears to be composed of amorphous quartz and undoubtedly represents the residue from the breaking down of a cherty limestone.

Tripolite has a great variety of uses; perhaps first in importance is its service in the pottery industry. When sufficiently firm and homogeneous, it is cut into filtering disks. The softer rock is pulverized and finds a variety of uses—as wood filler, in the making of paint, in metal polishes, for the facing of foundry molds, in soaps and cleaners, and in glass manufacturing.

DIATOMITE

Diatomite is a variety of hydrated, opalescent silica, which because of a misunderstanding has received a number of inappropriate names. Diatomaceous earth, while not strictly a mineralogical name is the name most generally in use. Infusorial earth is erroneous, since infusoria are rarely present, and tripolite is of entirely different origin, as is shown elsewhere. Kieselguhr is the German equivalent.

Diatomite, when dry, is a whitish, pulverulent substance, outwardly resembling chalk but very much lighter in weight and more porous. Its density is 0.33, and it will float on water until it becomes saturated. The infallible test for diatomite is the microscope, which will at once show the presence of the diatoms. It has been computed that a cubic inch of the material contains from 40,000,000 to 70,000,000 diatom frustules. The amount of siliceous material ascribed to diatoms at first seemed incredible, but when their extraordinary rate of reproduction was understood, all uncertainty was removed. It is said that a single individual, if placed under favorable circumstances, may have as many as 9,000,000 descendants in the course of a month.

The diatom belongs to a group of flowerless aquatic plants called algae, which secrete for themselves external cases of clear silica. They occur all over the globe, wherever water is found, either fresh or salt, hot or cold. Geologically, diatoms have many fields of interest. Their type, structure, abundance, position in the strata, etc., serve as indications regarding climatic conditions and the degree of alkalinity, acidity, and salinity of the waters in which they lived. Their possible association with the origin of the petroleum of the California fields is strongly contended by some of our best geologists.

When diatoms die, they fall to the bottom of the sea, where the organic parts decompose and are removed, while the skeletons (frustules) accumulate in beds of ooze. In time, these beds become a part of the sedimentary strata. During the Tertiary period, conditions seem to have been at their best for the widespread and prolific propagation of diatoms, for some beds that are known have a thickness of 2,000 feet. Some of the deposits are friable, while others are sufficiently compact to permit the material to be removed in the form of blocks.

For building purposes, diatomite was used by both Greek and Roman architects to decrease the weight of certain structures. It is said that in the sixth century, "swimming blocks," fashioned from diatomite, were used by the artisans of Emperor Justinian in the construction of the dome of the church of St. Sophia in Constantinople. The physical characteristics, great porosity, low density, and chemical inertness, fit diatomite for an increasing number of commercial uses. It is extensively employed as a filtering medium and as an insulator against heat, cold, and sound. A lesser amount is used as a filler in paints, in paper making, in cement, and in the hardening of rubber. Its great absorbing properties are made use of in the manufacture of dynamite, etc. As a mild abrasive, it is found in silver and dental polishes, in buffing powders, etc.

Diatomite is world-wide in its occurrence, but the United States leads as producer and as consumer. Most of our commercial deposits are located in the Western states, especially in California. The Lompoc beds in Santa Barbara County—the largest, purest, and most uniform commercial deposit known—cover approximately 5 square miles of area, with a total thickness of about 1,400 feet, and contain over 1,000,000 tons of commercial material. Actually, this is only a part of a great chain of diatomite deposits that extends through the coastal states from San Diego far north into Oregon, where there are other important deposits. Considerable diatomite is mined also in the Eastern states of New Hampshire, New York, Connecticut, Virginia, and Florida; and much of it is shipped abroad.

CHAPTER IX

The Cryptocrystalline and Amorphous Forms of Quartz

CHALCEDONY

Chalcedony is a cryptocrystalline variety of quartz, with a waxy or greasy luster and somewhat splintery fracture, identical with crystalline quartz in chemical composition. Chalcedony, in translucent or opaque, botryoidal, reniform or stalactitic masses, is composed of microscopic fibers. The fibers composing chalcedony are optically biaxial, while quartz is uniaxial. Also, the refractive index and fusing point of chalcedony differ from those of quartz. At times, it exhibits a surface coated with a distinct bluish bloom, of uncertain origin. Chalcedony receives its name from the ancient city of Chalcedon in Bithynia in Asia Minor, near which place it was first discovered.

Chalcedony is always of secondary origin, being deposited from colloidal solution in veins or cavities in various kinds of rock. Occasionally it occurs as pseudomorphs, as at Tampa Bay, Florida, where it has so impregnated corals as to preserve even the minutest detail of their structure. Sometimes it forms coatings of concentric rings on rocks. Such forms are known as "orbicular silica," or "*Beckite*," which is found in a number of places in this country, notably in the Black Hills of South Dakota. Much of this Beckite fluoresces under ultra-violet light.

Chalcedony frequently shows a faint banded structure, due to the alternation of layers of quartz, chalcedony, and opal.

There are several kinds of chalcedony, all appearing in a variety of dull colors. However, the transparent to translucent, waxy, cream- or milky-colored, faintly banded variety is chalcedony proper. In some localities it is known as "white agate."

Perhaps one of the most interesting occurrences of chalcedony is to be found in the vicinity of Crawford, Darres County, Nebraska, where the mineral occurs as a filling in nearly all the fossil bones which are found there in great profusion. When the bones are broken or are weathered away, these chalcedonic cores remain scattered over the ground. Moreover, it fills all the seams and cracks in the bone-bearing formation. This, after weathering, leaves walls of chalcedony of varying thickness and height projecting from the ground.

According to H. P. Whitlock, "Chalcedony was much used by the ancients as a medium for engraved gems; examples are to be found among the cylinders of Assyria and Babylonia, the intaglios of Greece, and the oval talismanic seals of Persia. Its modern gem uses include necklaces, bowls, and numerous small ornamental objects, most of which are carved in western Germany. To these we must add the figurines and vases carved from this material by the Chinese."

CHRYSOPRASE

Chrysoprase is a translucent variety of cryptocrystalline quartz with a leek- or apple-green color, though there may be a variety of shades, such as bluish green or yellowish green. The green color is due to the inclusion of about 1 per cent of nickel in the form of a hydrated silicate. Chrysoprase is very often near or associated with deposits of nickel, especially where the ore-bearing veins have been silicified. Nickel often exists as a silicate in rock, though usually present in only very small amounts. Percolating waters passing through a nickel-bearing rock may easily take into solution enough of the coloring matter to stain the quartz. Few deposits of nickel are to be found in the United States, and this may account for the scarcity of chrysoprase. Some years ago, good-quality water-worn pebbles of chrysoprase were to be found near Nickel Mountain in western Oregon, but now specimens are rarely found. The bright-green color made this gem stone eagerly sought for.

As an ornamental stone, chrysoprase has had a long popularity. It was a favorite among both Greeks and Romans as a

material for signets and seals, many of which show exceptionally fine workmanship, especially the intaglios and cameos. Even in a much earlier period we find the stone held in high esteem in Egypt, where it was usually set with lapis lazuli. Beads of chrysoprase were found as part of a remarkable necklace adorning the mummy of a young woman of noble rank of the Eighteenth Dynasty, that is, about 1500 B.C.

It is a difficult matter at times to be certain as to the varieties of stones an ancient writer had in mind when he wrote his descriptions of them. The chrysoprase of the moderns is certainly not the stone of that name described by Pliny and the Greek writers. As nearly as we can ascertain, the chrysoprase of the ancients was probably our chrysoberyl. Chrysoprase, as we know it, is of comparatively recent acceptance as a variety of gem stone.

JASPER—CARVED PAPER KNIFE

In more recent times, chrysoprase was very popular in Europe. Frederick the Great of Prussia, it seems, was a great admirer of this stone and, by offering rewards, did much to encourage search for it in Silesia, where it was discovered in 1740. Since it could be obtained in masses of considerable size, Frederick caused it to be used lavishly in decorating the palace of Sans Souci and the Old Palace at Potsdam, where it is still viewed and admired by throngs of visitors every year. Among the most striking objects to be seen in the Old Palace are two tables of this stone; each is three feet long and two feet wide. At a much earlier date, much of the Silesian chrysoprase was

140

used for mural decorations at the St. Wenzel Chapel in Prague.

Kunz, writing on the talismanic virtue of chrysoprase, states that it was once thought to be endowed with strange and wonderful powers. For instance, during the Middle Ages, it was believed by some that if a thief condemned to be hanged or beheaded should place this stone in his mouth, he would escape the just punishment for his misdeeds. In what way this miracle was to be accomplished is not definitely stated, but it is reasonable to suppose that the stone was believed to have the power to make the culprit invisible and thus enable him to escape the executioner. Several other stones were said to possess this peculiar power, if worn in a certain way, or if engraved with certain talismanic symbols.

Dame Fashion, it seems, plays strange pranks with our gem stones, as well as with the shapes of ladies' hats and the cuts of men's trousers. In England, in the early part of the nineteenth century, chrysoprase was valued so highly as to be used for brooches and rings set around with small brilliants. At that time a stone large enough for such a setting would cost from $50 to $100, the value depending upon its color. Only the very inferior stones were used for necklaces, larger sets, seals, etc.

The largest engraved gem of chrysoprase known to exist is now in the Maxwell-Summerville collection of engraved gems, seals, and talismans, at the University of Pennsylvania. This stone is in the form of a cameo, showing the head of Jupiter, and dates from the second century. It is exquisitely carved from a single piece of chrysoprase some six by five inches in dimensions, and shows the god with both the oak leaves and the aegis, or armor, a rare combination.

A note concerning the collection referred to above might not be out of place at this point. As a collection of engraved gems, seals, talismans, etc., it is, without a doubt, the finest private collection ever assembled. It contains over 2,000 pieces, brought together from every part of the world. Every phase of the glyptic art is represented, from the Assyrian and Egyptian cylinder seals to the curious Gnostic gems and

Aztec hieroglyphs. The entire collection is engraved upon some 56 different substances; however, a large number of the pieces are cut on various varieties of quartz. Any student of the quartz gems would do well to visit the University of Pennsylvania Museum and study this collection.

Chrysoprase has a rather limited distribution, and the supply of good gem-quality material is not nearly equal to the wide commercial demand; hence a great majority of the cut stones on the market were originally colorless chalcedony, which had been artificially colored green by the use of nickel salts.

Some ten years ago, mining claims were filed on a deposit of chrysoprase located several miles southeast of Ione, California. The gem stone was found as a seam nearly two inches thick, in a serpentine rock. The deposit evidently did not warrant extensive commercial exploitation. Excellent gem-quality chrysoprase has been found near Visala, Tulare County, California. Kunz also mentions several other places where the mineral has been found in this country: in Macon County, North Carolina; Chester County, Pennsylvania; Garfield County, Colorado; and St. Lawrence County, New York.

Until recently, nearly all of the world's supply of chrysoprase came from the vicinity of Frankenstein in Silesia, a limited amount being contributed by the Ural Mountains. Whitlock, in his recent book, states that the Silesian deposits are no longer producing.

PRASE

Prase is a translucent, dull leek-green or sage-green variety of amorphous quartz. The color is caused by a multitude of enclosed hairlike crystals of actinolite that crisscross in every direction; or, as some think, it may be due to ferrous iron salts or a metallic pigment other than nickel. While it is often fully as translucent as chrysoprase, because of its much duller color it ranks far below that as a gem stone. Both prase and chrysoprase, stained and natural, are widely used as cheap imitations for jade and other valuable green-colored gems. Prase occurs with deposits of agate.

PLASMA

Dark-green to leek-green subtranslucent or opaque amorphous varieties of quartz are classed as plasma. Some writers include massive translucent quartz in this group, but, to avoid confusion, it seems best to exclude the distinctly translucent green-colored silicas. This is a much coarser variety of quartz than is prase, approaching jasper in texture and appearance. The green color is said to be due to the presence of chlorite. The name "plasma" means image and refers to the use of the stone in olden times for seals and signets. It has no distinctive pattern, and, while usually it is of a dull, dark, grass-green shade, there may be very small areas of white or yellow present. When green plasma is intergrown with red or other colors or grades into translucency, it will fall into some other subvariety.

Plasma is a rather common mineral and may be found in large masses or deposited in thick veins. Agate and other varieties of jasper may be associated with it or found near by. The best qualities are obtained from India and China. The so-called "Oregon jade" found in quantity near Durkee, Oregon, is a dull green-colored, opaque plasma. Good-quality plasma is also found in many localities in California, Nevada, Idaho, Utah, and Colorado. The Bell Mountain Mine, Clarke County, Washington, produces a gem-quality green plasma (grading into prase), some being mixed with small veins of red jasper. It has also been found in the Black Hills, South Dakota, and in North Carolina.

HELIOTROPE, OR BLOODSTONE

One of the fascinating features connected with the study of the quartz minerals is the diversity of forms in which they occur. The bloodstone is a form both peculiar and interesting. Heliotrope is a translucent, dark-green plasma containing scattered spots of bright, blood-red jasper. The green color is due to chlorite, and possibly ferrous iron salts; the red, to hematite.

Bloodstone is usually cut for sets in signet rings bearing crests or monograms, and other small ornaments. The best quality shows a dark-green color, and the jasper spots should be small and uniformly distributed. Much of the bloodstone fails to meet these requirements in one way or another. Either the green matrix will be of a dull color, or the red areas will be too numerous or angular in outline.

The ancient Egyptians and Babylonians held the bloodstone in high esteem, using it extensively for seals and other small, ornamental objects. The specific name "heliotrope" was early applied to this stone, and because of this precedent, it was favored by Dana. The name is derived from Greek words meaning "sun-turning," and refers to the old-time belief that the stone, when immersed in water, would turn the image of the sun to blood-red. The water was also said to boil and blow up the apparatus containing the magic mineral. About the middle of the seventeenth century, during the time when ignorance and superstition were rife in Europe, bloodstone was used as a cure for dyspepsia, and, when powdered and mixed with honey, it was considered a remedy for tumors. Also, if one of these stones was rubbed with the juice of a bloodstone (whatever that might mean), it was supposed to render the wearer invisible. Bloodstone was used for stopping the flow of blood, either by putting it directly upon the wound or by wetting it in water and having the patient hold it in his hand.

The early church called the bloodstone "St. Stephen's Stone" and held it in great reverence, using it frequently as the medium for carved sacred objects. On several occasions it has been used most effectively for carvings representing the head of Christ. A very fine specimen of this sort is in the French Royal Collection in Paris, so executed that the red spots of the stone very realistically resemble drops of blood. Still another piece may be seen in the Field Museum in Chicago. The use of the stone for this purpose was, no doubt, suggested by the ancient tradition that the stone originated at the time of the crucifixion of Christ, from drops of blood, drawn by the spear thrust into his side, falling on a piece of dark-green stone at the foot of the cross.

While bloodstone may be found in any locality where jasper occurs, practically our entire supply is obtained from India, especially from Kathiawar Peninsula, west of Cambay, where agates, carnelian, and chalcedony are obtained from the Deccan traprock. Other sources are Australia and Brazil. Some fine material has been found in several places in Scotland, especially in the basalt of the Isle of Rum. It occurs also in Siberia and in the Hebrides. The demand for high-grade material appears to be greater than the available supply, and first-class stock commands a good price.

In the United States, the finding of good bloodstone is of rare occurrence; some stones of good quality have been reported from Newport Beach, Oregon, while less desirable material is more or less common in many Oregon localities. Some blood-stones showing very fine markings have been found in Chatham County, Georgia. In Colorado, the stone has been reported as coming from near the South Fork and below Uncompahgre, near Grand River. It also occurs as veins in slate at Blooming Grove, Orange County, New York. A fair quality of coarse-grained heliotrope, is found in California. The so-called "bloodstone," a combination of large red and green jasper, is quite common—sometimes found in large deposits—but usually the red areas are patchy and irregular, and fail to resemble "drops of blood on green stone."

JASPER

Jasper includes, in a general way, nearly all varieties of impure, opaque, colored, amorphous quartz. Under the microscope it is essentially a very fibrous quartz—a characteristic in which it differs from all other varieties. The members of this group are extremely numerous, mineralogical literature listing about seventy different varieties, of which we will discuss but a few of the more outstanding forms.

In color, jasper may be red, yellow, brown, green, bluish, or black. These different colors are due to the inclusion of different impurities, such as, clay, iron in varying stages of oxidation, or organic matter, and possibly admixtures of other minerals in minute quantities. At times, these impurities may reach a quantity as high as 20 per cent, and, since they are not always evenly distributed or uniformly oxidized (if it be

JASPER—VARIETY ORBICULAR
Spherical areas of red jasper in matrix of massive white quartz. Cut cabochons (below) from William B. Pitts collection.

an iron compound), the color may vary perceptibly within a small area.

The usual origin of jasper is in a colloidal solution of silica gel. Jasper, *in situ*, is most commonly found in regions of recent lava flows. Porcelain jasper, which is merely a baked clay, having a gray to red color and a conchoidal fracture, has been formed by contact metamorphism, often thirty or forty rods from trap dikes. The heat of the igneous activity likewise increases the capacity of the underground water for carrying silica in solution, and when conditions become right (a drop in temperature would be sufficient), the water deposits the dissolved silica along with the impurities, to form jasper.

Although at the present time jasper is little used, aside from cabinet specimens, except for mosaic work and for small ornaments, the ancients esteemed it highly and employed it extensively. In olden days, the term "jasper" included several stones that we do not now include in that group. The jasper of antiquity was in many instances distinctly green, probably a chalcedony or even chrysoprase. According to the Mosaic instructions in the Book of Exodus, a jasper was to be the eleventh stone of the breastplate of the High Priest of the Hebrews. Moreover, one of the gates of the Holy City, as described by St. John in Revelation, was to be made of it.

146

The ancients were accustomed to engrave upon it; for instance, the jasper mentioned as being set in the High Priest's breast-plate was engraved, as were all the other gems.

During the Middle Ages many strange beliefs persisted concerning the efficacy of jasper to prevent sorrow. If the jasper chanced to be mottled and was suitably engraved, it was believed to be capable of protecting the wearer from death by drowning. Moreover, it was believed to have the power to ward off scorpions and spiders, and to keep the wearer free from ailments of the chest, lungs, and stomach. Considering these things, we are not at all surprised by the popularity of the stone in Europe during those times.

CLASSIFICATION OF JASPER

Next to agate, jasper is probably found in as many sub-varieties as any of the other types of the amorphous quartz minerals. The varieties classed as jasper are generally opaque or only subtranslucent, and various names have been given to this fascinating gem material. Many of the terms assigned to jasper have principally a local significance, like the name "oregonite"; this material would be termed simply orbicular jasper when seen elsewhere. Terms of this kind, while useful to designate some types of jasper, are also confusing, since they do not apply to a distinct mineral species. The use of the designation, Jasper, variety "oregonite," would do much to clarify the confusion that results from using the variety name alone.

There is considerable difficulty in distinguishing some jaspers from cherts and flints. Obviously, they grade into one another; although their mode of deposition might be different, chemically they are identical; hence the matter of naming is often one of opinion. Usually, material which is well colored and suitable for gem purposes is termed "jasper," although actually in origin it may be a chert. On the other hand, low-grade or inferior-colored or impure jaspers are sometimes termed "chert."

While jasper occurs in a multitude of colors, shades, and mixtures of colors, the reds, browns, and greens are the most common. Opaque jasper may be intergrown with agate or chalcedony. It is then referred to as "jasp-agate" or some similar name. As in the case of agate, the color of jasper is due to the presence of small amounts of metallic salts, generally iron and manganese. The oxides of iron produce red and brown colors, while the ferrous iron salts may give excellent green colors or merely a faded and dull green. Jasper is frequently highly variegated, with numerous patterns, bandings, spots of color, and similar markings—a fact which has given rise to the long list of local terms. Generally, color is not a factor in distinguishing jasper from agate; the term "jasper" is applied when the material is more or less opaque, and as translucency is approached, it grades into the agate family, but, as in other instances cited above, there is no distinctive rule of terminology.

From time immemorial, the jaspers have enjoyed wide popularity as gem stones. They take a splendid, glossy polish, wear well, are attractive in appearance, and justly deserve popularity. Since jasper is not translucent, unless cut into very thin sections, the gem must depend upon some definitely pleasing color or patterns to make it suitable as an ornamental stone. The jasperized wood of the great petrified forest of Arizona is of a remarkably fine quality, a riot of colors and available in large specimens. Often, along the borders of sections of limbs are found the black dentritic markings of manganese (pyrolusite); these are cut into cabochons to resemble forest scenes and are widely used in costume jewelry and for the local tourist trade.

So generally is jasper distributed throughout the country, there are perhaps few areas where gravel deposits are found which will fail to yield specimens of some type or other. In some of the Western states and along the beaches, jasper is found in profusion and often in high-grade quality. Scattered over the desert areas of America are innumerable localities where good specimens are found loose upon the surface, resting

148

where they were deposited after weathering from the surrounding rock. Generally, the jasper found in stream gravels and along the beaches is small in size, having been long exposed to attrition, but the specimens may be of excellent quality and of a size suitable for gem cutting, no sawing being indicated to reduce them to proper size for the grinding wheels. On the Mojave Desert of California a variety of fine jasper is found; one type, consisting of a yellow matrix with dentritic growths, is termed *moss jasper*, a very attractive cabochon material.

JASPER LOCALITIES

In many deposits, jasper appears to have an origin similar to that of chert and is thus found in veins or seams, frequently of considerable size, where large masses may be quarried. Probably one of the most noted localities in the country producing large masses of jasper, is the Morgan Hill district, Santa Clara County, California, where immense amounts of orbicular jasper are found. The bright red matrix, with circular areas of white and gray-colored silica, makes an attractive contrast, rendering it suitable for gem cutting, large ornaments like book ends, paper weights, cabinet specimens, and similar uses. The William Pitts collection at Golden Gate Park Museum, San Francisco, exhibits some choice examples of orbicular jasper. The Dr. M. Groesbeck collection at Porterville also includes numerous fine specimens of California jasper.

Jasper seems to occur at numerous localities along the western side of California. During the sinking of the foundations for the famous Golden Gate Bridge at San Francisco, large bodies of an exceptionally attractive yellow-and-red jasper were encountered by the drills, and a limited amount of the material was obtained. In all probability, the foundations of that great suspension bridge rest, in part at least, upon jasper.

One of the largest masses of gem-quality jasper ever found (not in matrix) in America, was the specimen encountered a few years past by a farmer plowing a wheat field at Antelope, Oregon. This mass was so large as to require two strong horses to drag it from the field. For some time, collectors visiting the area were invited to break off from the mass whatever they desired, until the specimen was finally so reduced in size that some hardy soul could venture to transport it to a collection. The specimen was mainly of a bright-red color, with areas of subtranslucent moss jasper. For a long while, this locality has supplied the Western gem-cutting trade with excellent quality of jasper, moss jasper, and jasp-agate in bright red and green colors, often with both colors in the same specimen. Much of this material is fully equal to the moss agate which has been found for centuries in India and the inland parts of China.

Idaho. Throughout central Idaho a great many localities are known where excellent jasper, chalcedony, agate, geodes, and agate-filled nodules are found in the lavas or encountered in mining operations. At MacKay, in the Alder Creek mining district, the ores carry a red-and-yellow, ferruginous jasper of a colorful pattern. Nodules of brown jasper, with crusts of chloropal, are also found there.

In Bear County, at the Humming Bird Mine, in Paris Canyon, a fine quality of red-and-green jasper is mined. At one time, an effort was made to produce this material in quantity for the gem-cutting trade, but, probably through inability to find a ready market in America, the project was abandoned. In the Tertiary lavas of Blaine County, especially to the east of Little Wood River, jasper is found in profusion in the usual red and green colors. This area and others throughout central Idaho are comparatively little known to collectors; future prospecting by those familiar with semiprecious gem minerals in the rough will bring to light many additional deposits. Long ago, Idaho was given the title "The Gem State."

SUBVARIETIES OF JASPER

Agate Jasper. This variety is an intermediate form between true jasper and chalcedony. It presents a great range of colors. This variety is often met with in the petrified woods of our Western states.

Boakite. The brecciated and cemented green-and-red jasper found in Nevada has been given this name locally. It occurs in large-sized masses and takes an excellent polish.

Catalinaite. Water-worn pebbles of a variegated jasper found on the beaches of Santa Catalina Island, off the coast of southern California are named "catalinaite." It occurs in numerous assortments of colors, some of which are attractive as a gem-cutting material and are sold as such. This material has never been found plentifully, and the deposits are now said to be largely exhausted.

Creolite. This is a red-and-white banded jasper, found in Shasta and San Bernardino counties, California. The better quality is used for gem cutting and specimens.

Egyptian. The orbicular jasper found in small pebbles along the beaches at Joyce, Clallam Bay, and Port Angeles, Washington, is sometimes termed *Egyptian* jasper. This material is very similar to the *oregonite* found north of Holland, Oregon. Both varieties have small, circular, gray or white areas distributed in a uniform manner over the bright-red background. They are used widely for gem cutting. The name Egyptian is used also to designate a banded yellow, red, and brown jasper, thought to have been originally found at some locality in Egypt.

False Lapis. Bluish jasper is the rarest of the entire group— so rare, indeed, that in Germany chalcedony is artificially colored a deep blue to simulate this stone. Sometimes it is known as "false lapis," that is, "false lapis lazuli."

Ferruginous. In the Lake Superior region, some jasper is found which is so highly impregnated with iron oxide that it is termed "ferruginous jasper."

Green. Jasper whose color is ordinarily due to the inclusion of iron silicate, chlorite, or chromate salts is a very popular stone for ornamental purposes, because it works up with a wonderfully pleasing polish. At present, our chief source of the material is the Siberian Urals. The Chinese especially have been very partial to this variety.

Iolanthite. A banded reddish jasper in the gravels of Crooked River, in central Oregon, iolanthite is found only in limited quantities but it is often well suited for gem cutting.

151

Jasperine. This variety corresponds to banded jasper of various colors and shades. The name is not in general use.

Jaspillite. In the iron regions, where the processes of metamorphism have been carried on for untold ages, jasper is found interlaminated with bands of hard hematite iron ore; this is known as "jaspillite." When in a solid, unweathered state, it will bear cutting and polishing, the alternating bands of different colors producing pleasing effects.

Jasponyx. This is layered onyx, where some of the bands consist of jasper rather than onyx, or where the material is opaque and grades into jasper, yet retains the essential appearance of agate onyx.

Kindradite. Very attractive jasper of a maroon-red color, with spherulites of colorless or nearly colorless quartz, is found in the vicinity of San Francisco, California, and at various localities to the south, including the noted Morgan Hill district. The spherulites are quite circular and usually do not consist of pure quartz but are intergrown with iron-stained silica; they are crystalline when examined under the microscope.

Kindradite and some of the varieties of orbicular jasper are identical; the only difference may be in the size of the spherulites and the nature of the staining and the contrast in color with the surrounding matrix. A large amount of this type of jasper is found widely distributed in California, available in large masses free of objectionable flaws, and is used for gem and specimen cutting. Sometimes the matrix surrounding the spherulites is yellowish in color, due to the presence of limonite, the hydrated iron oxide, hematite iron causing the dark-red colors. The jasper termed "oregonite" comes under this class, as well as the *bird's-eye quartz* of Roseburg, Oregon; the latter variety is without a bright-colored matrix. Jasper with circular white areas is widely distributed and found in many localities throughout the world.

Moss-jasper. This is an unusual form that shows a mixture of colored jasper and opaque or pellucid chalcedony. It is not uncommon among the petrified woods of Arizona and New Mexico.

Oregonite. (See Egyptian Jasper and Kindradite.)

Oriental Jasper. This is generally taken to be another name for bloodstone, but the term may be applied also to any type of jasper originating in, or thought to come from, some Asiatic locality.

Paradise. A variety of jasper found at Morgan Hill, California, paradise presents an unusual variegation of red colors mixed.

Poppy Stone. A type of orbicular jasper found in Paradise Valley and Llagas Creek, California, this stone has a good, bright-red color and is used widely for cabochon cutting.

Porcelainite. Hard masses of partly silicified or baked clays, carrying dull red or green colors, are sometimes incorrectly classed as a form of jasper. The fused shales and clay that occur in the roof and floor of burned coal seams are termed "porcelainite" and are often seen in low-grade coal deposits. When of a red color, these masses are sometimes termed "porcelain jasper."

Puddingstone. This name is given to a brecciated or conglomeritic jasper, cemented into a compact mass by chalcedony or hematite or some other mineral, and found in good gem quality in Michigan and elsewhere, especially as a basal conglomerate of the Pennsylvania coal measures. *Brecciated agate* cemented with chalcedony is essentially a similar formation. *Ruin agate* is identical and belongs to this type; the cemented fragments in this type may present some areas showing banding or other types of agate.

Riband. Jasper with broad, ribbonlike stripes of alternating colors, is termed "riband," also, "striped." This type of jasper is similar to onyx, except that the bands are much wider. Combinations of white and red, red and dull green, are the most common. It is found over wide areas.

Rogueite. This is the local name given to a greenish-colored jasper found in the gravels of the Rogue River, Oregon.

Sioux Falls Jasper. At Sioux Falls, South Dakota, is found this variety of quartzite, which in some respects resembles jasper. (See Quartzite.)

Texas Agate. This is a colored variety of jaspagate found in the gravels of the Pecos River in Texas, along with other quartz minerals.

Variegated Jasper. Good-quality gem-cutting jasper of a variegated type is found quite widely distributed in the region around San Francisco, California, and south of it. The gravels along some of the beaches yield good pebbles, especially after storms, when the deposits are reworked.

Zonite. Variously colored jasper and chert are found in many parts of Arizona, and one of the types has been given the name "zonite."

GASTROLITHS

Strange as it may seem, the huge, birdlike reptiles of the dim geological past swallowed fragments of bright-colored rock to aid the grinding of food, as do our modern fowls. The extinct, birdlike dinosaurs that lived at least a hundred million years ago were equipped with gizzards and would swallow bright-colored pebbles, often two inches or more in size. Jasper, agate, chalcedony, and other varieties of quartz seem to have been favorites in the diet of these ponderous masses of life.

At localities where fossil dinosaur remains are found, these pebbles are sometimes encountered. They are called "gastroliths" or "dinosaur gizzard-stones." Not all rounded and worn pebbles found in dinosaur graveyards are gastroliths; in fact, perhaps very few of the specimens labeled as such are authentic. In some instances where the pebbles have been actually found with the fossil bones, and where otherwise no gravel deposits exist, the specimens doubtless are authentic. Circular scratches and markings on the surfaces of the pebbles are taken as evidence of their having been within the animal. On the other hand, specimens showing straight lines of abrasion can be considered to be ordinary river pebbles. Experts are generally guided solely by field evidence and the actual presence of the pebbles with the skeleton remains.

At various localities in Montana, Wyoming, Utah, Colorado, and other Western states, well-rounded and colored gastroliths of jasper have been found. But, in all probability, authentic stones are not nearly so numerous as would be inferred from the quantities of suspected material collected.

BASANITE

Basanite is a deep velvety-black variety of amorphous quartz, of a slightly tougher and finer grain than jasper, and less splintery than hornstone. It was the *Lydian stone* or *touchstone* of the ancients. It is mentioned and its use described in the writings of Bacchylides about 450 B.C., and was also described by Theophrastus in his book on "Stones," a century later. It is evident that the touchstone that Pliny had in mind when he wrote about it was merely a dense variety of basalt. Some touchstone is, in reality, a very fine-grained sedimentary stone allied to quartzite, but it may be just as useful for testing purposes.

This stone is in general use by jewelers for determining the purity of the precious metals. Its value for testing purposes depends upon its hardness, peculiar grain, and jet-black color, so that a metallic streak upon the surface can be readily seen and judged by contrast. A smooth—but not polished—surface is used for this purpose; and the gold to be tested for approximate carat is drawn across it, leaving a metallic streak. Different alloys of gold and silver, or of copper, give different colors to the streak on the stone. From this it is possible, by comparison with a set of standards of known carat, to determine the fineness of the metal to an accuracy of about one carat, provided the alloy is above six carats. Gold-plated objects can also be readily detected; a few strokes across the stone reveal the difference between the color of the gold and that of the base metal. In the hands of an expert, the touchstone is a very quick and efficient means of determining the purity of the precious metals, where only a small amount of the metal is to be tested. However, if a considerable amount of gold is involved, the streak test by basanite would, of course, not be utilized.

Basanite in the form of water-worn pebbles is found in stream gravels with jasper and is common to many localities in

America. The smooth, water-worn surfaces are suitable for testing the fineness of gold without further preparation. Good-quality basanite is found in practically all the stream gravels of the West, wherever silica minerals abound, but the specimens really suitable for testing purposes comprise only a small percentage of the whole supply. The best basanite in use today is imported from India.

Kunz mentioned Centerbury and Cornwall, New York, as the only localities in the United States where the stone has been found in place. However, specimens have been picked up from the glacial drift in the vicinity of New York City and along the Delaware River from Easton, Pennsylvania, down to the state line. Glacial drift has furnished collectors with specimens of basanite in many other parts of the country, as well. An unusual use of this hard, tough stone, in the form of a five-inch spear-head and several arrow points, came to light near Statesville, North Carolina. The original source of the material is conjectural.

CHAPTER X

Agate — Chalcedony

INTRODUCTION

Definition. "Agate" is the term generally applied to chalcedony or chalcedonic silica, having a definite color, pattern, layers, bands, scenes, or markings of some description. The terms agate and chalcedony are often used loosely and interchangeably, and where to cease calling chalcedony an agate, and vice versa, is a matter of debate and personal opinion.

In general, any compact mass of silica free of definite color, cryptocrystalline (also termed "microcrystalline") in structure, not wholly opaque, and lacking in markings of any kind, is referred to as chalcedony. Sometimes chalcedony that appears highly translucent or transparent is termed "agate." The term "chalcedony" is an old name of uncertain origin; in 1546 the spelling was given by Georg Agricola as *chalcedonius*.

Popular Classification. A popular method of classification is the application of the term "agate" when the material is suitable for gem cutting, or would be useful as such if free of flaws. Specimens not suited for some form of lapidary work are termed "chalcedony." Any opaque or subtranslucent colored varieties fall into the jasper class. This distinction is a simple and handy one and, in general, follows the definitions given by Dana and other authorities. Dana refers to agate as "a variegated chalcedony," which implies that some pattern or markings must be present.

Quartz Names. No attempt has been made by the authors to list all the known names which have been applied to the various quartz minerals. A great many of these names are of purely local origin and meaning; carrying no significance, they are usually confusing and frequently in duplication. As a good illustration, we may take the term "Cornish diamond"—the crystal quartz of Cornwall, England. Crystal quartz and water-worn pebbles of quartz are found in practically every country in the world; hence the term is futile, bearing no connection with the diamond. It is suggested, therefore, that local names

RIMROCKS OF OREGON

Agates, crystal-lined geodes, agate-filled nodules, jasper, moss agate, and numerous other quartz minerals occur in the basalts of the Western states. Quartz specimens are more resistant than the surrounding rock matrix and may be picked up loose, being released through weathering.

or others which lack specific meaning or which duplicate more appropriate terms, be dropped from usage. Names like cloud agate, cloudy chalcedony, eye agate, topographic chalcedony, jasp-onyx, and numerous similar ones, are descriptive within themselves, convey some definite meaning, and therefore are good usage.

Many local names ending in "ite" which have been assigned to some varieties of quartz are confusing and should not be used where they may be confounded with a distinct mineral species.

In a reference to "creolite" of California, it should be listed: Jasper, variety "creolite." The quotation marks will at least serve to call attention to the fact that it is not a distinct mineral species. The number of names of this type is so great and so many additional ones are constantly being invented that few of them are ever listed or recognized in standard textbooks on mineralogy. In labeling a specimen of coral agate, for example, it should not be marked *beckite*, but rather the label should read: Coral agate, variety "beckite." While very many varieties and subvarieties of quartz have been described, all of these can be divided into a small number of groups. Thus "Cornish diamond," "Irish diamond," "Alaska diamond," would fall into the crystal quartz class; while "creolite," "oregonite," and "kindradite" belong to the jasper group. In this work, an effort has been made to place in their respective categories the subvarieties described.

PHYSICAL PROPERTIES

Composition. Chemically speaking, agate, chalcedony, opal, jasper, and the numerous varieties and subvarieties, are essentially identical. The colored varieties merely carry a small percentage of metallic salts or oxides, usually iron or manganese, and, more rarely, nickel, chromium, and copper. Silicon dioxide (SiO_2), more often referred to as "silica," is the composition of all varieties. The amorphous types, like opal, have a variable amount of water present. Heated in the closed tube, the crypto-crystalline varieties yield a small amount of water.

Luster. The luster is nearly like that of wax; a weathered or long-exposed surface may be somewhat duller than a freshly broken surface.

Color. The principal colors of chalcedony are white, grayish, and pale brown, with numerous intermediate shades. Much chalcedony is seen to be lacking in any distinctive color, and this is often referred to as "colorless."

In agates we find a much greater diversity of color, mixtures, and shades, the most common being red, brown, yellow, green, blue, gray, and black. The green colors caused by ferrous iron salts are fairly common, but the splendid, bright, apple-green color caused by nickel or copper is much rarer. To describe the colors seen in an agate is often a task beset with difficulty. Nature is liberal to the agate in this respect; hence, we find innumerable variations. Owing to the manner in which agates are formed, we may expect to find numerous alternating bands of color in a single specimen. The degree of translucency in an agate also has its effect upon the color; the delicate "depth" of color is dependent upon the lack of opacity.

Hardness. The hardness of the quartz minerals serves to aid in distinguishing them from minerals of lesser hardness which they may resemble. In Moh's scale of hardness, quartz ranks as seven. Agate, chalcedony, and jasper are generally considered to be equal to other quartz in hardness, but in some specimens there will be a slight variation. The slight difference in hardness of the different faces of a single quartz crystal is well known.

Agate and chalcedony, mostly lacking cleavage and being composed of microscopic-sized crystals closely bound together, are often tough, and this has led to the assumption of superior hardness over quartz. The cryptocrystalline varieties are much tougher than crystal quartz but not harder. Any cryptocrystalline or amorphous form of quartz carrying a perceptible percentage of water in chemical combination presents an inferior hardness. In the cutting of quartz crystal by the diamond saw, the disk will readily section the crystals, but cutters often note the toughness of some varieties of agate.

Specific Gravity. Like hardness, the specific gravity of quartz will vary slightly, depending upon purity, compactness, and the amount of water present, but it usually ranges from 2.6 to 2.64 for all varieties.

Cleavage. The cryptocrystalline varieties have no distinct cleavage; the fracture surface is either subconchoidal or hackly.

THE DEPOSITION OF AGATE AND CHALCEDONY

Occurrence. Agate and chalcedony (and jasper) occur in a wide range of deposits and forms. While crystallized quartz frequently is found as a primary mineral, the cryptocrystalline varieties are generally a secondary deposition, filling seams, fissures, veins, and cavities in rock.

Stalactite growths of chalcedony are seen in numerous localities, and often these assume fantastic shapes and forms. Sometimes the constant blast of air through certain caverns will cause the percolating waters to evaporate and leave their burden of silica in positions and forms contrary to the laws of gravity. Off-center stalactite growths of chalcedony, while

CAVITY LINED WITH DRUSY QUARTZ

Note cavity at left, lined with drusy quartz and partly filled with common white opal. The work of ages, which nature did not complete. Nye County, Nevada.

not as common as those of calcite, are nevertheless well-known in numerous localities.

Botryoidal, concretionary, and mammillary growths of agate, chalcedony, and jasper are common. The "grape" agate of San Raefael Swell, Utah, is an excellent example of this class. Quartz-crystal-lined geodes are frequently noted, with a layer of chalcedony covering the exterior, forming a "shell" or base for the later deposition of the crystal growth. Perhaps the following ancient Chinese description of a quartz-crystal-lined geode will be of interest. An early writer described a geode as a "petrified" cocoanut, the dark outer exterior representing the

161

shell of the cocoanut, the chalcedony layer of the geode representing the meat of the nut, and the milk within finally forming the interior crystal lining. This is plausible perhaps, but certainly not probable.

Neither chalcedony nor agate is ever found in distinct crystals, but pseudomorphic forms are common enough. These types often fill cavities left by other mineral crystals, or the pseudo form may occur by a direct replacement of the original mineral present.

In all probability, both surface and magmatic waters play a role in the deposition of agate and chalcedony. Silica is almost wholly insoluble under ordinary conditions; but waters under pressure, subjected to high temperatures or charged with alkalies or other substances, have a much greater ability to dissolve silica from the surrounding rock through which they pass. Analysis made of surface waters and hot spring waters indicates a much higher silica percentage in the latter. In short, the great areas of silicification throughout the world are undoubtedly associated with magmatic-water deposition.

It is sometimes difficult to account for the many phenomena of silicification, and no attempt will be made here to carry the reader into any voluminous discussion. Some of the phases of silicification and the genesis of quartz minerals are yet in doubt and defy scientific explanation. Until some of these feats of nature are duplicated in the laboratory, we shall doubtless be forced to content ourselves with theories and speculations.

Even in the instance of the seemingly simple process of wood replacement by silica, we are still in some doubt as to how this is accomplished. Dr. R. G. Weiland, a noted scientist, who has made an extended study of the petrified forests of the world, states in effect, "Until Science succeeds in duplicating Nature's silicified wood in the laboratory, we shall never fully understand the phenomenon." Perhaps this is one reason why the study and collection of the fossil woods are so fascinating and so popular.

Silica Colloids. It is well known that colloidal solutions of silica, iron hydroxide, and aluminum hydroxide play an

important part in mineral deposits formed at or near the surface. Lindgren, an authority on mineral deposits, states:

There is, however, an increasing mass of evidence that colloid silica
or silica gel is of considerable importance in the origin of deposits
(mineral) formed relatively near the surface by ascending waters.
Some quartz filling in such veins is extremely fine-grained and bears
evidence of having been deposited as a stiff jelly, which soon after-
wards was crystallized in chalcedonic or cryptocrystalline form. Clear
evidence of this is seen in some filled veins in the Tintic District,
Utah, where the original delicate banding by deposition is still seen,
though the substance is now microcrystalline quartz.

There is also good evidence to show that in the Tintic district,
some deposits formed at moderate depths and not very high temperatures, limestone and dolomite may become silicified by the action of
percolating waters bearing silica gel. . . . Later metalliferous solutions passing through deposit sulphides in it. Sometimes a banding
has been produced which strongly recalls the so-called Liesegang rings
in artificial gels and indicates a rhythmical precipitation of sulphides.

Gold in Quartz. Native gold is frequently carried in veins
of crystalline quartz, but chalcedony and agate may also be
gold-bearing. In the Republic mining district of Washington,
finely divided gold is found in chalcedony in some of the richer
veins. Dr. Francis T. Jones, of Pacific University, has demonstrated in the laboratory the manner in which gold-bearing
solutions may be made to grow into beautiful treelike forms in a
silica gel. Gold in solution is so finely divided as to be invisible
to the eye, yet large visible masses can be made to accumulate
in a silica gel under properly controlled conditions. In all
probability, the fantastic growths of gold so often seen in
quartz, "grew" from gold-bearing solutions in a silica gel of
some kind, in a manner similar to the demonstrations made by
Dr. Jones.

FORMATION OF AGATE

The manner in which agates are formed has long been a
matter of speculation and discussion. It is agreed that these
colorful nodular masses are deposited by some type of silica

solution or gel, but the mechanical mode of deposition is not easy to explain in all instances.

Some agates may consist of bands or layers so coarse as to be freely visible to the eye, while other specimens show as many as 17,000 or more distinct layers to a single inch. Further, the microscope proves that these very fine layers are not made up of amorphous silica but consist of very minute crystals resting at

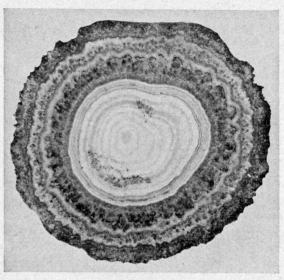

NODULAR GROWTH

Spherical mass, eight inches in diameter, cut and polished to show concentric and alternating layers of chalcedony, crystal quartz, and amethyst. Note that the quartz and amethyst crystals point *outward*, whereas crystal-lined geodes invariably have crystals directed inward. Inyo County, California.

right angles to the banding, and interlocking with the crystals of the adjoining band. The fact that the layers or bands in agate vary in porosity can doubtless be accounted for by the closeness with which these microscopic-sized crystals are packed into position.

Early Theories. Probably one of the most interesting of the early theories used to account for the mode of agate formation is the "sweating" theory. It was thought that the surrounding rocks, by changing in temperature and moisture content, would cause successive solutions to pass into and out of an adjacent cavity. In this manner, very thin layers of silica would be deposited within the cavity. For a long time this theory was generally accepted.

The ancients ascribed various origins to the agate, including its formation within the bodies of some animals and transformation from other substances. Red-colored agates were thought by some early peoples to represent the solidified blood of demons and were, therefore, believed capable of warding off evil spirits.

The layman, not familiar with the deposition of agates, generally has a vague idea that in some way they are molten droppings originating from volcanic activity, the small, rounded, transparent specimens being considered as fused masses, like molten glass.

Modern Theories. More recently, Noeggerath pointed to the tubes and channels seen in some agates and advanced the hypothesis that these were open ducts by means of which the solutions found their way into the interior. These apparent ducts resemble channels through which percolating solutions could have passed and thus deposited agate, layer by layer. It is probable that some agates may actually have been formed, in part at least, by the presence of open ducts. While these are seen in numerous specimens, there are probably just as many agates that show no vestige of any duct, canal, or any other opening leading into the interior. This fact constitutes the main objection to the theory.

Bauer, a noted gem expert, adheres to the "duct" theory. In his work on gemstones, he states that agates are formed in this fashion, and cites the geysers and hot springs of Yellowstone Park and other places, where waters rise and fall at intervals. Bauer assumes each successive rise of water to enter the rock cavity and thus leave a thin layer of agate, the water passing in and out of one or more ducts, which remain open until the interior is completely filled and finally the ducts themselves are closed by silica.

Silica Gel Theory. The presence of a colloidal solution, with the silica so finely divided as to form a silica gel, is the most recent explanation. The German chemist Liesegang was one of the first to experiment with the silica gels, and called attention to their similarity to agates. The bandings of color produced in artificial silica gels are often referred to as "Liesegang rings."

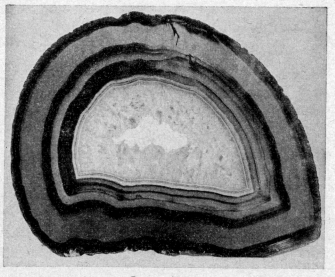

BANDED AGATE

Alternating layers of red and white agate. The center is filled with colorless crystalline quartz. These occur in profusion in the basalts of our Western states.

Experiments made in the laboratory, using both silica gels and organic gels (made from ordinary gelatine), would seemingly indicate the gel theory to be the best explanation for the formation of agates. Nearly every type of pattern and markings seen within agates can be artificially produced within a silica gel, using various metallic salts as the coloring agents and acids to hasten the solidification of the mass. In other words, from a chemical standpoint, agates can be manufactured in the laboratory; physically, of course, the finished product is different. But can we expect to obtain a product in the laboratory in a few hours that will duplicate the specimens upon which Mother Nature labored for perhaps hundreds or even thousands of years?

In brief, the silica gel theory assumes the presence within a cavity of a liquid mass of silica in the colloidal state, plus the presence (in solution) of some metallic salt. Next, percolating solutions must bring in some acid substance to change the silica to a semisolid or a "gel," as it is termed. A second agent is then required, to react with the dissolved metallic salt to produce an insoluble (colored) oxide or hydroxide, or some other product which is precipitated within the gel. The remarkable part of this process is the fact that the chemical, placed even at the edge but in contact with the gel, will eventually permeate throughout the entire mass. This spreading takes place slowly and continues as long as the supply of reagents lasts. Moreover, this permeation of the gel can take place in various ways, to form bands, lines, and irregular growths; in short, it is possible to duplicate practically every design seen in agate.

A solution of silica (or gelatin can be used) can be made to fill a very thin film between two pieces of glass, and, by the introduction of the proper reagent at one side, in time the reaction will spread by osmosis over a large area. Or, a thin layer can be poured out on a glass plate, and a small fragment of a soluble salt placed at one side will slowly dissolve and spread to form some definite pattern, resembling agate. The following experiment will serve to illustrate. Dissolve twenty grains of ordinary gelatin in one ounce of water, adding a few drops of vinegar and a small pinch of salt. Heating and shaking will hasten solution of the gelatin. Pour out a thin layer on a clean glass plate. Then, with a glass rod dipped in a strong solution of silver nitrate, place a band of the solution around the edge of the gelatin. Set the plate in a cool place, away from direct sunlight, and observe the silver nitrate creep into the gelatin and react with the salt to form a white insoluble silver chloride. The reaction will continue for a few days or until all the silver nitrate has found its way into the gelatin gel.

If chemicals that give colored precipitates are substituted, then colored bands and lines will appear. The requirements for this experiment are (1) a silica (or gelatin) solution of proper concentration, (2) the presence of a soluble salt within the silica solution, (3) the introduction of an acid to "gel" the solution, (4) contact with an agent to react with the salt in the gel, to give a precipitate.

By successive advancement of the contact agent (4) into the gel, and the formation of areas of saturation and precipitation, a regular banding may be noted in properly controlled gels. Fortification, moss, dentric, and an endless number of other types of patterns, which closely resemble those seen in nature, can be duplicated in the laboratory.

Diffusion Experiments. A small fragment of hardened gelatin (10 per cent of gelatin dissolved in warm water) is placed in a solution of colored salt, like ammonium bichromate. The salt will diffuse slowly into the gelatin. After a time, the gelatin can be placed in a dilute solution of silver nitrate; thereupon, the ammonium bichromate will react with the silver nitrate, to give a deep-red-colored precipitate of silver chromate. Under controlled conditions, the silver chromate can be made to deposit and grow in beautiful parallel bands, like those seen in agate.

A solution of gelatin can also be poured out on a plate, and, when hardened, the above experiment can be repeated in a different manner. A few drops of 10 per cent ammonium bichromate solution and a small amount of lemon juice are added to the gelatin solution; when this is cool and solidified, a ring of silver nitrate solution is drawn around the outer edge of the solidified gelatin. After a few days, the colored rings will have penetrated far into the gel. Variations in the gelatin solution and the concentration of the reagents used will all affect the rapidity of penetration and the patterns obtained as well as the density of color.

These and numerous other experiments all point to the fact that channels and ducts are not necessary for the deposition of agate and the colored markings seen within. In nature, the deposition is undoubtedly very much slower. As further proof of the gel theory, attention is called to the discovery of pockets of silica gel deep down in the earth, during the construction of a tunnel in the Swiss Alps. There are many phases of agate formation that we still do not fully understand and cannot explain; one is the way in which the silica gel hardens when water is lost.

Crystal Growths in Agate. The manner in which crystals may be deposited within an agate is also taken into consideration in the silica gel theory. It is thought that crystals cannot grow in a colloidal solution, owing to surface tension; but when tension is relieved by the shrinkage of desiccation, crystals could then be deposited. In this way, the crystalline growths seen within some agates would represent a residual deposition from the gel mass, unless we assume the presence of ducts to bring in a secondary solution. Possibly, the fine coatings of drusy quartz seen lining the interior of some hollow agates are residual from the gel, while the larger areas of crystal masses have been fed by additional silica solutions.

CRYSTAL GROWTHS IN GEODES

Geodes, having thick walls of chalcedony lined with large quartz crystals, as well as other minerals, are undoubtedly fed by percolating solutions. This seems to be proved by the fact that large quartz-crystal-lined geodes are seen with large crystals of calcite and other minerals growing over the quartz. Or, the otherwise hollow geode may be completely filled with massive calcite, after the quartz has ceased to grow. At some geode localities like Keokuk, Iowa, a dozen or more minerals may be found within the specimens; however, these do not present a preliminary thick shell of chalcedony lining the cavity. Enormous-sized geodes which show three distinct depositions: (1) a thick layer of chalcedony lining the cavity within the lava, (2) quartz-crystal growth covering the chalcedony, and (3) large calcite crystals resting on the quartz, are found at Antelope, Oregon. In this case, a silica gel may not have entered into the picture; the chalcedony may have been deposited directly from percolating solutions, which then changed in temperature to deposit crystals; and finally, after silicification ceased, calcite-bearing solutions may have entered the cavity. Proof of this mode of origin would be indicated by the fact that distinctly banded and well-colored agate is rarely, if ever, seen comprising the outer shell of a hollow quartz-crystal-lined geode.

While it is generally thought that quartz crystals cannot grow in the presence of a colloidal solution, owing to the surface tension, there is some question concerning this supposi-

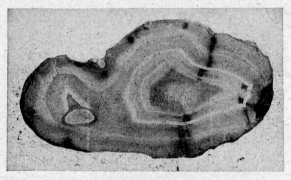

FORTIFICATION AGATE

Note presence of ducts and channels, where silica-bearing solutions may have found access. Miniature agate is seen filling cavity at left side. Bandings are alternating colors of brown, red, and white. Lake Superior, Michigan district.

tion. The crystal-lined geodes of the Keokuk, Iowa, locality are sometimes completely filled with a thick, viscid petroleum oil. Certainly, the presence of a liquid of this kind would create considerable surface tension, but the quartz crystals seem to thrive and grow in the medium. Moreover, field evidence obtained by carefully opening dozens of specimens indicates that the petroleum oil was included in the geode simultaneously with the silica solution or gel. Specimens of large size are known which contained at least a quart of oil. Some are found with walls two and three inches thick, composed of solidly packed crystallized quartz, and a very small cavity in the center, filled with petroleum oil and quartz crystals pointing their terminations directly into the liquid. In examples of this kind, there is no evidence of any duct or channel into the center; and the only possible manner in which the oil could be introduced into the central cavity, would be under enormous pressure.

Assuming that the crystallized quartz seen comprising the central core of some agates is the result of residual silica from the gel or was brought in by additional solutions through ducts, how then can we account for the presence of water in some agates? Invariably, these fascinating specimens (enhydros), often carrying a considerable amount of water sealed within a thin shell of silica, are composed of chalcedony rather than colored agate. Rarely, if ever, do we see an enhydro exhibiting a banded or colored appearance; the shell is simply a drab-appearing chalcedony. In all probability, the mode of origin of enhydros is different from that of the colorful banded and layered agates.

From laboratory experiments it would appear that agates are undoubtedly formed from a silica gel of some kind or other. The authors are of the opinion that *both* silica gels and percolating silica-bearing solutions must be given consideration in the genesis of the agate. Numerous examples are seen with and without a central core filled with crystalline quartz, with various solutions, channels, and ducts, and some wholly lacking in these. Some specimens present a "secondary" agate within a larger one. Some large spherical masses of silica are built up of dozens of alternating layers of white agate, colorless chalcedony, quartz crystals, and amethyst crystals, all packed in close together and with the quartz crystals pointing outward. *Generally*, the quartz crystals in a geode point *inward*, the mass having been deposited from the outside toward the center. Inclusions of various minerals are seen in agates, including even native gold, and numerous other phenomena, all difficult to account for in considering only a single mode of origin.

FLUORESCENCE OF AGATES

Although thousands of agates, from various localities throughout the world, have been tested for fluorescence under ultraviolet light, relatively few places are known to produce agates or chalcedony which exhibit this phenomenon.

For some unknown reason, the agate, agatized wood, and chalcedony found throughout Wyoming will frequently show a fairly strong, bright-green fluorescence, when exposed to ultraviolet light in a dark room. This is especially true of the small but fine-quality moss agates found near Granite Mountains, Sweetwater County, Wyoming. This well-known locality is about ten miles from Split Rocks, and about seven miles east of the main highway between Lander and Rawlins. At least 75 per cent of the Sweetwater moss agates show a good green color; cutting into cabochons seems to bring out the green fluorescence even more strongly. This can probably be accounted for on the basis that grinding the rough pebble to shape also removes the thin outer coating of altered agate, thus enabling the ultraviolet light to gain deeper and better penetration.

The agatized wood and agate casts of wood found in Eden Valley, Wyoming (north of Rock Springs), may also exhibit a good fluorescent color. Recently, W. A. Brox, of Rawlins, discovered a new find of large masses of chalcedony at Specimen Hill, north of Medicine Bow, Wyoming. The Specimen Hill chalcedony fluoresces a strong green, nearly equal to that of some of the Sweetwater agates. In general, all agate and agatized wood found in Wyoming is likely to exhibit fluorescence, while similar material found elsewhere is generally negative.

Why the agate and chalcedony of Wyoming are generally fluorescent is a matter of conjecture. The authors advance the following theory—one which has not yet been substantiated by scientific investigations, but is supported by field observations. It is known that many of the sandstones and rocks of Wyoming are radioactive to an abnormal degree; hence it can be assumed that long exposure to these feeble, but ever-present, radium emanations has rendered the agate fluorescent. Or again, during the deposition of the silica by percolating solutions, minute amounts of radioactive minerals could easily have been picked up by the solutions and deposited with the agate.

Moreover, it is thought that the smoky quartz found in the Swiss Alps owes its color to long exposure to radium emanations. Experts familiar with the smoky crystals of the Alps can judge with reasonable accuracy the elevations at which they are found; the rocks, varying in radium content at different elevations, thus affect the color of crystals differently.

A deposit of chalcedony found near Oatman, Arizona, shows green fluorescence in some areas. This, however, appears to be due to intergrowths of common opal, rather than to the chalcedony. The common opal found at one small mine in the Virgin Valley (Nevada) opal field, shows remarkably powerful greenish fluorescence, even under the little argon bulb. Not all the common opal of Virgin Valley reacts; only the slightly yellowish, opaque variety from the one limited area exhibits fluorescence.

Some of the silicified wood of Nye County, Nevada, shows a feeble fluorescence, but there are few other localities in the country that produce agate or silicified wood which reacts under ultraviolet light.

Types of Lights. The Braun Fluorolight and the R. & M. light, equipped with a special cobalt and nickel glass filter, appear to be best suited for demonstrating the fluorescence of agate and chalcedony. Some specimens are wholly negative without the filter. The NiCo lamp and the "Black Bulb" types are also excellent in some instances. The little, inexpensive, argon-gas-filled bulb has limited use; but, if it is fitted with a special glass filter, its scope of usefulness can be increased.

For demonstrating the fluorescence of minerals or any other substance, let it be remembered, no single type of light is wholly satisfactory in all instances. Minerals react differently to the various wave lengths of ultraviolet light, and since different types of lights have differing Angstrom Unit capacity, the reactions will not be alike. In a single case, a specimen may be wholly negative under one light and yet fluoresce brilliantly with another lamp. The Braun type of light, giving off only 6 per cent of visible light and the remainder invisible, is perhaps the best all-round source of ultraviolet light for the demonstration of fluorescence of quartz and other minerals.

A specimen of agate, chalcedony, or petrified wood should always be tested prior to sawing with the diamond saw, when kerosene or lubricating oil is employed. These petroleum products show a strong blue fluorescence, even in very thin coatings.

Rarely, if ever, do the crystallized forms of quartz show fluorescence, except in some few instances where inclusions or coatings of some other minerals are present. Fossil woods are sometimes found coated with a thin layer of calcite or mineral other than silica, and these may fluoresce. Wood may also be petrified with some mineral other than silica, which may be fluorescent.

The authors know of no instance where any of the varieties of jasper, chert, or flint gave a reaction with ultraviolet light, unless inclusions of other minerals or common opal were present. Frequently, specimens are seen which have alternating layers of chalcedony and common opal, the latter mineral showing a greenish fluorescence. Of all the minerals of the quartz family, the hydrated form of silica-opal is the most likely to fluoresce.

Fossil bones or teeth which have been preserved by the infiltration of agate or common opal, may show a slight fluorescence. Agatized teeth are sometimes seen presenting a rather strong greenish or yellow color. Agatized fossil shells may also prove positive.

HOW AGATES ARE COLORED

Historical. The well-established fact that different layers in an agate vary in porosity enables the stone to be colored by artificial means. A great many of the agates of commerce, particularly those showing quite bright colors, have either been altered by some form of heat treatment or have received their "beauty bath" in the dye vats, by the use of various chemicals.

Just when the artificial coloring of agates was first known and applied is not definitely recorded in history. It is thought, however, that some of the methods of heat treatment were known to the Romans, probably having been discovered accidentally. Medieval writers make reference to boiling agates in honey and various acids to improve their color, but the modern commercial methods were not applied until about

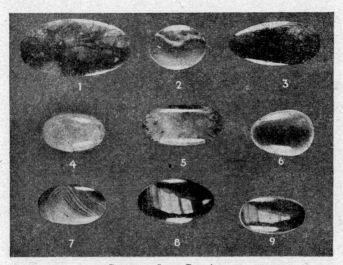

CABOCHON STYLE CUT AGATES

1. Red and green moss agate. 2. Fortification. 3. Yellow and brown moss. 4 and 5. Cloud agates. 6. Moonstone variety. 7, 8 and 9. Ribbon and banded, red and green alternating bands of color.

1815, when the well-colored agates found in the Oberstein-Idar district were nearing depletion. Agates imported to the German cutting center from South America, at about that time, were found to be lacking in color; hence, the Germans started their studies in artificial-coloring methods.

Two General Methods. The methods of artificially coloring or altering the color of quartz gems can be divided into two general groups. The heat treatment applied to crystallized quartz is widely used to produce the dark-brown and yellow colors of citrine quartz and Spanish "topaz." Inferior-colored amethyst and some types of smoky quartz are used to produce the brown and yellow quartz, which is often sold as "topaz."

It has been found that crystal quartz has what might be termed a critical temperature, at which the color change takes place, if at all. In the modern method, the material is heated in an oven controlled by a thermostat and containing a glass window, through which the color changes can be observed. Not all quartz will respond satisfactorily to heat treatment, and there is more or less loss and waste. If the temperatures are insufficient or too high, the proper results are not attained.

Some of the citrine and amethyst quartz of commerce is also made by various fusion methods, where crystal quartz is fused and colored as desired. These gems have the identical hardness, specific gravity, and color of the natural gem, but the fused material lacks in crystalline structure. It can best be distinguished from the natural gem by its optical properties. Even the dichroscope is unreliable in distinguishing the fused gem, as we may note a slight dichroism.

Heat treatment is also applied to produce carnelian and sard and perhaps other varieties, from colorless or nearly colorless chalcedony. This method is referred to under Carnelian. Some of the chemical methods are combined with heat, where the stone is boiled in the solution or heated after soaking. The heat treatment of the quartz gems, particularly the crystal varieties, is looked upon as a trade secret, hence, more definite information is lacking.

*Chemical Methods.** "Respect much more all that has been, than what now is seen." This utterance of the great mineralogist, Liesegang, can be applied to agates. Artificially colored agates are often difficult to distinguish at a glance, especially if the gems are cut *en cabochon*, but in the instance of large cut and polished specimens, the connoisseur can generally detect in an instant those which have received beauty treatment. In large museums, artificially colored agates are frequently dis-

---

* See Frontispiece, Plate I, for examples of the various chemical dye effects.

played together with natural examples; these, while confusing to the layman, are easily detected by the expert.

Since the dyeing of agates and chalcedony depends upon the variation in the porosity of layers, it follows that the coloring will not be uniform. In delicately banded agates, the colors are absorbed in such a way as to present minute variations in color. Again, the porosity of the layers may not follow straight lines; the coloring matter may "run" and appear messy, or, if minute fractures are present, the color will follow these small seams. Naturally stained fracture lines occur in agates, however, so this cannot be taken as a definite criterion. Perhaps the best and most reliable means of distinguishing a dyed agate is to grind off a thin layer of the specimen; as the color rarely penetrates deeply, uncolored agate will be encountered. Large, nodular masses of agate, from which specimens are cut, frequently have a central filling of crystallized quartz into which the dye permeates, thus making the crystalline material appear red, green, or blue, or whatever color has been applied. Bright-colored crystalline quartz of this kind is rarely, if ever, seen in nature.

The coloring matter used by nature is frequently one of the iron salts or oxides, from which various shades can be had, including reds, browns, yellows, and greens. Solutions of iron are also widely used in the artificial methods, in addition to various other metallic salts and even organic compounds and aniline dyes.

Brown and Black. These colors can be produced by first soaking the cut and polished stone or specimen in a strong solution of ordinary sugar. Into some agates the sugar will penetrate more rapidly than into others; hence, in practice, it is customary to continue the soaking for at least two or three weeks. Boiling occasionally appears to hasten penetration. The agate is then placed in concentrated sulphuric acid until the desired color appears. Heating the acid will hasten the carbonization of the sugar. Before attempting to dye any specimen, it should, of course, be cleansed of any oil or grease. This operation is termed "extraction" and is carried out by various cleansing agents, including bicarbonate of soda, gasoline, and lye. Sometimes the agate is given a dilute nitric-acid bath, following the soda treatment.

Reds. The red shades of color can be produced by various means, but iron compounds are most frequently used. One method consists in soaking the agate in a warm solution of iron nitrate (about a 10 to 15 per cent concentration is sufficient) for a few weeks, to a month or more, depending upon the porosity of the gem and the thickness of the mass. In practice, the rule followed is: the thicker the specimens, the longer the soaking; but in any case the solution is not likely to penetrate to a depth greater than about one-half inch. Should an excess of iron nitrate penetrate the agate, through low porosity or longer soaking, it will only result in deeper final red color and may also, of course, render the agate more opaque, like jasper.

The iron-nitrate solution which has penetrated must now be altered to an iron oxide, to yield the red color. This is accomplished by first gently heating the agate for several days in a low-temperature oven. While still warm, the specimens are placed in an iron container, covered with sand, and strongly heated for several hours, the iron crucible being kept at a low red heat. The agate is not removed from the container until it is entirely cooled.

Certain stones will fail to respond to a single treatment by any of the artificial-coloring methods in use; or they may be only slightly stained. By repeated treatments, the desired color can usually be attained.

Since most of the chemical methods of coloring depend upon saturating the stone first with one substance which is freely soluble in water and then by a second process altering the salt to an insoluble and colored oxide, variations of the stated methods can be used. Some methods depend upon the precipitation of an insoluble and colored compound, using two or more chemicals.

Aniline dyes are said to be useful in obtaining a wide range of colors, but, since these are organic dyes, they will tend to fade with age. However, it is thought that some commercial use is made of aniline dyes, by employing a mordant to fix the color and render it more permanent; but these methods are not so reliable as the metallic pigment methods.

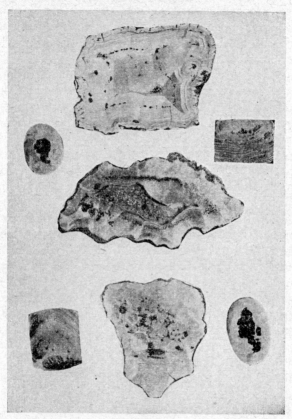

MOSS AGATES

Moss agates of delicate structure and texture, combined with bandings and colored iridescent (iris) layers. Cut and polished thin sections, ½ natural size.

Blue. The soluble ferrocyanide salts are frequently utilized to obtain the deep-blue and stained-blue effects in agate. Copper and ammonium salts can also be used.

In one method, the agate is soaked in a 25 per cent solution of potassium ferrocyanide,* for periods ranging from a few weeks

* Poisonous. Handle with caution.

to several months. The specimens are then placed in a warm concentrated solution of copper sulphate for several weeks, or until the proper blue shade is noted.

The ferricyanide salt can be used in place of the ferrocyanide, and if the solution is acidified slightly with nitric acid, the depth of blue can be varied.

A great deal of colorless chalcedony is treated chemically, to obtain blue or green stones. These are sometimes sold as lapis or chrysoprase, green jade, or other semiprecious gems of similar colors. Chalcedony used for this purpose must be free of lines or bandings; otherwise, the colors will appear in layers and not uniformly throughout. The massive chalcedony is treated after it has been worked, as the color would fail to penetrate into deep masses or would require many months of treatment.

Nickel Green. To obtain the beautiful shade of apple green in imitation of the natural chrysoprase, the stone is soaked in a solution of nickel nitrate and then heated, to convert the salt into oxide. This method is identical with the one discussed under red and follows the same type of chemical reaction.

Any soluble metallic salt which, when strongly heated, is converted into an insoluble colored metallic oxide, can be substituted for nickel nitrate. The final color will, of course, depend on the color of the oxide.

Bluish Green. Salts of chromium, including ammonium bichromate and chromic acid, yield various bluish-green shades. The agate or chalcedony is soaked in a strong solution for a few weeks and then strongly heated, as prescribed for red.

The coloring of agates at the German cutting centers of Oberstein-Idar is performed chiefly by the cutter of the agates. Since much of the agate cutting in Germany is carried on in the home of the lapidarist, we find the artificial dyeing of agates a process often accomplished in the kitchen.

In the larger agate-cutting establishments of Oberstein, large vats are filled with the coloring solutions. The agates may remain in the vats for months, or until sold. Time is not an important factor in most of the dyeing or coloring methods, for, after all, the treatment is limited in penetration; longer periods would only tend to deepen the color, if they made any difference.

Clear, translucent, yellow-to-red agates are referred to as sard and carnelian. Those with a more reddish tint are termed "carnelian," while the yellowish and brownish varieties are called "sard."

Owing to the fact that sealing wax does not adhere readily to polished agate, these gems were widely used as seals at one time. The hardness of the mineral and its romantic and talismanic properties were also factors in its wide utilization, in addition to the beauty of some cut stones. The sardius mentioned as forming one of the stones of the High Priest's breastplate, was probably a carnelian. One of the peculiar uses made of carnelian at one time was that of a toothpick. Certainly it would give long service in that capacity.

Gem Quality Scarce. Good-quality carnelian or sard, free of fractures and with the color penetrating evenly through a specimen of good size, is not at all common. Undoubtedly, the cause of color in the gem can be attributed to the presence of small amounts of impurities in the form of oxides of iron-hematite and limonite. Hematite would tend to produce reddish shades, while limonite would predominate in yellowish and brownish shades. The color range is extensive, grading from flesh tones to a deep, clear red in the carnelian, through the brown and yellow reds in sard. The deep rich colors are the most highly prized.

Color Alteration. Small amounts of iron in one form or other are often present in agate or chalcedony, but not in a form to present colors suitable to class the specimen as carnelian or sard. Colorless or nearly colorless chalcedony can often be altered to carnelian or sard by proper heat treatment in ovens, and many of the gems of commerce emanating from the foreign cutting centers have been heat-treated or dyed to obtain the proper color.

Natural Stains. How does nature produce the delicate shades of color noted in some carnelian and sard? Field evidence would indicate that long exposure to sunlight will change some color-less or nearly colorless chalcedony into carnelian or sard. So far as the authors can learn, this variety of agate is not found *in situ* but always lying loose upon the surface or among alluvial debris or gravel deposits.

Assuming that the maximum heat of the sun's direct rays, even in the blazing desert lands, does not exceed 140°F. to 150°F., it would appear unlikely that this temperature alone would suffice to cause a marked change of color. The artificial oven treatment requires a much higher temperature, to be effective.

The action of the oxidizing effect of ultraviolet light from the sun, possibly hydration of an iron salt through long exposure to moisture—these, coupled with the low heat, are all factors in bringing about a very gradual improvement in the color of carnelian and sard. Perhaps, this occurs in some-what the same manner as the familiar change of colorless glass to an amethyst color by the desert sun. In the instance of glass, it is known that the small amount of manganese oxide present as an "impurity," is altered to a permanganate (purple), a change that usually requires from ten to fifteen years.

Field evidence further points to the fact that the longer the exposure to sunlight, the deeper will be the color and the depth of penetration. Specimens exposed for shorter periods will be colored only in a thin exterior layer. Localities where carnelian and sard are found will frequently yield well-colored specimens lying loose upon the surface, while those dug from some depth and undoubtedly from the same original source will show much less color.

Localities. Carnelian and sard are found in many localities throughout the world. The gems used by the ancients were, no doubt, found loose upon the surface, much as they are today. The great Arabian and Egyptian deserts were sources for the rough gem.

The Far Western states, including California, Oregon, Washington, Nevada, and Idaho, produce specimens of high-grade gem quality. The supply, however, does not appear to meet the demands of commerce, and this situation long ago was a factor which led to the development of the heat-treatment method for the artificial production of carnelian and sard.

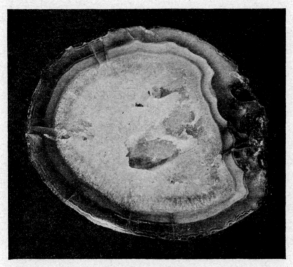

TREE CAST IN LAVA

Mould made in lava by tree, later filled with chalcedony and agate (outer portion), and crystallized quartz. Tree casts of agate are found in old lava beds throughout the West.

In California, the Jenne Creek locality, northeast of Hornbrook, and the desert regions in the southern part of the state, are among the best known localities. In Washington, the best known localities are the gravels of Salmon River and Cedar Creek, east and south of Toledo, where large, well-colored boulders are found each year, following periods of high water. The Salmon River gravels are noted for the large specimens produced, some being nearly a foot in diameter, but, of course, colored only superficially—not uniformly throughout. Smaller sizes are more likely to exhibit deeper and better color and to be better suited for gem cutting, in that the color penetrates throughout the stone.

Beach localities along the Washington and Oregon coast have produced many small but excellent specimens, well suited to gem cutting. The gravels of any of the Western streams are likely to yield at least an occasional specimen. Recently large, water-worn boulders of good-colored carnelian and sard have been found in the Nehalem River gravels, northwest of Vernonia, Oregon.

The desert and mountainous areas of Nevada, Utah, and Arizona, also produce carnelian and sard. In the Midwestern states, the glacial drift debris carried down from the North during the Pleistocene Ice Age, has produced excellent-quality gem material, but not in profusion, and usually of smaller sizes.

LOCALITIES AND SUBVARIETIES

Wart Agate. This curious variety of carnelian, occurring in mammillary and small spherical growths, is found in San Raefael Swell, Utah. Specimens are often termed "wart" or "grape" agate, owing to their resemblance to a mass of warts or a bunch of grapes. The "warts," frequently of an excellent reddish color, are seen coating and covering colored masses of agate.

Pigeon Blood. The bright-red agate found on the desert south of Cisco, Utah, is in reality a carnelian; but it is known locally under the name "pigeon blood." Some of this variety is banded with layers of white agate. Specimens are found also along the Colorado River.

Carnelian-onyx. Here is another of the numerous instances where two words are used to designate one of the subvarieties of agate. In this case, the double terminology applies to agate with alternating red and white bands. Terms of this kind are found throughout the literature on agate; they are generally self-explanatory. "Chalcedony-onyx" and "chalcedonyx," are names applied to varieties lacking bright-colored bands. The use of the term "white carnelian" to designate very pale-colored carnelian is misleading. It fails to give any adequate description of the color and should not be used.

Cer-agate. This variety is a chrome-yellow-colored agate found in limited quantities in Brazil.

Sardoine. A quite dark-colored red or brownish carnelian found in the desert deposits of the West is the sardoine.

Wax Agate. Yellow or yellowish-red agate, with a wax-like luster, is known as wax agate.

THE AGATE PROPER

Fortification agate. The lines of banding in an agate may be roughly parallel and deposited in a zigzag manner so as to represent an aerial view of old-time fortifications. These are termed "fortification agates." The bandings may or may not be of contrasting colors, but the name is usually retained only for those not brightly colored, the rest grading into some of the other varieties. Fortification agates may present quite attractive and delicate outlines; generally, they are cut and polished with a flat surface that will best show the design.

Good-quality fortification agate is found at hundreds of localities throughout the country. Wherever deposits of agate occur, this type is likely to be found. The Lake Superior district in Michigan and the adjoining states yield excellent specimens. Antelope and the Warm Spring Indian Reservation, in Oregon, continue to produce exceptionally fine cabinet specimens. The fortification agate found on the Indian Reservation is of an unusual type, tending to dark-brown and nearly black lines and matrix, yet quite translucent, often with a central core of snow-white crystalline quartz. In contrast of colors, beauty, and large size, it is safe to say that the fortification agate of the Warm Spring Indian Reservation area cannot be excelled by that of any other locality in the world. It occurs scattered over a rather large area and has been gathered by the ton.

In Mint Canyon and Soledad Canyon district, some fifty miles north of Los Angeles, California, high-grade fortification agate is found. Numerous other varieties of quartz, including jasper, geodes, and nodules, are found there.

Topographic Agate. This can be considered a variety of fortification agate. Finely banded agates with curved lines sometimes have the appearance of a topographic map, showing many fine curved lines which simulate mountainous country, hence the term.

Lake Superior Agate. The agates found in the Midwestern region, around Lake Superior, the other Great Lakes, and to the south, are frequently termed "Lake Superior agates." They are found largely in the glacial drift brought down from the north during the Glacial Epoch of the Pleistocene Age. Where streams cut through old drift deposits, the gravels are reworked and the agates are farther scattered. The deposits extend from about Port Arthur on the north, thence to the south and west for a considerable distance, defined by the limits of glaciation. Hence, the agates found on the prairies of Nebraska and Iowa are substantially of the Lake Superior type and were undoubtedly brought down by the same ancient continental glaciation. Deposits of a reddish-colored clay, termed locally "Superior clay," are also productive of good examples of this type of agate. The dry gravel beds and stream beds, however, appear to yield the largest numbers in good quality.

The traprocks of the Upper Peninsula of Michigan carry agate as well as amethyst crystals. Just how much of the Lake Superior agate is of local origin is a moot question, but in all probability the greater part of the agates found scattered over the Midwest had their origin much farther north.

Generally, the Lake Superior agates are well rounded, and the average size is perhaps but a few inches, although larger examples up to ten inches and over have been found. Red and brown colors, with circular lines of banding, predominate, while the bluish shades are more rare. Many excellent specimens have been picked up over a long period of years. Since these agates were transported a considerable distance and subjected to wear and pressure by ice transportation, they may present fractures and flaws which sometimes detract from their appearance as cabinet specimens. The shores of Agate Bay, in Michigan, have in the past yielded fair quantities of colorful agate.

Some of the agates of the Fox River, in Illinois, and those of Minnesota are of local origin and were probably not all derived from the glacial debris, in many instances being weathered out of the local deposits of cherty limestone. Many of the agates of the Mississippi River gravels, below the mouth of the Missouri River, doubtless had their origin in the mountain states far to the west; Montana-type moss agates are known to have been found in these gravels.

Lake Superior agate is not to be confused with the mineral *thomsonite*, which occurs in the igneous rocks of the north Lake Superior district. Although *thomsonite* does resemble agate in markings and bands, it is a member of the zeolite family, one of the more complicated silicates.

Polka-dot Agate. The name "polka-dot agate" has been given (locally) to the enormous deposit found on Pony Creek, near Madras, Oregon. The gem material occurs in a large vein, which outcrops on the side of a steep hill; weathering has broken off tons of fragments, which are strewn down the slope. The matrix of polka-dot agate is an opaque to subtranslucent, colorless chalcedony, somewhat granular in appearance. Small circular dots of red, yellow, and brown, due to iron stains, are distributed throughout the chalcedony, giving the gem an appearance of spotted calico cloth.

The colored spots, which average less than one-fourth of an inch in diameter, are areas of spherulitic growths of quartz, iron stained. Tons of fragments have been gathered by gemstone cutters, and a considerable amount is well suited for either gem cutting or polished specimens. The supply seems nearly inexhaustible, although the better quality surface supply has been removed. The vein occurs in a matrix of hard rhyolite rock, and agate-filled nodules which are found on the far western side of the rounded hill are no doubt of contemporaneous deposition.

St. Stephen's Stone. This variety of agate is described differ-ently by various writers, some stating the gem to be a dark-green plasma, with rounded, blood-red spots. Others describe it as a translucent chalcedony with round, blood-red areas. It would appear that the former type of stone should be classed as bloodstone; therefore, the present writer considers St. Stephen's stone in the group with polka-dot agate. This dis-tinction is clear, for polka-dot agate presents variously colored spots in a white matrix, while only blood-red spots appear in St. Stephen's stone. *Dot agate* is another type, presenting rounded colored spots similar to polka-dot agate.

Frost Agate. Translucent drab or gray-colored chalcedony carrying inclusions of white markings like snowflakes or patches of snow is found in a number of localities in Montana and elsewhere. The close resemblance to frost accounts for the name. Good specimens are also found on the Mojave Desert in California. The frostlike markings appear to be due mainly to growths of some siliceous material within the agate, of a slightly different composition from the surrounding matrix and characterized by the lack of any distinctive color.

Glass Agate. Clear, nearly colorless chalcedony is sometimes classed as "glass agate." However, the term is also incorrectly used for black obsidian. "Iceland agate" is another name given to obsidian. All these terms are erroneous and should be discarded.

Cloud Agate. This is an agate of light gray, transparent, or translucent chalcedony, with dark or black spots more or less circular in outline. It is generally found in stream gravels or along ocean beaches, in the form of water-worn pebbles. When the rounded surfaces are ground and polished, they have the appearance of dark clouds in a gray sky. The dark, cloudy areas are due to finely disseminated iron or manganese oxides.

Eye Agate. Concentric rings of a color contrasting with that of the surrounding matrix may have the appearance of an eye. Some specimens are so perfect as to be slightly oval in shape and show smaller inner colored rings to represent the iris and pupil of an eye. The rarer specimens are those which show two "eyes" on the same polished surface, spaced at an appropriate distance.

Eye agates similar to the eye or eyes of a human being or some animal, may be found at any locality where agates with circular bandings are present. In order best to show the eye, the surface is cut and polished. The fine eye agates from Brazil, with contrasting bands of black and white, are often artificially colored, the black bands being brought out by the sugar and sulphuric acid treatment. An old name for the eye agate is "Aleppo stone." Agates with concentric circles of different colors, but not having so close a likeness to an eye, are often called "ring agates." Specimens having a single eye are termed "cyclops agate"; those

BRECCIA AGATE
Fragments of agate cemented by silica. Also termed "ruin agate."

with double eyes may resemble the orbs of an ox or owl and are named accordingly.

Brecciated Agate. This agate, probably one of the most peculiar forms, is by no means of common occurrence. These stones consist of angular fragments of agate jumbled together without any semblance of order and recemented into a solid mass by the infiltration of silica. Such agates when cut and polished show very pleasing and unusual arrangement of the agate fragments. This makes them attractive additions to any collection. The cause of the shattering of the agates is thought by some to be analogous to the shattering of a cold glass dish when it is suddenly heated. This variety is sometimes called "ruin agate."

THE IRIS AGATE

Definition. Clear, colorless quartz crystal showing a play of colors has been known for centuries and was popular at one time as a gem material. It is recorded that the Empress Josephine, wife of Napoleon, had an array of remarkable jewelry made of "iris" quartz.

The color in iris (or "rainbow") quartz is due to the presence of minute fractures and can be produced artificially by the heating and sudden cooling of crystal quartz. The "rainbow" effect in iris agate is, however, due to a wholly different phenomenon.

Iris agate (chalcedony) has until recently remained practically unknown, for various reasons. Agate cutters would perhaps encounter the gem in a more or less accidental manner, but evidently looked upon the material as a curiosity and made no further search for additional specimens. It remained for Fred S. Young, a Portland, Oregon, gem cutter, to make a close study of the occurrence of iris agate and bring to light a supply of specimens.

Iris agate is a type of chalcedony which, when cut thin, polished on both sides and held toward a light, will show a play of brilliant "rainbow" colors, with red, green, and blue usually predominating. As a rule, the iris effect is more likely to appear in a chalcedony which shows fine and minute lines or bandings; but the proof is in the final cutting of the gem, properly oriented according to the arrangement of the lines of structure. Experts have a method of chipping a small, rough fragment from a specimen, dipping it in kerosene, and holding it toward a strong light, and thus judging the presence of a "rainbow."

The extraordinary play of colors in an iris agate is due to the deposition of very thin layers of agate which cause the thin specimen to act as a diffraction grating. These minute layers number from 12,000 to 20,000 or more to the inch. If fewer (or more) are present, the specimen will fail to show a play of colors. Heat treatment and similar methods have failed to produce this play of colors in chalcedony. Only nature can make an iris agate. Relatively few examples of agate will show any iris effect; in all probability, this can be accounted for on the basis stated above—namely, the spacing of the layers of agate as deposited by solutions must be within the correct limits.

Only approximately one agate in 10,000 will show any iris effect, and the patterns are innumerable in variety. No two specimens will show exactly the same pattern, even when cut from the same piece—a condition that is due doubtless to the change of curvature and of structure. In order to view an iris agate to best advantage, it should be held at arm's length, directed toward a strong open light or sunlight; indirect lighting is not so effective. Cut stones mounted in a small frame, with holes cut in cardboard, and covered with glass on both sides, make an effective means of displaying this gem. The frame can be mounted with a light behind it or placed in a window with sunlight on the outside.

Localities. While iris agate doubtless occurs wherever agates are found, relatively few localities are known to have produced this gem. It is known that specimens occur in the South American agate fields, but cutters have probably not searched for the material. After an agate has been dyed by soaking in chemicals, the iris effect is lost permanently, even if it was originally present.

The best known American localities for iris agate are those of the Yellowstone River, in Montana, and Antelope, Oregon. The Yellowstone River iris agate is often combined with a "scene," which greatly enhances its value as a specimen; trees and similar landscape scenes may be in the foreground, with a blazing play of colors resembling the northern lights, above. Probably the iris agate of Antelope is more brilliant in color and is available in much larger specimens, but there it is never found combined with any scenic effects; it is merely plain banded chalcedony. While enormous quantities of agate have been found both along the Yellowstone River and at Antelope, in Oregon, only a relatively small portion of the material is iris. This fact has been proved by the expert examination of large lots of rough material; often tons, picked up at random, will yield only a small amount of the coveted gem.

Iris agate has been found also in Wyoming, Idaho, and in a number of localities in California. The Willamette River, Oregon, and the Oregon agate beaches have yielded iris, but not in quantity. Until recently, practically none of this gem was in the hands of collectors or even represented in the large museums. In all probability, when a closer study is made of the agate of other localities, cutters will find additional sources of supply.

SAGENITE AGATE

Types Included. The inclusions seen in agate are similar to those noted under quartz. While perhaps not scientifically correct, it is customary among agate fanciers to class all types of agate having acicular inclusions or similar structures as sagenite.

A rather large number of minerals are seen in needlelike growths within agate, and many of the finest specimens are those with fibrous hydrous silicates and zeolites. Or, the line or needlelike growth may be not another mineral but an open duct or "air tube"; some of these were once filled with mineral matter which has been removed by surrounding percolating solutions.

Since both zeolites and agates are common to lava rocks, it is not strange that a delicate acicular growth of some silicate mineral like natrolite or mordenite should first form in the cavity. Later, through a change in solutions entering the cavity, a filling of chalcedony was deposited around the first mineral growth. Rutile, hornblende, tourmaline, and actinolite are also seen as needlelike growths in agate.

Localities. Sagenite agates are found in many localities; in fact, wherever the mineral is discovered, specimens of this type can be expected. One of the finest sagenite specimens ever found in western America was a water-worn boulder about four inches in diameter on the beach near Yachats, Oregon. This specimen was cut into thin sections, to be viewed as a transparency. It presented large bundles of white and yellowish-brown "needles." Numerous other specimens, often of good

192

quality, are found in that locality from time to time, generally after a storm, when the beach deposits are reworked by the waves and additional material is revealed. Curiously enough, they are all of the same type, about the same size, and found in a restricted area. Perhaps, in a small area, acicular zeolitic minerals were first deposited in cavities which were later filled with agate.

SAGENITE AGATE

Yellow, brown, and red acicular inclusions (below) with "turtle-back" effect (above). One of the finest ever found; diameter four inches, cut and polished. Yachats Beach, Oregon. (*From collection of J. Lewis Renton, Portland, Oregon.*)

Some of the inclusions in sagenite agates resemble deer hair or straw, and these are termed "deer hair" and "straw" agates.

Organic matter or carbon has been identified as an inclusion in agate by Dr. Esper S. Larsen. Possibly some of the black areas seen in cloud agates are a colloidal form of carbon. The sulphide of mercury, cinnabar, is often seen intergrown with chalcedony or common white opal, providing highly attractive gem-cutting material. The bright-red color of the cinnabar against the nearly snow-white color of the opal or chalcedony makes a vivid and pleasing contrast.

During the deposition of the massive varieties of quartz, various other minerals may be included in the mass. Metallic sulphides, often deposited with chalcedony, include stibnite, pyrite, and marcasite. The inclusion of native gold in agate has already been referred to. Jasper may also be permeated with a metallic sulphide, generally disseminated in small masses or crystals. Marcasite—a low-temperature form of iron sulphide—is a rather common inclusion in jasper.

Byssolite. This term is not to be confused with the mineral bysolite, spelled with only one *s*. "Byssolite" is a variety of quartz or agate showing inclusions of greenish, hairlike mineral, possibly asbestos or actinolite. "Crispite," used in a similar manner, is a name equally undesirable. Sagenitic agate, a more inclusive term, would be more appropriate.

MOSS AGATE

The term "moss" agate properly belongs to the moss, fern, and tree-like (dendritic) inclusions sometimes seen in colorless chalcedony. These inclusions are black in color and are due to the presence of an impurity in the form of manganese dioxide, the mineral pyrolusite. Identical growths of this kind are frequently seen on sandstones, where the percolating solutions carry the manganese into the minute fracture seams. The water evaporates, leaving the typical and characteristic mosslike structure.

However, the term "moss" is often used to include similar inclusions of various colors, including shades of red, green, yellow, and brown. Generally, these inclusions are due to iron or some other substance present as an impurity in the percolating, silica-bearing solutions from which the agate was formed. Usually these growths, while colorful and attractive, are not so uniform and characteristic as those due to pyrolusite. Specimens showing red and green make a pleasing color contrast and are especially attractive, although many combinations of shades of color occur. Superb examples are found in large masses, often a foot or more in diameter, at localities in central Oregon. Excellent colored moss agate is found also in Nevada and California. The green moss agate of India, which has been known for centuries, has supplied commercial gem cutters for many years.

The manner in which the "moss" is deposited within the solid mass of agate is a subject of interesting speculation, and a number of theories have been offered. If we accept the

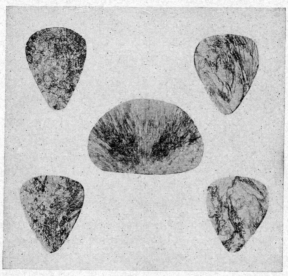

MOSS AND SAGENITE AGATE

Cut gems of agate with colored inclusions of dendritic and needlelike growths.

gel theory to account for the genesis of the agate, then the pyrolusite could segregate into dendritic growths prior to the final solidification of the mass. Another popular theory assumes that no pyrolusite is present in the gel, but assumes that the mass, on solidifying, leaves minute cracks, due to shrinkage of desiccation. These are filled later by secondary percolating, silica-bearing solutions carrying pyrolusite, which deposit the moss and at the same time seal the seams. If we adhere to the theory of the agate's having been built up slowly, layer by layer, from silica-bearing solutions, we can consider the pyrolusite to have been brought into the agate at various times. In this manner, an area of dendritic growth would be deposited on the surface, to be covered later.

The deposition of the pyrolusite directly from a silica gel carrying this mineral as an "impurity" is probably the most simple and logical theory. Moreover, this theory can be demonstrated in the laboratory by the use of a variety of substances with an artificial silica gel, whence a very wide range of types of moss is obtained. But regardless of what theory we may elect to accept or formulate, the common lay supposition of the presence of actual plant life in the agate is incorrect.

Man is sometimes ingenious in imitating the work of nature, as shown by the cheap glass doublets which are sometimes sold as moss agate. These frauds are merely two pieces of glass or agate cemented together, with a too-perfect "tree" sealed within. The imitations are made in a manner similar to the manufacture of laboratory moss agates and will frequently fade or turn brown when exposed to the sun. The expert, or even the novice, can detect these clever fakes quite readily; but the layman will accept them with considerable confidence.

MOSS AGATE LOCALITIES

Montana. Montana is, without doubt, the most noted state for the production of moss agate with inclusions of pyrolusite. For many years, these specimens have been gathered for commercial use along the Yellowstone River, which runs through southern Montana. Masses of moss agate, averaging perhaps four inches in diameter, are found mixed with the stream gravels on bars in the river at various places. The origin of these agates is in question. Seldom, if ever, have they been found in their place of origin; presumably, the matrix where they were originally deposited has long since been eroded away, leaving the agates free to travel on their journey down the river. At present, most of the moss agates of Montana are found by searching the gravel bars, generally during periods of low water, when the bars are well exposed. Specimens are also discovered resting on the surface of the low, sage-covered hills which border the Yellowstone River at some points. In past years, specimens were much more plentiful than at present; recent intensive commercial collecting has somewhat diminished the visible supply, but each year additional specimens are taken from the reworked gravels. It will be of interest to note here that moss agate of excellent quality, identical in appearance with the characteristic Yellowstone River type, is found in northern Wyoming, some distance from the river.

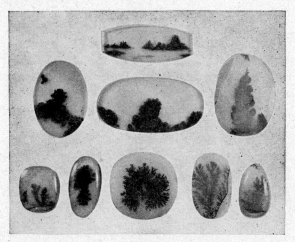

Moss Agate—Cut Gems

Upper row, Yellowstone River, Montana. Lower row, Central Point, Oregon. (*From collection of J. Lewis Renton.*)

During the World War, when the supply of agate for use in the industries was not available from foreign sources, the United States turned to Montana as a source of supply. Large quantities of non-gem Montana agate were worked into spatulas, mortars, balance-beam knives, and similar implements. Unfortunately, this important local industry was not retained in the state.

Montana moss agate is typical in appearance and, as a rule, can be instantly recognized as such, even in the cut gem, by the agate connoisseur. The large waterworn pebbles or boulders also can be readily recognized by the agate cutter or collector.

The rough masses are frequently oval in shape, with a nearly opaque, rough exterior. Relatively few specimens are of the quality best suited for commercial cutting. A specimen is sampled by chipping or sawing a portion at one end. Sometimes a single specimen, six or eight inches in diameter, will bring from $5 to $10 or more, but an inferior one is worth only a few cents. A high-quality rough agate may yield dozens of good commercial gems, with pleasing designs, which are classed and sold as "scenic" agates. Some outstanding single cut agates of this type have been known to bring $100 or more, but the average stone is valued at but a few dollars, when sold at retail.

In some instances, a boulder of Montana moss agate shows a splendid play of iridescent colors, when cut into flat shapes, fairly thin, and polished on both sides. In such a case we have a landscape or some other scene, combined with a play of prismatic colors across the specimen, seen when the agate is held at arm's length toward an open electric light or the direct rays of the sun. Fancy specimens of this kind are in high demand and often bring a heavy premium, but not many such specimens are produced. No other locality yields gems of this type and quality, although iris agate (without the moss inclusion) of greater brilliance, is available elsewhere. The iris "rainbow" of brilliant shades lends color to the black dendritic scene or landscape.

Wyoming. The Sweetwater agate bed, near the Granite Mountains, has been known locally for a number of years, but only recently has come into wider prominence. This deposit, which is located seven miles off main highway 287, between Lander and Rawlins, near Split Rock, is unique in many respects. Specimens are not so plentiful as in the past, though the author, visiting there in the summer of 1937, experienced no difficulty in picking up hundreds of moss agates on the sage-covered hills in a few hours' search.

The moss agates of that locality, while carrying pyrolusite as the inclusion, are wholly different from those of other localities. Like the moss agates of Montana, the Sweetwater specimens are not found in the original matrix. They may have been associated with a deposit of common white opal, for a number of moss agates have been found surrounded by opal. The average size is about one inch; they are well rounded and waterworn and possibly have been subjected to sand blasting. In any event, thousands of these excellent little gem pebbles are found on the low, rounded hills, some exposed on the surface and others covered by loose surface debris. The small size does not detract from their value for gem cutting; the lapidarist can grind them to shape without the necessity of sawing. Some of the specimens are wholly free from moss, but the majority show a pleasing arrangement of moss patterns.

Few agates and very little chalcedony display good fluorescence under ultraviolet light. In this respect, however, the Sweetwater specimens are the exception. Ultraviolet light fitted with a purple corex glass filter will reveal a remarkably strong green color in over half of these moss agates. The Braun Fluorolight, with filter, shows the phenomenon very well. For some reason or other, after the stone is cut, the fluorescence is even stronger, possibly because of the removal of a thin outer layer of partly altered silica, which could shield out some of the ultraviolet light. Very few localities in the world boast agates which will fluoresce; those of Sweetwater are equal to the best yet seen.

Laramie County, Wyoming, is a producer of moss agates of a type similar to those of Montana. Some of the moss agate of Laramie County is found in veins from a few inches to two feet or more in thickness, cutting nearly vertically across limestones of the Carboniferous age. The vein agate is more opaque than that deposited in cavities in igneous rocks.

Yellowstone Park. Although specimen collecting is forbidden in Yellowstone National Park, there are agate connoisseurs who cannot resist picking up the excellent moss agate found in some of the stream gravels. The moss agate of Yellowstone is similar to that found in Montana and Wyoming.

Bare Hills, Maryland. In the well-known mineral locality, Bare Hills, northeast of Baltimore, Maryland, high-grade moss agate has been found. Mineral collectors working that area for specimens, from time to time, pick up an occasional moss agate. Unfortunately, like most of the agate and jasper localities of the Atlantic Coast states, the Bare Hills region does not offer the profusion of specimens found in the localities of the West. Various crystallized quartz minerals, suitable for cutting and polishing, are found in a number of Eastern localities, but, in general, the cryptocrystalline varieties are almost wholly lacking.

VARIETIES AND SUBVARIETIES

White Moss. Translucent or transparent chalcedony, often snow-white in color, but resembling the more common black

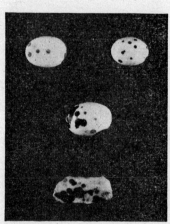

POLKA-DOT "AGATE"

Circular areas of red, yellow, and brown jasper in matrix of white chalcedony. Cut stones above, rough specimen below.

type, sometimes contains artistically formed areas and is referred to as "white moss agate." Although presenting a dendritic pattern and a pleasing appearance, white moss is coarser in texture and usually does not present the wide range of landscape and similar scenes noted in its close relative, black moss. Though not nearly so common as the black and colored types, white moss agate is found in numerous Western agate fields, including desert deposits, and beach and stream gravels. Excellent specimens are found along the Pacific Coast. Some undetermined non-metallic mineral matter, included in the silica gel, causes the white and nearly opaque mosslike growth.

Red-top Moss. Sometimes specimens of Montana moss agate exhibit a distinctly reddish color, bordering the black dendritic growths; these are termed "red-top moss agate" and are classed as a subvariety. Specimens of this kind, of good quality, are quite scarce. The reddish tinge seems to be due to the presence of a slight amount of iron, which separates and draws aside as the manganese assumes its characteristic dendritic form.

Variegated. Red-, green-, and brown-colored, mosslike growths in agate are quite common, but generally these do not assume any definite pattern, although they are often attractive. The mixtures of colors in a single specimen, with perhaps bright red in one area, and green, brown, or yellow in other sections, would seemingly tend to support the gel-mode theory of origin. Generally, mixed colors are seen only in specimens of substantial size, possibly as a result of solutions slightly different (chemically) being brought in contact with various sides of the large mass and reacting differently with the metallic salts carried by the gel. Sunflower Flat, in Oregon, and the lavas of California and Nevada have yielded superb examples.

BANDED AGATE

Alternating bands of snow-white and jet-black agate, with central core filling of crystalline quartz. From Warm Springs Indian Reservation, Oregon.

The colored varieties of moss agate are, as a rule, much coarser in texture, compared with the black types. The chemistry of the silica gels, as shown by laboratory demonstrations, has proved the ability of pigmenting agents carried in a colloidal solution to pass through a very minute opening and then grow into relatively large masses under proper conditions. In all probability, the black and the colored types have a different mode of deposition, but in all cases they are not crystalline but wholly amorphous, in spite of their pseudo-crystal appearance.

Flower Agate. In September, 1937, a new type of moss agate was discovered on the Priday Ranch near Madras, Oregon, a locality once very productive and thought to be nearing depletion. This area had been visited by hundreds of collectors during the past several years, in search of the admirable agate-filled nodules; but seemingly the "flower"-filled specimens had been overlooked. The wheat fields and sage-covered hills which comprise the large Priday Ranch have probably been more productive of superb agate-filled nodules than any other similar area known, and it remained for this locality to yield still another and even more attractive type.

Flower agate is known also by the name of "plume agate," but the former term is much more suitable and should be used. This beautiful variety of colored moss agate occurs as a filling in nodules. From outward appearances, the stones are no different from hosts of others. The average size is about four inches in diameter, and the "flower" growths are seen up to two and three inches in length, resting in a matrix of nearly colorless, translucent chalcedony. Strong imagination is not at all necessary for recognizing the close resemblance to a flowering plant; the green leaves, topped with a growth of red, brown, or yellow moss leave little to be desired in the way of any added beauty. The translucency of the matrix permits the "flowers" to be viewed in threefold dimension—not simply on a flat surface.

Not only are the specimens well suited to be cabinet specimens, when cut in the middle or into sections about one-fourth of an inch thick, but cabochons also can be worked from the choicest areas. The finished cabochon has the appearance of a delicate plant, growing from a single stalk and in full bloom, sealed within the gem. Without doubt, these are equal in beauty and color to the moss agate found anywhere. The color in flower agate is due to iron salts and iron oxides, including goethite. Nodules of flower agate are usually not found lying loose on the surface, but occur a few feet below, in a matrix of disintegrated rhyolite, from which they can readily be removed without fracturing. To date, the production has been limited.

Seaweed Agate. Curiously enough, on some of the Western beach localities, a type of moss agate is found which has the exact appearance of a submarine garden growing within the translucent chalcedony. Often this variety of agate can be worked into attractive cabochons or cabinet specimens. Various types of red, green, yellow, and brown seaweed agate may also be found as a filling in nodules.

Amberine. A type of yellow-green moss agate found in Inyo County, California, is known as "amberine."

Mocha Stone. An old term for dendritic or moss agate is "Mocha stone." It is seldom used now. "Indian agate," "river agate," "tree agate," and "tree stone" are other terms sometimes used locally.

Medfordite. This is a local name for a massive white quartz, showing streaks and patches of green and brown moss. "Medfordite" occurs in large masses and is suited for polished cabinet specimens rather than cabochon cutting. The name is derived from the town of Medford, Oregon.

Moss Opal. Moss agate sometimes grades into common opal or may be intergrown with it. Recently, in the Virgin Valley, Nevada, opal fields, a large vein of common opal with inclusions of dendritic growths was exposed in one of the opal diggings. The matrix is a subtranslucent, nearly white opal, with small areas of moss; it is well adapted to gem cutting and is unique, in that it usually shows a strong green fluorescence under any type of ultraviolet light. A gray-colored moss opal is found in Kern County, California; it is sometimes called chloropal.

ONYX-AGATE, ETC.

Agate consisting of parallel, alternating layers of different colors—white and black, white and red, and similar combinations—is used widely for cameo cutting. To be classed as onyx, this gem must present layers in straight lines and of uniform thickness. It is generally more opaque than translucent. The true agate-onyx is not to be confused with the much softer ornamental variety of calcite onyx.

For centuries, onyx has been used for cameo cutting, and the museums of the world are replete with exquisite examples of this art. Sometimes, three successive bands of color are seen in onyx, and, if the material is of suitable quality, these bands are taken advantage of in carving a cameo with three reliefs, in place of the usual two. To be best suited for cameo cutting, the bands must be neither too wide nor too narrow. A great many of the cheaper cameos on the market either are cut from dyed agate or are in the form of "doublets" of some type— often, a small colored-glass casting cemented to a piece of glass of another color. Cameos can be cut from almost any of the gem minerals; recently, Australian opal has been utilized for cameo cutting, with pleasing results.

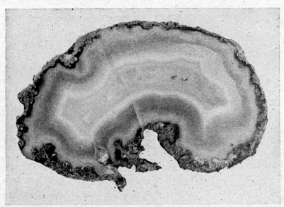

FORTIFICATION AGATE

The lines and layers appear to represent the outline of "fortifications." Note the crystalline quartz in center, common in specimens of this type. From Inyo County, California.

Onyx is found widely distributed, but little of it is suited for high-quality cameo material. Wherever agate and jasper are found, onyx is likely to be encountered. Black-colored agate, without any banding, is sometimes termed onyx in the gem trade. There are various substitutes in use, including common black glass and porcelainlike ceramics.

An extensive deposit of onyx was discovered in Madison County, Montana, a few years ago, and worked on a commercial scale. The onyx occurs in a vein which outcrops at the surface and can be traced over a distance of several thousand feet. The quality of the stone is excellent, and it is well suited to cutting and polishing and cameo cutting. It is found in a multitude of colors, which form beautiful tapestry designs.

Onicolo. A subvariety of onyx, which has a layer of white on the upper surface and is used for cameo cutting, is called "onicolo."

MOONSTONE

Cut and polished gems which show a pale-blue moon effect on the rounded cabochon surface, are sometimes called moonstone. The name properly belongs to the mineral feldspar, which reveals this light effect better than any variety of quartz. "Blue moonstone" is sometimes used to designate the blue agate of the Barstow region in California, the white and gray chalcedonies being called "California" and "Mojave" moonstone. Small, nearly colorless, agate pebbles found in stream gravels and beach deposits, when cut and polished, bear a slight resemblance to the feldspar moonstone.

The slight change in luster or opalescence, without any play of colors, causes the effect of a "moon" passing over the surface. This chatoyant effect is seen in some varieties of quartz, and when the luster change passes over the surface in line, the stone may be termed "cat's eye."

MYRICKITE

Cinnabar intergrown with common white opal or translucent chalcedony has been given the name "myrickite," after an early and prominent Nevada prospector—"Shady" Myrick. The variety in common opal is sometimes known as "opalite." While not as well suited to gem cutting as the more translucent chalcedony, this makes attractive specimen material.

Cinnabar in opal or chalcedony is found in practically all cinnabar deposits, though sometimes in only very limited amounts. The type of translucent chalcedony carrying streaks and finely disseminated "clouds" of bright red cinnabar, is best suited to gem cutting; good specimens come from Nevada, California, Arizona, Washington, and Oregon. The cinnabar mines of the Yellow Pine district, Valley County, Idaho, are productive of good myrickite.

CHAPTER XI

Geodes, Thunder Eggs, Etc.

GEODES

A geode is a hollow ball; at Oberstein, in Saxony, are found hollow balls of agate (chalcedony) lined with crystals of quartz or amethyst, which are termed Geodes.

Phillip's "Mineralogy," 1828.

With this old definition, which is probably one of the first ever written for geodes, we shall proceed to the discussion of these interesting forms. No collection of minerals should be considered complete that does not contain at least one specimen, and a complement of them, showing different shapes, sizes, and inclusions, makes a display of which the collector may well be proud.

In general, a geode consists of a hollow shell of amorphous quartz, usually chalcedony. Most shells show evidence of consecutive growth in bands of different colors, such as white, gray, or bluish. The shells differ in thickness; in fact, some geodes are entirely filled with quartz or other minerals.

Few mineral forms have occasioned more questions, with fewer satisfactory answers, concerning their origin than have the geodes. Most geodes are rounded in shape; but there are some which do not remotely resemble this shape, being very irregular. Some are flat, even pancake-shaped. It is now quite generally conceded that the shape of the geode depends upon the original configuration of the preexisting cavity in which it was formed—whether spherical or irregular.

Geodes vary from those the size of a pea up to giants three or four feet in diameter. One of these huge geodes, almost three feet in diameter, was recently found in the Keokuk area of Iowa, and may be seen in the United States National Museum in Washington. A still larger geode, nearly four feet in diameter —probably holding the record for size—was found a few years ago by the Schneider brothers in the well-known Antelope locality in Oregon. This huge geode, weighing about 300 pounds, is nearly round in shape, and, when opened, displayed an interior lined with clean, clear quartz crystals, each an

QUARTZ CRYSTAL-LINED GEODE

One of the largest ever found in America. Greatest diameter four feet, weight nearly 300 pounds, depth of cavity nearly 2 feet. Found (1935) in the loose surface soil, Antelope, Oregon. (*Photograph courtesy Gus Brockmann.*)

inch or more in length. Since these represent the extremes in large size, the majority of the geodes naturally come in between their dimensions and those of the tiny variety, the usual size ranging from a few inches up to a foot in diameter.

In most cases, the shells of the geodes are composed of chalcedony, although there are exceptions, some having shells of jasper or calcite or even of quartz. Those most highly prized by collectors are hollow and have the inner walls lined with crystals of quartz; or in some cases they may contain beautiful crystals of calcite or pink dolomite. However, not all geodes are hollow, for in many cases the collector finds that the process of growth was prolonged until the inner cavity was entirely filled with crystalline quartz. The opening of one of these "duds" is an excellent test of the strength of the collector's right arm and the temper of his hammer. In some instances, the space within the quartz layer will be taken up by a mass of nailhead crystals of calcite, or the calcite may be simply a mass or "blob," with no form or comeliness. North of Keokuk, near Montrose, Iowa, there are some geodes the interiors of which are filled with a mass of chalcedony composed of loose pieces that readily fall out when the shell is broken. These would seem to represent a state of arrested crystallization, in which the water was evaporated from the silica gel, leaving the quartz in the amorphous form. Also, occasionally the entire interior of the geode is lined with a thick layer of white, bluish, grayish, or black botryoidal chalcedony.

One of the very attractive features about geodes is the unexpected number of adventitious minerals that are found in them. Some of these are scattered crystals upon the quartz lining of the shell, adding much to the attractiveness of the specimen. Some of the minerals most often met with may be listed as calcite, galenite, sphalerite, dolomite, pyrite, millerite, and ankerite. In Uruguay some of the geodes are lined with deep-colored amethystine quartz. Van Tuyl reported some twenty different minerals noted in the geodes of the Keokuk area. Sometimes the mineral matter found in the geodes does not make them very desirable cabinet specimens; for instance, at Niota, Illinois, some peculiar geodes filled with a black, viscous bitumen are to be found. This strange occurrence has not been reported from any other geode locality, so far as can be learned. What is probably the acme of peculiar inclusions ever found in geodes was brought to light in the Pioneer Mine, Napa Valley, California, where quartz geodes were reported to be found nearly filled with pure mercury.

The origin of the geodes found in stratified rocks has long been a moot question, because any theory advanced to account for these strange structures must also explain the origin of the preexisting cavities. The origin of the cavities in the Antelope area of Oregon is not difficult to explain, because of the well-known fact that they represent steam holes in the basaltic rock; but to explain the origin of cavities in limestone or shale is not so simple a matter. Naturally, there has been no lack of theories suggested to account for structures so interesting. One of the first of these was put forth by Dana in his "Manual of Geology" (1895), in which he states that they were formed by the deposition of mineral matter in cavities formerly occupied by sponges. This idea was not favorably received and now has been abandoned for lack of substantiation. No sponges of the proper size and shape have been found in the geode beds.

A similar suggestion was made by Prof. N. S. Shaler in a paper published in 1899. After a careful study of the geodes of the Knobstone shales of Kentucky, he came to the conclusion that they had been formed in cavities resulting from the heads of crinoids, these, of course, being greatly enlarged during the process of growth. This hypothesis has also been much questioned by geologists, because of their failure to find the necessary plates of the crinoid heads embedded in the shells of the geodes. Van Tuyl examined several thousand geodes from the Keokuk area and found but two that showed traces of fossil remains. Examination showed that these fossils had merely been enveloped in the siliceous shell of the geode during the process of growth. Some have even suggested that the cavities were produced by the bulbous roots of certain crinoids, but again evidence in support of the theory is lacking.

One of the most recent and the most satisfactory contributions made to the solution of this problem was put forth by Dr. F. M. Van Tuyl, in his report on the "Stratigraphy of the Mississippian Formations of Iowa," to be found in Vol. 30 of the *Reports of the Iowa Geological Survey*. After noting carefully the occurrence of geodes in the numerous exposures in Missouri, Iowa, and Illinois, he concludes that their origin is intimately related to the calcareous concretions which may be observed at some of the exposures. According to Van Tuyl, these nodules, being more readily removed by solution, provided the necessary cavities in which the geodes could form. Moreover, he noted that, when present, these calcareous concretions occupy the same stratigraphic relationship to the containing strata, and possess the same shapes, as do the geodes.

It is thought that, as soon as the process of removing the concretions began, a layer of silica gel was deposited about the outside, forming the shell. In confirmation of this supposition, many calcareous concretions may be found enclosed in a shell of chalcedony, a geode in the making. In fact, starting with unaltered calcareous concretions, it is easy to secure a complete series of intermediate forms which show all gradations up to the completed geode. It would seem, then, that the formation of the geodes involved several successive steps, somewhat as follows: first, the formation of the calcareous concretions in comparatively shallow water on the sea bottom; then the development of the siliceous shells upon these nodules, followed by the removal by solution of the developed calcareous matter; and lastly, the deposition of the mineral matter on the inner walls of the empty siliceous shells. This was followed in some instances by the deposition of the adventitious minerals, such as calcite, galenite, sphalerite, pyrite, and many others, upon the quartz. Occasionally, geodes from the more shaly matrix will be found filled with kaolin in the form of a white, impalpable powder, which represents, for the most part, the residue from the disintegration of the enclosed calcareous concretion, the disintegrating process having stopped before the residue was removed from the cavity. Some wags with more humor than historical and geological knowledge have dubbed these "Cleopatra's powder boxes."

Near Farmington, Iowa, a reddish-colored variety of geode occurs that appears as if vitrified. Since in outward appearance these geodes differ so strikingly from those found in other sections of the geode-bearing area, some have assumed for them a quite different mode of origin, even going so far as to consider them to have been formed in molten masses of rock that contained much gas, the expansion of the gas preparing the cavities, and the infiltration of mineral matter giving rise to the geodes. Since no igneous rocks exist in the Farmington region, it is difficult to conceive how such an idea could have gained any credence. A still more preposterous idea attributed a meteoric origin to these geodes. Geologically, the explanation for the peculiar appearance of these geodes is not far to seek. In the vicinity of Farmington the geode beds of Mississippian age are in direct contact with the coal measures of the Pennsylvanian age. The latter formation is composed largely of argillaceous shales containing a great deal of iron sulphide, which readily oxidizes when subjected to weathering conditions and in so doing generates sufficient heat to impart a reddish, vitrified appearance to the shales and enclosed rocks. Similar occurrences may be seen anywhere in the coal-mining regions, where old culm piles have been weathering for some years.

Dr. W. H. Over, director of the South Dakota State Museum at Vermillion, reports that beautiful little geodes with translucent chalcedony shells are to be found in the Bad Lands, especially south of Imlay in Washington County, where in places they are very numerous. None are especially large, the size ranging from that of marbles up to something slightly larger than baseballs. A few are nearly solid, while others have very thin shells; however, all are characterized by having brilliantly sparkling quartz crystals lining the interior cavity. According to O'Harra, no other mineral, except for the rare occurrence of selenite, has ever been found in them. Occasionally, some of the crystals are loose and rattle about when the geode is shaken; hence, they have received the name of "rattlestones" among the homesteaders of the region.

The hydrolites, or "water stones," from Uruguay, as described by English, are of especial interest to the mineralogist, not only suggesting the possible manner in which the quartz and other minerals came to be crystallized in the geodes, but also accounting for many other similar occurrences found in vugs, cavities, and veins in the rocks themselves, which should not be confused with geodes proper. These are similar to, though slightly different from enhydros discussed elsewhere.

A hydrolite possesses a shell of chalcedony, the interior of which is partly filled with a watery solution that contains considerable dissolved silica in solution. The instructive point is this: in such cases, where the water has been removed by evaporation, the silica remains behind on the inner wall of the geode as minutely small, clear quartz crystals. Conceiving, then, that this simple process was repeated over and over again an infinite number of times, through an indefinite period of time, we have the secret of crystal growth. As said elsewhere, nature is prodigal of time and infinite in patience, and the beautiful crystal lining of our favorite geode may represent a lapse of time far beyond our human conception. After all, Dame Nature is our chief chemist and, quite contrary to popular conception, her work, like that of the good housewife, is never completed. On the contrary, the processes that she has employed since the beginning of the world are still in operation and will continue to operate until time is no more.

The geodes of the well-known Antelope area in north central Oregon were formed in steam or gas vesicles in a basaltic lava. They range in size from a few inches up to three or more feet in diameter, and fragments of shells seem to indicate that at one time even much larger geodes existed there. All of these geodes are more or less rounded in shape, and generally hollow, with thick chalcedony shells. However, as is the case in other geode-bearing areas, some that are found are entirely filled with crystalline quartz or calcite. The hollow geodes are completely lined with well-formed quartz crystals, some few of which show slight tinges of amethystine color. Many of these geodes have large scalenohedral crystals of calcite that have formed upon the quartz crystals. Formerly, these geodes could be found in great profusion lying loose upon the surface of the ground. However, in recent years so many have been removed by collectors that the number has been greatly reduced. Good specimens may still be found after heavy rains, in the near-by plowed fields.

Geodes of various sorts occur in widely separated localities in the United States; with the exception of the areas heretofore described, however, the localities are small and furnish little material. In Colorado, geodes may be found near Florissant and in the vicinity of Fort Collins. The geodes there are for the most part small and knobby, with small central cavities. Some show a tinge of amethystine color on the quartz crystals.

"CINDERELLA'S SLIPPER"

Portion of a large geode, lined with quartz and calcite crystals. Calcite crystal at left. From Antelope, Oregon. (*Collection of Walter Nelson.*)

Contrary to reports, Dr. D. H. Newland, State Geologist of New York, announces that there are no geodes, in the full sense of the term, to be found in the Little Falls dolomite or the Lockport dolomite. It is evident that crystal-lined vugs in these formations have been mistaken for geodes. However, Dr. Newland does cite the occurrence at Lloyd's Neck, Long Island, of some peculiar concretionary masses of limonite containing cavities which are at times lined with various secondary iron ores. Strictly speaking, these can scarcely be considered as geodes.

The discovery in Riverside County, California, of quartz-lined geodes of a peculiar nature, has been reported recently. The geodes from that locality consist of a shell of silicified rhyolite, which is the unusual feature of this occurrence. Some of the enclosed quartz crystals are small and doubly terminated. This is also unusual. Platy and skeletonized quartz crystals are to be seen in the interiors of some of the geodes.

It is not at all strange that a formation as peculiar as the geode should excite the imagination of those whose minds were governed by superstitious beliefs. As a natural result, there are many interesting legends and stories associated with them. We cite the following as an example: In the Near East there is a story of ancient origin that purports to explain the appearance of great numbers of geodes scattered over the fields about Mt. Carmel, not far from Jerusalem, in the land of the ancient Hebrews. It seems that the prophet Elijah was walking one day along the stony road. Suffering from the heat of the noon-day sun, and seeing many melons in a nearby field, he asked the farmer if he might not have one with which to quench his thirst. The farmer, so the story has it, was in anything but an amiable frame of mind and replied, "Those are not melons, they are stones." "So be it as you have said," the prophet answered, and to this day the hollow rocks fill the farmer's fields in that part of Palestine. Just how this tradition helps in accounting for the appearance of geodes in other parts of the world, will have to be left to the reader's imagination.

AGATE-FILLED NODULES ("THUNDER EGGS")

The remarkable and colorful agate-filled, spherical masses of silicified claystone and disintegrated rhyolite found throughout the Western states of America are known by the popular name of "thunder eggs." An old legend of the Warm Springs, Oregon, Indians tells us that these spherical masses were once hurled from the craters of Mt. Hood and Mt. Jefferson, when the Spirits of the Mountains were angry. According to the legend of the aborigines, the "Thunder Spirits" who lived in the craters hurled the nodules, to the accompaniment of much lightning and thunder, hence the term "thunder eggs." The Indian, in his field observations, noted the thunder eggs of various sizes strewn about, far out in the foothills of Mt. Jefferson, on the reservation which is just to the east. Very often "thunder eggs" are found within sight of some snow-capped peak; so the old legend certainly has some basis

AGATE-FILLED NODULES

Two huge agate-filled nodules (in foreground). Specimen at left partly broken, exposing interior filling; specimen at right is intact. Nodules are found up to four feet in diameter, filled with colorful siliceous minerals. Des Chutes River Canyon, Wasco County, Oregon. (*Photograph by Gus Brockmann.*)

of fact in the mind of primitive man. Various names, including rhyolite bombs, nodulites, septuary nodules, spherulites, and others, have been given to these unique formations, but the sobriquet "thunder eggs" seems to predominate in popularity.

Mode of Origin. Very rarely are two specimens identical in colors and pattern; every one in thousands may be cut into halves, yet no two will be found to be exactly alike. Specimens from the same locality will resemble one another, and the collector familiar with the region will recognize them, yet the pattern and colors will differ from the general run of nodules from other localities.

One of the chief characteristics of the agate-filled nodule is the stellate, or starlike, outline seen when the spherical or oval mass is cut in the middle. According to Dr. Esper Larsen, of Harvard University, this septuary outline represents the shrinkage outline of a "mud" which once filled the interior of the cavity in the volcanic rock. Subsequent silica-bearing solutions completed the task of filling. Agate-filled nodules are invariably found in rhyolite rocks or associated with them. At some localities in central Oregon, they appear associated with an altered and disintegrated obsidian, essentially rhyolite in composition. More recently, in the Berkeley Hills, California, locality, agate-filled nodules have been found by the thousands in the surface soil, resulting from the weathering of rhyolite; and deeper down, at a depth of fifteen to twenty feet, the specimens are encountered in the mother matrix-rhyolite. So plentiful are the agate-filled nodules at Berkeley Hills, that, according to the late John Melhase, who was a local geologist, hundreds of specimens are to be encountered in the course of digging the foundations of an ordinary dwelling-house. The Berkeley specimens greatly resemble those found in other Western localities, occurring in essentially the same matrix and manner, and having the same rough exterior appearance.

The original "mud," lining the cavity in the rhyolite in which the nodules had their birth, is a disintegrated rhyolite rock, altered later by additional silicification, at the time when secondary solutions deposited the agate filling. The "mud" represents one stage of deposition, when magmatic waters were dominant in action, and later, when this activity ceased, normal percolating, silica-bearing solutions (in part juvenile waters) completed the task. It is very logical that a gel-like mud of high silica content, filling a cavity, should upon desiccation assume a starlike outline, and that is exactly the pattern seen in the majority of nodules. The matrix comprising the outer walls of nodules is quite hard and takes an excellent polish. Moreover, microscopical examinations of thin sections point to a composition identical to rhyolite, except for a higher silica content. So far as can be learned, the agate-filled "thunder egg" does not occur in any but the high-silica-content rocks, mainly the rhyolites. Generally, the rhyolites in which they occur are of comparatively recent origin, dating from Eocene, Miocene, and later stages.

Types. Each locality yields a distinctive type of nodule, some being dominantly blue or gray in color, while at other places green and red moss types may be seen. Banded and layered varieties are very common, but red bandings are scarce. Sizes varying from four to eight inches in diameter appear to predominate in most localities, and these are the most suitable for cabinet and museum display. In some localities in central Oregon and Nevada, sizes will vary from as small as one-fourth of an inch up to three feet or more in diameter; in both instances the comparative thickness of the rhyolite shell and the amount of silica filling will be proportional. This would certainly seem to indicate a common origin of some kind, and in all probability the theory of "mud" as an original filling holds true. A very finely divided mud, like a colloidal silica gel, is out of the picture; microscopical evidence clearly shows much larger fragments present in the matrix, which has often been termed a "silicified rhyolitic mud."

Flattened, irregular shapes are not so common as the more spherical forms. Angular-shaped examples are unknown—a condition which indicates definitely the deposition of the nodules in circular cavities, gas, or steam pockets in lava rocks. The color of the rhyolitic matrix surrounding the agate is usually dark brown or reddish, but yellowish-brown and gray shades are seen in some localities. The exterior resembles that of some quartz crystal geodes, roughened, ragged, or in other cases quite smooth. Specimens found in a given area resemble one another so closely that experts familiar with nodules can instantly recognize them. Even the fillings, although quite different in pattern, are very much alike in general color.

Some nodules are filled with attractive and scenic patterns, alternating bands of color, fortifications in various colors, water scenes, outlines of animals, and virtually all the other types seen in ordinary agates. Nodules can often be cut into thin sections and viewed as transparencies with good effect. Specimens filled with common colored opal are quite rare and are found in few localities. Those of Coyote Springs, Humboldt County, Nevada, carry a filling of blue-colored, transparent, colored opal, while those of Opal Butte, Morrow

NODULE—EXTERIOR AND INTERIOR

Rough exterior of agate-filled nodule (left). Cut and polished surface of onyx agate of alternating colors. Note angular, starlike outline of matrix, typical of many specimens. Berkeley Hills, California.

County, Oregon, carry similar opal, with green and bright red colors predominating. Curiously enough, the opal-filled nodules from these two widely separated localities are identical in exterior appearance. Those of Oregon, however, are larger, ranging up to twelve inches or more in diameter. They make highly attractive cabinet specimens.

Localities. Nodules are likely to be found anywhere where the higher-silica-content, rhyolite rocks are found; seemingly the basalts and traprocks are wholly devoid of specimens of this type.

Oregon boasts no less than twenty nodule localities, principally in the central part of the state, in southern Wasco

County, Warm Springs Indian Reservation, and Deschutes County. The town of Madras is about in the center of the nodule-bearing area. Oregon localities of note include the Deschutes Canyon, Priday Ranch, Donnybrook, Antelope, Mitchell, Ashwood, Pony Creek, Trout Creek, and numerous others. Specimens have been gathered by the thousands and, after being cut and polished, adorn museum and private collections. Perhaps one of the outstanding private collections of nodules in the country is that of J. Lewis Renton, Portland, Oregon, comprising over 300 cut and polished examples, no two exactly alike, and representing all known localities. Included in the Renton collection are some unique and rare nodules, not filled with the usual agate, but carrying opal and zeolites, natrolite and mordenite. The discovery and development of the agate-filled nodule as a cabinet specimen and gem-cutting material has been made only within the past few years. Owing to the rough and drab exterior of the nodules, they have generally escaped attention as potential gem-bearing rock. At the Berkeley, California, locality, nodules were encountered from time to time in building operations, but it remained for a member of the Northern California Mineral Society to recognize them recently for their intrinsic worth.

Other notable California localities are the Mojave region, where blue chalcedony filling is found in specimens, with the rhyolite matrix largely eroded away. Chocolate Mountain nodules are characterized by a red-colored shell and colorful fillings. Red Rock Canyon, Afton Canyon, and a number of other localities in the southern part of the state have produced good specimens.

Nevada has remained more or less unexplored for agate-filled nodules, yet rhyolite rocks are common throughout the state. Known localities include Virgin Valley, Coyote Springs, Beatty, Pahute Mesa, and Duckwater.

The late John Melhase, a prominent geologist and mineralogist of Berkeley, California, was of the opinion that numerous nodule deposits will be found in Nevada and the adjoining states, where rhyolite rocks are dominant.

Few localities for nodules have been found so far in Washington, Idaho, Montana, Utah, and Colorado; possibly, a search would reveal additional localities. The Midwest and far Eastern states appear to be wholly barren of this unique type of agate. In New Mexico, two miles east of Laguna, a rounded hill on the north side of the highway yields fragmentary colored agate that shows every indication of having had its

NODULE—MOSS-AGATE TYPE
Filling of red and green moss agate in a matrix of nearly colorless chalcedony. Diameter eight inches—cut and polished. Nye County, Nevada.

origin in nodules. Agate-filled nodules are generally found lying loose upon the surface or in the loose surface debris; those which are resting within the hard rhyolite matrix present a difficult problem of removal without breakage.

SILICEOUS OÖLITE

In a number of places, such as Centre County, Pennsylvania, and associated with the Cambrian limestones of the Upper Mississippi Valley, there is to be found a peculiar oölitic rock, seemingly formed by the deposition of chalcedony about minute grains of sand. Blocks and fragments of the rock lie scattered about upon the ground, the resistant residue from the weathering and erosion of limestone formations. A polished surface, when viewed under a hand lens, shows the concentric structure and the regularity in size of the spherules so characteristic of oölitic structure.

Similar oölitic structures are being formed and deposited today as chemical precipitates along the shores of Yellowstone Lake and Great Salt Lake, in situations where the water is saturated with calcium carbonate, which collects around minute nuclei of sand or other substances until the mass becomes too heavy to be buoyed up by the water, at which time it sinks to the bottom and growth ceases. This accounts for the evenness in the size of the oölitic grains. Since no similar situations are known where chalcedony is being deposited in the form of oölitic grains, we may conclude that the siliceous oölite was originally calcareous in nature, and in its present state represents a replacement product and, hence, is allied to the cherts. The finding of transition stages between the lime and siliceous oölite, in the same geological horizon, in Centre County, Pennsylvania, adds considerable evidence to this theory of its mode of origin.

SILICA GLASS (TECKTITES)

In a book such as this, it is thought not entirely out of place to include a brief discussion of the unusual forms of natural glass included under the name of *tecktites*.

The natural glasses, usually found as small, much worn, and pitted pebbles, scattered about on the earth's surface or in alluvial deposits in a few restricted areas, have long presented a puzzling problem. They were first known in Bohemia and Moravia, and the first printed description of them was by Josef Mayer in 1787. In fact, it is known that prehistoric man used this material in the fabrication of implements of the chase and warfare. Similar glasses have since been found in several other localities, namely: in the Dutch East Indies, the Malay States, Australia, Tasmania, French Indo-China, the Philippines, and the Ivory Coast of Africa; more recently Dr. L. G. Spencer has reported them as occurring abundantly over a considerable area in the Libyan Desert. Nearly all these glasses have received names referring to the region where they occur, such as Moldavite, Australite, etc.

In 1900, Prof. F. E. Suess, of Vienna, included all these glasses under the term "*tecktites*" and suggested the theory that they were of meteoric origin. No definite proof of so peculiar an origin of the stones has yet been forthcoming, neither has it been shown that they are of terrestrial origin.

AGATE- AND OPAL-FILLED NODULE
Silicified mass of claystone with filling of agate and common colored opal. Note outline of head of duck in foreground. From Madras, Oregon.

As a matter of fact, none of these glasses has actually been found in connection with a known meteorite fall. Moreover, they differ radically, both in chemical nature and structure, from any meteorite actually seen to fall. But, since they differ from all known terrestrial rocks, except those recognized around meteorite craters, it is not at all strange that a meteoric origin has been ascribed to them.

It is a well-known fact that meteors, while in their rapid passage through the earth's atmosphere (velocities from 26 to 150 miles per second have been recorded) become so intensely heated by friction that their outer portions become fused and slough away, forming the fiery tails of the fireballs. Some of the materials of the meteor have been actually vaporized and glow with an incandescent light. When meteorites reach the ground, most of them possess a crust of glassy material formed in this way. These observations point to the fact that a temperature sufficiently high to fuse silica (3110°F.) had been attained, to produce this crust. Most elements will vaporize at temperatures much lower than that. It is evident that such meteorites as reach the earth's surface are only a fraction as large as when they entered the earth's atmosphere. Physicists tell us that a large mass passing through the atmosphere would attain a greater velocity and generate a greater heat than a small one, which readily accounts for the long tails noticed, following some of the fireballs. Moreover, this greater velocity and attendant heat would suggest that considerable of the molten material on the surface of the meteorite would be sloughed off the mass before it had become thoroughly vaporized. This material naturally would accumulate as particles of various sizes, which would follow the meteor in the partial vacuum of the tail, until they reached the earth. This might easily explain the partly rounded and pitted surfaces of the glasses as found.

More and more, since the promulgation of the *planetesimal theory of earth origin*, by Drs. Chamberlin and Moulton, the tendency has been to regard meteorites as constituting "world stuff." This is not a new idea, having been suggested by Chladni as far back as 1794. Space does not permit of a lengthy development of the analogy; let it suffice to say that the suggestion fits nicely into the facts as we find them.

According to Dr. Henry Washington, of the United States Geophysical Laboratory, we now conceive the earth to be constituted essentially of three parts, one grading gradually into another. In the center there is a huge iron or nickel-iron core, accounting for about one-sixth of the whole planet. This is surrounded by an intermediate shell composed of mixed iron and silicates, about 800 miles thick, which represents about one-fourth of the whole volume. Outside of this is an outer shell, about 1,000 miles in thickness, occupying about six-tenths of the volume, which is composed almost altogether of silicates.

Also, the arrangement of material outlined above is postulated for all the solid members of our solar system. Hobbs, Clarke, and others, believe meteorites to represent detached portions of disrupted small asteroidlike bodies, which, coming within the earth's sphere of gravitational influence, are drawn into our atmosphere, where the smaller masses are burned up and a residue of the larger reach the earth's surface.

It follows that if the meteor mass chances to be a fragment from the inner core of one of these disrupted planetoids, the composition will be iron or iron alloyed with nickel. Or, if it chances to be from the intermediate zone, it will show a mixture of iron and silicates. If it is a fragment from the outer shell, the composition will be largely of the silicates. All these main varieties of meteorites have been found—as well as all gradations in between—and may be seen in our museums and private collections.

AGATE-FILLED NODULE
Fantastic growth of silica in nodule. From Chocolate Mountain, California.

In this latter case, the heating of a silicate meteor while it is passing through our atmosphere would result in the production of a glasslike substance rich in silica, such as we find in the tecktites. Analysis made of samples of the various finds show the tecktites to contain from 70 to 98 per cent of silica, while ordinary glass seldom contains much above 50 per cent of silica.

In recent years, the presence of silica glass in considerable quantities has been recognized in connection with meteorite craters, as at Coon Butte, Arizona; Wobar, Arabia; Henbury, Australia; and recently in connection with the Great Siberian Fall of 1908. In all these instances, the glass has been formed by the fusing of the sand or sandstone in the intense heat generated by the impact of a very large mass of meteoric iron. Such glass does not occur in the rounded, pebblelike masses so characteristic of the tecktites, but is more generally found in the form of a glasslike glaze upon the rocks near the crater.

CHAPTER XII

Unusual Quartz Types

CRYSTAL PSEUDOMORPHS

It may be a complete surprise to some of our readers to learn that quartz readily responds to replacement processes and is often found masquerading in many unexpected crystal forms. Indeed the word "pseudomorph" means "false form" and is a term used by mineralogists to indicate a mineral that has replaced another of entirely different crystal form and composition. In other words, as Bayley puts it, "A pseudo-morph is a body possessing the form of one substance and the chemical composition of another." For example, the finding of a quartz crystal which has assumed a cubical shape, as at Loma La Jata, Guanabacoa, in Havana Province, Cuba, would ordinarily be looked upon with suspicion, since that is not the normal crystal habit of the mineral; nevertheless, this may actually occur and the phenomenon has a plausible explanation.

A study of chemical processes involved in the several instances of replacement in which quartz plays an important part, makes up a very fascinating phase of mineralogy. Whether the replaced material be a crystal, a fossil, or some organic substances, such as in the petrification of wood, the process in each case is a similar one. Molecule by molecule, the material is dissolved out and carried away by percolating ground waters, and in its place are deposited molecules of silica which are carried in in the same manner. So slowly and gradually is this process accomplished by nature, that the shape or form of the original material is scarcely at all disturbed.

Quartz Family Minerals

Quartz is singularly facile in the formation of its pseudo-morphs, assuming the crystal form of no small number of minerals which it is capable of replacing. At Paterson, New Jersey, advanced collectors are ever on the alert, watching for quartz pseudomorphs after the various zeolites, and many collections containing choice specimens of these are extant. At the same locality quartz pseudomorphs after natrolite are said to occur, sprinkled thickly with small crystals of quartz and making very handsome specimens. G. L. English, dealing in minerals at the close of the last century, advertised quartz pseudomorphs after crocidolite. Quartz has been known to take the form of fluorite cubes, and haydenite is a pseudomorph after datolite, etc.

Some very interesting pseudomorphs of quartz after twin crystals of feldspar were found by Mr. Elmer Benge at the Old Copper Mine near Shannonville, Pennsylvania, the largest being over five inches long, coated with drusy quartz, and standing in relief in a thick shell of chalcedony. Asbestos altered to quartz, is found at Marple, Pennsylvania; and at Newton, what is said to be serpentine altered to quartz is found in large masses, with cavities in it filled with minute quartz crystals of bright-brown color.

Lincoln R. Thiesmeyer in a recent number of the *American Mineralogist* describes in detail an unusual occurrence of fibrous quartz after asbestos, which caps the Blue Ridge in Fauquier County, Virginia. In this locality "thousands of lenticular seams of cross-fiber actinolite asbestos in all stages of replacement by transparent to milky quartz" are to be found scattered over a distance of thirteen miles. This form is of rather rare occurrence, and the finding of so large an area thus silicified furnishes a remarkable opportunity for study of the changes involved in the process of replacement. The veins range in width from hairlike veinlets up to two and a half feet in width, and all stages of replacement may be found in the area, grading almost insensibly from one into another.

For some reason or other, agate and chalcedony have a propensity for replacing calcite crystals or stalactite growths of this mineral; specimens of this kind are common wherever agate and calcite are found. The jasper pseudomorphs after selenite found in Utah are colorful and interesting specimens.

TIGER-EYE

Tiger-eye, a gem-cutting material which is again coming into popularity, is another good example of a quartz pseudomorph. It is an asbestos mineral (crocidolite) which has been completely silicified, and the original fibers have altered to the yellow oxide of iron-limonite. The original color of the asbestos was a dark blue. Yellow-colored tiger-eye is the most common and plentiful variety, but red and dark blue are also found at the locality in Grieualand, Southwest Africa. The red color is due to the presence of red iron oxide (hematite), the dark blue representing another form of iron. Tiger-eye is often beautifully chatoyant and very durable. It was quite popular in the past as an ornamental stone, especially for carving cameos and intaglios for ring sets. A similar variety known as cat's-eye differs in that its chatoyancy is of a rich greenish cast. Petrified asbestos is another popular name for this silicified crocidolite.

ORGANIC PSEUDOMORPHS

Wood turned to stone, one of the most common forms of pseudomorph, is found in large quantities, especially in our Western states. In such instances, the wood has undergone a complete change; particle by particle, the organic substance has been turned to stone. Further discussion of this interesting subject may be found in Chap. XIV.

Fossils are, for the most part, pseudomorphs of a mineral substance after organisms or parts of organisms. The process of transformation is analogous to those employed in the changing of a crystal. The original organic material may be replaced, molecule by molecule, by the mineralizing substance, as was noted in the case of petrified wood; or the organic material may be removed from the rock in which it was embedded, leaving a cavity, which later is filled with some mineral matter, thus preserving the form. The fossils resulting from this latter process may be likened to casts that show only the outer forms of the original objects.

Fossils of Jasper. As with woods, jasper can also be a fossilizing agent for the preservation of the many organic forms. Generally, bone structure is well preserved; the organic matter in the bone cells is replaced by jasper, but the original lime of the bone usually remains in place.

There are several notable areas in the country where dinosaur bones have become permeated with bright-red jasper. Several localities in Colorado and Utah yield large quantities of jasperized bone, mainly of a fragmentary nature, but of a good color, quite compact, and often suitable for cutting into ornaments. In the noted Como Bluff, Wyoming, locality, situated on United States Highway Number 30, a large museum has been constructed of jasperized dinosaur bones. Excellent specimens of intact bones are also on display. The jasperized bone of Como Bluff is somewhat darker than that of Colorado and Utah, but attractive and suitable for cutting. Quantities of jasperized dinosaur bones are cut into ring-sets and sold as souvenirs to tourists. The novelty of having a ring set fashioned from the bones of an extinct reptilelike form of life that lived over 100,000,000 years ago makes this material popular. Agatized and jasperized dinosaur bone is found also in Red Deer Valley, east of Calgary, Canada, and some specimens show the interior, originally filled with bone marrow, now lined with sparkling drusy quartz crystals.

Replacements by Agate. Agate, chalcedony, and the other forms of quartz have a propensity for permeating and replacing other materials, and acting as fossilizing agents. Almost all forms of organic life, especially woods, bones, and even entire skeletons of ancient and extinct animals, are frequently found preserved by some form of quartz.

Agatized Bones. One of the most remarkable and outstanding instances of this class is the fully agatized and nearly complete mastodon skeleton seen on display at the Field Museum in Chicago. This enormous, heavy skeleton was found in Utah and presented a problem in constructing the steel support for the articulated bones. It was necessary to drill holes through the bones and pass cables through them to join the parts; and since some bones are nearly a foot in diameter, considerable time was spent in sinking holes through the hard, agatized mass. Ordinary iron pipes, slightly flattened on one end to cut clearance,

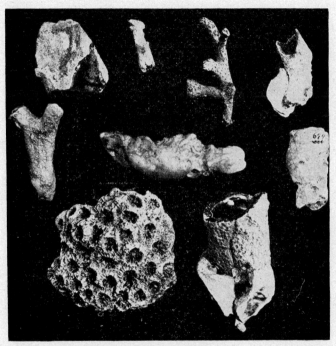

CORAL PETRIFIED BY CHALCEDONY
Tampa Bay, Florida.

rotated by power, and fed with a mixture of silicon carbide grit and water, were used for sinking the holes.

Agate and chalcedony also replace numerous other forms of life, including corals and shellfish life. Sometimes agate is seen filling casts in sandstone cavities once occupied by clams or oysters. Excellent specimens of this type are found in Florida and along the Pacific Coast. Since the forms of quartz are so much more enduring, animal life preserved in this manner will resist disintegration much longer and better than that preserved by other fossilizing agents like calcite and gypsum.

LIQUID INCLUSIONS

It is not uncommon in collections to see crystals containing small cavities in which are bubbles of some fluid, usually water, but sometimes liquid carbon dioxide, petroleum, or substances such as gases other than air. Rev. C. W. King, writing in his book "Antique Gems," says: "I am informed that in California, in early days, the miners often met with large nodules of quartz thus filled, and were often killed by drinking the liquid contained therein, so strongly impregnated was it with silica." So far, we have been unable to verify this statement, but on the other hand we have no good reason for doubting it. These are the "Enhydros" of Pliny and the medieval mineralogists, who looked upon this phenomenon as one of the most wonderful miracles of all nature, to judge from the numerous epigrams; it was also thought worthy, by the Claudian and other poets, of celebration in verse:

EPIGRAM VIII, ET SEQ.

When the Alpine ice, frost-hardened into stone,
First braved the sun, and as a jewel shone,
Not all its substance could the gem assume;
Some tell-tale drops still linger in its womb.
Hence with augmented fame its wonders grow,
And charms the soul the stone's mysterious flow,
Whilst stored within it from Creation's birth,
The treasured waters add a double worth.

Mark where extended a translucent vein
Of brighter crystals tracks the glittering plain
No boreas fierce, no nipping winter knows
The hidden spring, but ever ebbs and flows;
No frosts congeal it, and no Dog star dries,
E'en all-consuming Time its youth defies.

Unusual Quartz Types

A stream unfettered pent in crystal round,
A truant fount by hardened waters bound,
Mark how the gem with native sources foams,
How the live spring in refluent eddies roams!
How the bright rainbow paints the opposing ray
As with the imprisoned winter fights the day!
Strange nymph! above all rivers' fame supreme,
Gem yet no gem; a stone, yet flowing stream.
Erst, while the boy, pleased with its polish clear,
With gentle fingers twirled the icy sphere,
He marked the drops pent in its stony hold,
Spared by the rigour of the wintry cold;
With thirsty lips th' unmoistened ball he tries,
And the loved draught with fruitless kisses plies.

Streams which a stream in kindred prison chain,
Which water were and water still remain,
What art hath bound ye, by what wondrous force
Hath ice to stone congealed the limpid source?
What heat the captive saves from winter hoar,
Or what warm zephyr thaws the frozen core?
Say in what hid recess of inmost earth,
Prison of fleeting tides, thou hadst thy birth?
What power thy substance fixed with icy spell,
Then loosed the prisoner in his crystal cell?

Girkie, Dana, and others mention the occurrence of liquids and gases in minute quantities in crystals, but they seem to consider them to be accidental inclusions of foreign material occurring during the formation of the crystal. In the genuine enhydros the liquid is of so large an amount, it would seem probable that it is the remainder of the liquid solution from which the chalcedony walls were deposited. We are at present concerned only with the small bubble inclusions with which all collectors are familiar. Enhydros proper will be appropriately discussed later.

These liquid inclusions seldom completely fill the cavities— a condition which permits the liquid to move about from place to place and to be seen as a bubble. All prolific quartz localities afford liquid inclusions of some kind, but where the liquid involved is water, one must bear in mind that to avoid freezing the deposit must either exist in some tropical country, such as Brazil, or at some little depth below the surface, if in colder regions. We are, therefore, not surprised to learn that many of our best "bubble quartz" crystals come from Brazilian deposits.

In the issue of the *Mineral Collector*, for December, 1895, there is a picture of a magnificent crystal enclosing a floating bubble, which moves through a zigzag cavity over two and one-half inches long. E. Mitchell Gunnell has in his possession a Brazilian crystal which shows ten distinct and separate bubbles. He says:

I am certain that in many instances there is definite orientation of the liquid inclusions in quartz crystals. This is bound to be so, because these liquid inclusions are merely occupying the oriented cavities in skeletally developed crystals. I do not say that this is always the case: I know it is not—but in my own experience I know it to be often true. By such "orientation," I merely mean that the bubble is free to move only in the direction of elongation of the cavity which contains it—which is parallel to crystal faces, and causes these bubbles in turn to likewise be so oriented.

Although it may not appear so, even quartz crystals are somewhat porous to water and therefore the water inclusions therein are always more or less difficult to preserve. Some crystals enclosing liquids have been cut into gem stones, but it is said that the removal of the original crystal surface causes the liquid soon to disappear. If they become frozen, they are most certain to be ruined, and utmost caution should be exercised by everyone so fortunate as to possess one to avoid its destruction by that means.

The question is often raised as to how any gas, such as carbon dioxide, could possibly become liquefied and at the same time be entrapped within any crystal growth. This is not difficult to understand, when we realize that in many places —for instance, Colorado, Texas, Mexico—the rocks are literally charged with carbon dioxide gas, which escapes in vast quantities from wells that have been drilled for oil, and that this gas readily liquefies under such rock pressure as may occur at no greater depth below the surface than 500 to 700 feet. In places, this gas emerges through openings in the earth's surface under such tremendous pressure as to immediately create carbon dioxide snow or ice.

Transparent quartz crystals have been found at Guntersville, Alabama, enclosing one or more cavities which are filled with petroleum. There is one pleasing feature about these crystals: they will not freeze or shatter if left in a room with the temperature below freezing, as will most other liquid inclusions familiar to collectors.

A large glass-manufacturing concern was once asked to cast glass with movable bubbles containing water. After experimenting for a considerable time, they reported that in their opinion this would ever remain an impossibility. Here, then, is truly one of nature's seeming miracles which will probably never be duplicated by man's feeble efforts; and so, anyone so fortunate as to own any of these very interesting objects need never fear that it is a counterfeit production. Every one is a genuine article.

CHALCEDONY ENHYDROS

The intriguing masses of chalcedony which carry water sealed within are called enhydros or "water agates." Generally, the shell surrounding the water is of a translucent chalcedony, which may not permit viewing the water within. The manner in which enhydros were formed is doubtless similar to the genesis of geodes, and the water within may represent a residue from the silica gel; or the water may have been forced into the hollow cavity by external pressure. One of the most interesting features of enhydros is the fact that they seldom present anything more than a colorless shell of chalcedony. Why does this shell never have a banded structure, and why should distinct colors be lacking? No definite explanation is forthcoming other than the fact that this would doubtless indicate a different mode of deposition for colored or banded agates.

The writer has seen hundreds of enhydros from localities throughout the world, but never one where the shell could be classed as agate.

Some enhydros carry only a single drop of water, each. It may be in the form of a movable bubble, which will turn about as the specimen is rotated. Those from Brazil may enclose an ounce or more of water, with enough space left so that the splashing can be heard when the specimen is shaken. Some enhydros are prone to lose their water content by the slow seepage or evaporation of moisture through the thin shell. In some instances, it is possible to restore it by long immersion in water, or by placing the specimen in a pressure cooker under from ten to twenty pounds of steam pressure for a few hours. The fact that the water can be restored in some specimens by steam pressure may be taken as an indication that the water originally entered the cavity under external pressure.

Water agates carrying large amounts of water are really scarce, and are found in few localities in the world. Specimens showing a few drops of water are fairly common and may be taken from any locality where agates occur. Freezing temperatures will generally fracture an enhydro, and this may account for the scarcity of specimens showing large amounts of liquid. Unfortunately, most of the South American enhydros carrying large quantities of water have thin shells of nearly opaque chalcedony, which do not allow a view of the water sealed within. Sometimes it is possible to grind and polish a small area on the surface so as to permit viewing the water, but this is fraught with the risk of breaking into the cavity. Small enhydros, carrying only a few drops of water apiece, usually have thick shells, making it possible to grind and polish one side, if the chalcedony lacks transparency.

Enhydros may be found wherever agates occur, but rarely are they in great profusion. Along the Oregon and Washington coasts, the beach agate deposits yield a goodly number of excellent water agates. Where the enhydros are known to occur, perhaps one agate in a thousand will, after a careful scrutiny, prove to be an enhydro. Dipping the specimens in water and holding them toward a strong light will make possible a more ready detection of the bubble. Or, the specimen may be coated with a varnish of equal parts of Canada balsam and xylol, to render the shell more translucent; where the shell is thin, this method would be more desirable than grinding.

One of the most noted localities for enhydros is in the lava rocks east of Kalama, Washington. Here, admirable little enhydros are seen in their original matrix; frequently, several will be seen in a single, hand-sized rock specimen. They are also found by the thousands in the erosion debris at the foot of the rock cliffs. Most of the enhydros of this region are small in size, seldom over an inch in diameter, but they occur, perhaps, in greater profusion here than in any other known locality. The water in the Kalama enhydros will not tend to evaporate if the specimens are kept submerged in water; otherwise, some specimens will become dry after a number of months or years. Dr. J. L. Roach, a Kalama physician, was the first to call attention to this remarkable occurrence of enhydros.

Perhaps, one reason why the enhydros in the Oregon, Washington, and California beach deposits are more translucent, is that the surfaces have been partly worn and polished by the scouring action of sand and water. Many specimens are taken each year by visitors to the beach resorts. Specimens up to two inches and more in size have been found along the Oregon coast; the bubbles of water in some specimens follow a devious course around the inside as the specimen is rotated.

QUARTZ PHANTOMS

One of the chief differences between individuals of the organic and the inorganic world is that plants and animals assimilate their food inwardly and increase their size or growth from within, while crystals grow definitely by the accretion of material from without. It would be entirely too much to expect that all crystal growth, from the moment of its inception until its completion, would be a continuous process; therefore, we must assume that in the formation of most crystals there were many pauses, or periods when growth ceased altogether, due to lack or scarcity of the required material. Many of these pauses must have left traces or marks which even the most casual observer could not fail to see, and by means of which a skilled crystallographer might easily read the life history of the crystal in much the same manner that a trained forester might read the history of a tree.

PHANTOM-QUARTZ
CRYSTAL

Showing development of one crystal within another. (*Photograph, courtesy George L. English.*)

In rock crystals these pauses are revealed in various manners and habits. In the most usual form, the type of material of which the crystal is composed is homogeneous throughout, and each phase or stage of growth is shown by more or less faint mirror or ghost-like outlines or images, called "phantoms." Sometimes the enclosures show pyramids (seldom the prisms) of crystals distinctly outlined, but more generally they are but faint, feathery traceries, best observed when the crystals are turned at certain angles to the light, which suggest merely "phantom" forms of the earlier growths.

Phantoms may occur in groups, clusters, or a succession of forms, where the process is repeated again and again, resulting in a series of internal cappings. *Natural History Magazine,* (No. 3, 1933, pp. 271–272) illustrates a crystal showing multiple phantoms in quartz, in which "at least fifteen changes have taken place affecting the minor composition of the silica solution—during the period of its growth," and another unique specimen in which a thin coating of tiny mica scales reveals one gorgeous phantom and seventeen additional successive ones of later generation than the more obvious one, with the respective faces of each exactly parallel to it.

Occasionally, these cappings are separated by thin layers of foreign material, which are produced in the following manner. Imagine a rock-bound cavity lined with quartz crystals near and about which there is some other mineral, say actinolite. Every fresh surge or charge of silica which is beyond the ordinary rate of deposition carries with it particles of the actinolite, and the whole is precipitated upon the quartz crystals; then the process of crystallization is continued again for a time at its usual rate, until the disturbance once more occurs. In Germany are found large groups of capped opaque quartz crystals, with a micaceous deposit between every two series, which by careful labor may be separated. These are veritable caps, and A. C. Bates, an authority on quartz during the latter part of the nineteenth century, says: "I have seen four, one above the other, each free to be lifted."

Another form of "phantom," the cause of which is not so easy to explain, is called "smoky phantom," and is seen more commonly in crystals of colorless and amethystine quartz than in solely smoky crystals. Owing to their contrast in color with the embedding crystal, these phantoms stand out in a very strik- ing and unusual way. They have the appearance of one crystal's becoming buried within the growth of another. This may best be accounted for by changes in the source of supply and the conditions under which the crystallization has been accomplished. For a time, silica material suitable for the growth of smoky quartz crystals must have entered the cavity, and then, owing to forces of diastrophism, channel piracy, fresh checking or cracking of the rocks, material of a different character entered the cavity, producing profound change in the nature of the crystal growth. Doubtless, there is still as much to be learned about the nature of phantoms as there is knowledge to be gained by further careful study of the facts already in hand.

GLAZES AND COATINGS

Closely associated with the phenomenon producing cappings is the matter of glazes and coatings. The principal difference, it seems, is that these additions occur after the crystals have reached their full or final form, all growth by accretion having ceased. There are frequently seen on the faces of amethyst crystals beautiful reddish-brown glazes which, from their very nature, must have been produced by deposits from solution, although, from their vitreous appearance, the uninitiated might suspect them to be the work of fusion.

Under the lens, these coatings sometimes appear jasperized, and may be speckled with oölitic markings of distinctive color.

Connected with them may also occur fascinating surface markings which are slightly elevated above the surface and are thought to be associated with the phenomenon of twinning, whose patterns are usually isosceles (tepee-shaped) triangles with legs parallel to the edge of their adjacent facial angle.

In the vicinity of Henry, Lincoln County, North Carolina, have been found large numbers of what have been termed "porcelain-topped" crystals, which are both attractive and unique. The crystals bear every appearance of having been glazed or enameled with a pinkish-white substance resembling some porcelains; hence the name. The glazing is, however, upon close examination, found to be but a superficial coating upon the exterior of the crystals.

ETCHED QUARTZ CRYSTAL
Rough exteriors of crystal faces are due to etching.

Since there are so many inquiries regarding the proper method of removing foreign coatings from quartz crystal faces, we quote the following directions taken from an old volume of *Minerals Magazine*: "To clean quartz crystals that are coated with iron or foreign matter, place them in a kettle, cover with cold water, and for each gallon of water add one teaspoonful of oxalic acid crystals. Boil slowly (until the coating will scale off) adding boiling water whenever necessary to keep crystals covered. Do not remove crystals until the water has been allowed to cool."

CHAPTER XIII

The Opal

The opal is our most beautiful gem stone, from the standpoint of "colors at play." John Ruskin, in one of his lectures, says: "The opal, when pure and uncut . . . presents the most beautiful colors that can be seen in the world, except those of clouds." Certainly, this is ranking the opal high among the many lovely things of creation. Few, indeed, are those who will take exception to this estimate, for, as we view nature's handiwork in the kaleidoscopic changes of colors in the opal, we doubt if there is any other object on which so much beauty has been lavished in so small a space.

Edith M. Thomas, writing in *The Century Magazine*, many years ago, has given us a descriptive poem which is without doubt one of the most colorful known to mineralogical literature.

THE OPAL

Iris dwells in thee and throws
Rays of leaf-green and of rose.
Limpid amber courseth through
Violet glooms of fading hue.
If some stranger should inquire
Whence thy swift caprices came,
Morn-mist, closing evening flame—
Do thou, kindling answer bring,
Many-passioned, lambent thing;
Say with cosmic throe was born
All thy life of love and scorn,
Yet not chance but deathless law
Bred thy beauty from a flaw

Speak, thou, too, with perfect art,
For wild Genius' burning heart,
Whose perfection springs, like thine,
From some touch of scath divine.

MINERALOGY OF OPAL

Mineralogically, the opal is an amorphous form of hydrated silica, containing from 3 to 13 per cent of water. It is probable that opal, like chalcedony and agate, was originally a colloidal silica gel, but differs from them in containing a small amount of occluded water. Underground water is often subjected to great rock pressure and under such conditions can be heated far above the boiling point without vaporizing. When water is in this state, it readily dissolves out of the rocks silica and other minerals that may be present. When such mineral-laden waters ascend and come near the earth's surface, where the temperature is lower and the pressure is relieved, silica is often deposited in veins and fissures. In time, most of the occluded water may be driven out of the gel, and, if so, the mass becomes a vein of opal.

Opals may be divided into two great classes—*precious*, and *common*. All are of secondary origin and are found occupying seams and fissures in all types of rocks: sedimentary, igneous, and metamorphic. Opal also occurs as "petrified" wood and in other pseudomorphic forms. It is the chief constituent of the siliceous skeletons of various sea organisms, such as diatoms, which may ultimately accumulate in beds of great extent and thickness. Wherever found, opal is always a young mineral, probably the very youngest of our gem stones. Precious opals, with which most of this chapter is concerned, are usually found in regions of recent mountain-making activity, where they are associated with such eruptives as lava flows, ash beds, or fine-grained sedimentaries in contact with igneous rocks.

It is a difficult matter to generalize concerning the physical characteristics of the opal, since the numerous varieties differ somewhat one from another. Opal may occur in a variety of forms—either massive, or reniform, botryoidal, stalactitic, tuberose, or earthy, governed largely by the manner in which the silica material was deposited. Also, it is found varying in all stages from transparent to opaque. The numerous varieties may show vitreous, subvitreous, resinous, pearly, or earthy luster. The streak of all varieties is white.

The hardness of precious opal varies from 5.5 to 6.5. Its comparative softness constitutes one of the serious objections to the use of the stone for gem purposes. When so used, it should be shielded from hard wear. The hardness of the earthy varieties may be as low as 1.0. Massive opal usually breaks with a pronounced conchoidal fracture, similar to that of flint. Opal low in water content shows a refractive index of 1.406, while that with a high water content has an index of 1.46. Opal, though amorphous, behaves in polarized light as if it were a double-refracting body. Like quartz, opal has a high fusing point, 2110°F. The specific gravity of gem opal is about 2.2. Chemical analyses show many impurities present in the opal, including iron oxide, alumina, lime, magnesia, and some of the alkalies. These impurities in some instances so influence the formation of the stone as to account for some of the varieties.

BEAUTY OF COLOR

Every conceivable combination of the colors of the spectrum is displayed by the opal. It may be colorless or of any shade or delicate tint or combination of red, yellow, green, blue, black, or white. In the case of nearly every other gem stone, the color can be assigned to the inclusion of some known mineral salts But very little coloring matter is to be found in even the most colorful of the opals; and, when examined by transmitted light, the gem appears to be a solidified gelatinous mass, resembling a fragment of slightly milky glass. The fascinating display of prismatic colors is not apparent when the stone is viewed in this manner.

The fact that color is so essential to both the beauty and the value of the stone has influenced many scientists to investigate the mystery of its occurrence. It is at once apparent that the color tints change and ripple with the angle at which the light is incident and the relative position of the stone and the observer. Since the colors cannot be attributed to the presence of pigments, it is evident that they must be due to some structural peculiarity within the stone itself. Just what these structural conditions are, constitutes one of the most interesting of mineralogical problems—so far, not solved to the satisfaction of all.

The fact that some opaque stones may be caused to show a play of color for a short time after immersion in water has led some to contend that the color phenomenon of the opal is due to an uneven distribution of the water content of the stone. As an example, they cite the opalescent display of color of the variety *hydrophane* after it has been thoroughly saturated with water. While this answers the question nicely for hydrophane, it fails to satisfy all the conditions met with in other varities of opal.

Another writer claims that the play of color is caused by the interference of light rays reflected from thin layers of opaline material having different densities, but, for the lack of definite proof, this remains simply a theory. Sir David Brewster advanced the opinion that the color is due to the presence of myriads of microscopic cavities in the stone. This also lacks proof. Still others claim that the stone is internally a mass of small fractures and cracks upon which the rays of light are reflected and broken up, much in the same way as is sunlight on a soap bubble.

Probably the most satisfactory explanation yet offered was brought out by Behrends, a European investigator, who, after years of study, wrote a monograph on the cause of opalescence, in which he states his opinion that the play of color is due to very thin curved plates or lamellae, the refracting power of which differs considerably from that of the mass in general. These thin lamellae are thought by Behrends to have been originally formed in a parallel position, but during the solidifying process of the mass to have been bent, cracked, and broken. These fractures, reflecting the light, are conceived to be responsible for giving to the opal its perfect play of color; since they act as a diffraction grating.

It becomes apparent, therefore, that the varied colors of the precious opal are due to the interference of light upon very thin plates or lamellae of opaline substance. The true nature of these plates still remains unknown. That they are very thin, all are agreed—their thickness is probably comparable to the wave lengths of light—and since they are of different densities, they act like a grating to reflect, or refract, or absorb, portions of the light rays striking their surfaces. The angle of incidence at which the rays strike determines the thickness of the films that must be penetrated, and as this changes, some colors are permitted to pass, while others are cut out altogether.

In order to show the play of colors to their best advantage, the opal is cut in flat cabochon form and mounted in a closed setting, so that it can be viewed only by reflected light. Sometimes, thin sections of opal are mounted on a backing of some opaque substance, for the same purpose. Solidified silica gel is easily obtained in our laboratories, but it has not yet been possible to obtain anything resembling the precious opal. Pliny states that the ancients were very skillful in imitating the opal, it being almost impossible to distinguish between the real stones and their imitations. However that may be, modern attempts to duplicate the stone are so unsatisfactory that even a novice would have no difficulty in detecting an imitation.

FAVORITE WITH THE ANCIENTS

The opal has been known from ancient times, and the gem was highly prized by both Greeks and Romans. As far back as 500 B.C., Onomacritus wrote this sentiment concerning it: "The delicate color and tenderness of the opal remind me of a loving and beautiful child." Pliny valued the opal so highly that he ranked it next to emerald, and described it in such glowing terms that nearly every writer on opal quotes his description. Statements from the writings of many other ancient writers could be quoted to show that the stone was held in high esteem during their day.

That the opal failed to hold this place in the esteem of gem lovers is most deplorable. It is difficult for us to understand how the public mind could have been so influenced by an unreasonable and inexplicable superstition as virtually to shun the stone as something damned, for many long years. Sir Walter Scott in his book, "Anne of Geierstein," published in 1829, is thought to have initiated the superstition that vested the opal with the power to bring ill luck to its possessor. Previous to the publication of this book, opals enjoyed a wide popularity both in Europe and America, but in the course of a year thereafter the value of the stone had fallen off at least 50 per cent.

Scott's story, which evidently cast such a blighting influence upon the popularity of the opal, is an ingenious bit of fiction concerning an enchanted princess, Lady Hermione, who always wore in her hair an opal of rare beauty. It was enchanted and was credited with a sympathetic change of brilliance, corresponding with the moods of its wearer—glowing with a dazzling brilliance when she was happy and flashing red fire when she was angry. The stone faded immediately when, by accident, a few drops of holy water touched it, while the beautiful Lady Hermione sank to the floor of the chapel and died, and the next day only ashes remained where her body had been placed. How utterly foolish to malign so beautiful a gem because of superstition and an entertaining bit of fiction!

However, it is fairer to Scott to consider that the unfortunate misinterpretation of his book brought to a culminating point a distrust in the stone that had been growing for a long time. It appears that the opal was worn considerably in Venice when the plague occurred in the sixteenth century. At that time it was noticed that just before the death of one stricken with the disease, the stone would usually brighten on the victim's finger. It never occurred to the superstition-ridden people that the illness could enhance the glow of the opal; they simply took it for granted that the stone occasioned the illness. As a matter of fact, opals are affected by heat, and the fever, being at its height just before death, caused the colors to shine with unusual brightness. Accounts of these observations and the conclusions drawn by the observers were spread widely throughout western Europe, long before the days of Sir Walter Scott.

Superstition dies hard, and even to this day, there are seemingly sane persons who consider the possession of an opal as courting ill luck. Not many years ago, a man in Brooklyn gouged the opal set from his finger ring and smashed it to powder with a hammer because he had failed in business. Sometimes, it seems as though such men, as well as all those who patronize astrologers and crystal-gazers, have not advanced far beyond the Dark Ages.

However, there may be some genuine reasons for the unpopularity of the stone. The changes that occur in an opal are freakish. Some have been known to become dull and lusterless from the loss of water, while others have lost their color and regained it in what seems a very mysterious manner. Sometimes, solid stones have been known to fill with cracks (flaws) and even break into pieces from internal stresses. Some jewelers will not handle the stones for these reasons. Occasionally, an inferior stone is made to show good color by being rubbed with oil or glycerine, and is then sold to the unwary. In time, the oil becomes rubbed off, and the poor quality of the stone is apparent. While such mishaps are not general, they have not helped to popularize the opal. Even the warmth and moisture of the hand may temporarily change the color play of opal.

At present, opals are once more enjoying well-deserved favor both here and abroad. Much credit for this is due to the late Queen Victoria. No doubt, the Queen's actions were somewhat motivated by her desire to help her far-off subjects in Australia, where an abundance of opals had been discovered. In order to show her admiration for the stone and at the same time her disdain of the foolish superstition that had brought opals into ill repute, she gave opals to each of her daughters at their marriages. Very naturally this had its desired effect, and soon the demand for the opal was felt throughout the Empire. The dread taboo of "unlucky" seems to have had little effect upon the demand for the stone in the United States.

Geographically, the opal in some of its various forms is widespread in its occurrence; however, precious opal, suitable for gem purposes, is restricted to but few localities worthy of mention.

The Czechoslovakian opal fields—formerly known as the Hungarian fields—are without a doubt the oldest opal mines in the world. They were worked in the days of the old Roman Empire and furnished many gems for the beaux and belles of that day. At first, many of the stones were sent to India, and later, after cutting, they were returned and sold at very fancy prices, as Indian gems. Until the discovery of the extensive opal fields in Australia, all the best opals came from the vicinity of Czerwenitza, where they occur filling fissures in a weathered andesite lava. The mines in that region have been active for so long that now only small stones are being recovered. Opals from that field are well-known for their unusually fine display of color and can be readily distinguished from stones from other fields. Probably, the largest mass ever taken from those mines is now preserved in the Hofmuseum at Vienna. It is about four inches in diameter and, even though badly flawed, is remarkable for its exquisite play of color.

Mexico is noted for its limpid and deep-red fire opal, but the popularity of this variety is somewhat limited, because it is more transparent than ordinary precious opal and the colors are less pronounced and apt to fade. That the opal was well known to the Aztecs is shown by the fact that the head of their Sun God was carved from that material. It may be seen in the Field Museum at Chicago.

Mexican opals occur in cavities in an old spherulitic rhyolite. This rock is usually red, light pink, or green, and it is a notable fact that the character of the opal varies with the nature of the rock. Where the rhyolite is a deep red, opals with a fiery-red color abound, and where it is of a lighter color or mottled, lighter colored stones are the rule. At present, most of the producing mines are those in Queretaro, though some stones are procured in Hidalgo, Michoacan, Jalisco, and San Luis Potosi. Recently, opals have been discovered in western Chihuahua, but few stones of real value have been produced.

In eastern Australia, precious opal occurs over an enormous belt of country, roughly 250 miles in width, extending from New South Wales northward, well into Queensland. A small amount of good material is now being obtained also in South Australia.

The first discovery of opals in Australia was made in Queensland in 1872, but there was no active mining until several years later. In 1899, the White Cliffs field in New South Wales was opened, and in 1908, the Lightning Ridge field, famous for its black opals, was discovered. The first important discovery in South Australia was the Stewart's Ridge field in 1915. All these fields are located in an arid region, where both prospecting and mining are carried on under very adverse conditions, owing to the great heat and the lack of water. There are two geological occurrences of opal in Australia. The first is in a sandstone of Upper Cretaceous age, a unique occurrence not known elsewhere. The second is in a vesicular basalt of post-Cretaceous age. The veins of opal are seldom over one-half inch in thickness, and, as a rule, a great deal of waste material has to be removed before the veins are reached.

The Australian fields have furnished some very interesting specimens of opalized fossils. In some instances, bones, shells, and wood have been transformed into masses of precious opal. The British Museum possesses an opalized bone eight and one-half inches long and over four inches thick. In the Morgan collection in New York there is a larger specimen, some twenty inches long and five inches thick. Many other collections contain opalized clams, snails, and wood, some with teredos in place, all turned to gem opal.

In Honduras is found precious opal which is quite similar to the Australian, showing splendid flashes of "fire." Those of both localities have an opaque white matrix. The Honduras opal is slightly more translucent in the matrix; and while some very high grade stones have been mined in that locality, no great amount is being produced at present.

Quite contrary to some reports, there are in India a number of localities that furnish opals—notably, near Bombay, where is found a milk-white variety that shows a strong flamelike iridescence. Near Hyderabad City opals are found associated with chalcedony, amethyst, and agate. Opals are common also in the region about Madras. However, no opals comparable to those produced in either Mexico or Australia have been reported from the Indian mines.

DEPOSITS OF THE UNITED STATES

Very little precious opal has been found in the United States, but hyalite occurs in a number of places in New York, New Jersey, North Carolina, Georgia, Florida, and Oregon. Common opal is so widespread in its occurrence, in both East and West, that it is impossible to list here all the places.

The most noted deposit of precious opal in our country, both in extent and in the quantity of opals mined, is in Virgin Valley, Humboldt County, Nevada. Opal was discovered there in 1908, and intermittent mining has been carried on since that time. A surprising amount of excellent material has been found, including the famous Roebling black opal, discovered in 1919. This huge opal, weighing approximately seventeen ounces, was valued by the owners at a quarter of a million dollars. The stone was purchased by the late Colonel Roebling; the amount paid was never disclosed to the public, but is understood to have been perhaps half the price asked. The enormous black opal is undoubtedly the most spectacular opal ever mined in modern times—a mass of material appearing as black as a lump of coal, yet throwing forth brilliant and deep flashes of red, green, and purple fire. The stone has never been cut and may be seen today in the United States National Museum, just as it was originally mined.

The Opal

It is a matter of interest to note that the Nevada opal occurs under essentially the same arid climatic conditions that pertain in Australia. The Virgin Valley field represents the bottom of an old Tertiary lake, and the opals occur in a very definite horizon, in thin seams of semiconsolidated volcanic ash of Eocene age.

The gem material in Virgin Valley occurs entirely in the form of pseudomorphs, or casts after wood. In places, trunks of trees, branches, and even conifer cones are found turned to opal. Indications seem to point to a driftwood manner of accumulation of the logs and flotsam along the shore of the old Eocene lake, after which vulcanism buried the debris under a bed of ash, and the process of opalization proceeded to turn the wood into solid opal, replacing the wood structure, molecule by molecule. Many interesting problems, both mineralogical and geological, are suggested by the conditions that exist in the Virgin Valley field; but space will not allow our taking them up at this time.

Perhaps no similar area in the world has furnished so wide a variety of opals. These range from clear, colorless, limpid material to black and wholly opaque specimens; but most of the fire opal tends toward translucency rather than opacity. While large quantities of opal are to be found in the diggings, perhaps less than 10 per cent shows color play, and less still is suitable for gem purposes.

Unfortunately, the Virgin Valley opal has a strong tendency to fracture and has to be handled with extreme care, especially when first mined. This checking seems to be due to internal stresses. To counteract them, several methods of curing the stone are practiced by the miners. These include storing them in cans of dirt, soaking them in water, glycerine and water, oil, vaseline, etc., the idea being to permit the stone to dry out slowly and thus prevent the development of checks and internal strains. Even after curing for several years, these opals may fracture during the cutting process, or sometimes even months after it has been completed. Some gems, however, show no checking, even after years. Nevada opals are better adapted to being kept as cabinet specimens, owing to the fact that the cut stone is not likely to show any greater play of color than the rough conchoidal fractured surface of the specimen.

Small amounts of precious opal have been taken from time to time in a wide range of varieties, from various parts of the Western states, especially the Columbia River lavas of Wash-

OPALIZED WOOD—POLISHED

Complete tree section at left—colors, black and white. Found in volcanic ash between flows of Miocene lavas of fifteen million years ago. Swamp cypress (left) and redwood (right). Horse Heaven Hills, Washington.

ington, Idaho, and Oregon. Small deposits of precious opal have been found in various other parts of the United States, including California.

NUMEROUS VARIETIES OF OPAL

To list all the different varieties of opal recognized by miners, jewelers, and mineralogists would be a task in itself. In his "Opal Glossary," published in the *Rocks and Minerals Magazine,* for March, 1933, G. F. Shepherd lists some fifty-two varieties, all of which might merit some discussion; however, only the more obvious varieties will be taken up here. Such forms as diatomite, siliceous sinter, wood opal, and geyserite have been given fuller discussion elsewhere.

The Opal

Agate Opal. The true agate opal consists of alternate layers of chalcedony and common opal. When the opal is colored and the chalcedony is translucent, these make handsome specimens.

Black Opal. This is one of the most beautiful varieties of the precious opal. Its color changes from a glowing dark green to gold, blue to black or pale violet, or crimson, according to the direction of the light. Opal in a dark-gray or black matrix, showing a vivid play of colors, also is known as black opal. It is a rare variety, so far having been found only in the White Cliff region of New South Wales, Australia, and in the Virgin Valley field of Nevada.

Boulder Opal. This is not a variety of opal, but a miner's term applied to the concretions containing coatings of opal, as found in Queensland. Most of the boulder opal is well suited to cabinet specimens, consisting of scattered veins or coatings of opal enclosed in a brownish-colored rock.

Cacholong Opal. This is a milky-white, opaque, or feebly translucent, porcelainlike variety of common opal. It is very porous and readily adheres to the tongue. It somewhat resembles hydrophane, but does not show play of color when soaked in water. Its luster resembles mother-of-pearl, probably because of the inclusion of a small amount of alumina. Its color may be bluish white, pale yellow, or reddish.

Common Opal. Common opal is a translucent to opaque form which may occur in a variety of colors, but which does not show the play of colors so characteristic of the precious opal. It has a waxy or greasy luster, which is one of its best distinguishing features. Common opal occurs mostly as fillings in seams or cavities in igneous rocks, such as the steam vesicles in lava, etc. The remarkably beautiful-colored opalized wood found in quantity in central Washington is all classed as common opal.

The common pale-green opal found at only one mine in Virgin Valley, Nevada, is remarkable for its very strong and attractive green fluorescence under ultraviolet light. Specimens of this beautiful opal are to be found in collections of fluorescent minerals throughout the country. Even the little argon bulb exhibits the phenomenon very well.

Fire Opal. A yellow to red, translucent to transparent variety of precious opal, having a fiery play of color, irised with green or blue when turned in the light, is the fire opal. Some of the stones from Zimapan, Hidalgo, Mexico, are faceted, with very pleasing results. This is probably the only opal that will bear cutting in that way.

Float Stone. This is a remarkably porous variety of opal, which is sometimes confused with pumice. It is deposited in the vicinity of some hot springs, and is composed of a network of interlacing siliceous fibers enclosing numerous interstitial spaces, which confine sufficient air to cause the stone to float upon water, like wood.

Girasol Opal. A blue to white, translucent variety of precious opal, which shows a red play of colors when viewed in a strong light is known as the "girasol opal."

Harlequin Opal. The harlequin opal is a form of precious opal that flashes rainbowlike tints from angular surfaces. These colors change their position and character as the stone is turned. When the patches of color are regular in shape and size, and show a distinct checker-board arrangement of red, yellow, or green, this variety of opal is truly magnificent. By many it is considered to be one of the most beautiful, as well as one of the most uncommon, of the opals.

Hyalite Opal. When opal is pure, it is transparent and colorless, as is to be seen in this variety, which is sometimes called "Muller's glass," from its discoverer. This pellucid, opaline silica occurs as small globules or botryoidal incrustations on rocks or other minerals. It is occasionally found in masses large enough to be cut into gems; but as a rule, these stones seldom show sufficient fire to make them desirable as gems. Hyalite from some localities exhibits a beautiful, strong, green fluorescence when exposed to ultraviolet light.

Hydrophane Opal. This is doubtless our most curious and interesting form of opal. It is essentially a cloudy, white, dehydrated variety of common opal, which appears opaque and devoid of any opalescence until immersed in water. After it has become saturated, all the white color disappears, and the stone resembles transparent hyalite, even showing some play of color when viewed in a strong light. This condition lasts only so long as the stone remains wet; upon drying, it returns to its former opaque condition. The phenomenon can be explained by assuming that the stone contains a great multitude of cracks and cavities that are filled with air, causing the stone to appear opaque until the air is replaced by water, which possesses about the same index of refraction as the opal. The hydrophane was well known to the ancients under such names as "oculus mundi" ("eye of the world"), a purely fantastical name; or "lapis mutabilis," a variety which came from China and was eagerly sought for by the alchemists, who hoped that by its use they would be able to discover the "philosopher's stone," which would turn whatever it touched into gold. In Colorado has been found some hydrophane which absorbs an astonishing amount of water. The Virgin Valley field also produces fine hydrophane opal.

Jasper Opal (Jasp-Opal). This is a variety of common opal, colored and marked like jasper. It can be distinguished from jasper by its greasy, resinous luster, true jasper presenting a dull surface until polished. The color of jasper opal is due to the inclusion of several per cent of iron oxide. It is the analogue in opal of jasper in quartz.

Milk Opal. This is a milk-white variety of opal, with a glossy surface. Some milk opal shows deep-green flashes of color, when viewed by strong light. This is called "lechosos opal" by some. Milk opal grades into the white variety of precious opal. Some of this opal will lose its fire and become like a limpid piece of glass when soaked in water; but on drying, it will be restored to its original form.

Moss Opal. A milky variety of common opal, with black dendritic inclusions of manganese oxide, which resemble moss, is named "moss opal." W. Scott Lewis mentions an unusually handsome variety, from Virgin Valley, Nevada, which at times is nearly transparent. Very beautiful stones may be cut from selected material, and some will show a good green fluorescence.

Opalite (*also termed "myrickite"*). This is a name applied to impure forms of common opal. Those forms containing cinnabar as coloring material are very attractive, when cut and polished. There are large deposits of opalite in Nevada and in Lake County, Oregon.

Prase Opal. An apple-green opal which has no play of color, but at times can be cut into stones that very much resemble chrysoprase is called "prase opal."

Precious Opal. This term is given to all forms of opal which show a brilliant play of colors and are suitable for gem purposes.

Tabasheer. Tabasheer, our most unique form of opal, is formed in the joints of certain species of bamboo in India, Burma, and South America. It was originally a juice which, by evaporation brought about by some injury to the joint, changed into a mucilaginous state, then by further drying became a solid mass. It ranges from translucent to opaque. The color is white to bluish white by reflected light. On fracture, it breaks into irregular pieces resembling starch. Tabasheer has the property of strongly adhering to the tongue and, when immersed in water, gives off streams of air bubbles; when thoroughly saturated, it becomes transparent. It is doubly interesting, since we have here an organic product scarcely to be distinguished from the inorganic hydrophane.

George F. Kunz once wrote a paper setting forth the possibility that tabasheer is the same as the "snake stone," or "mad stone," of the Middle Ages. Also, we note that Jean Baptiste Tavernier, the great French traveler, described a stone that he saw in India which was considered an infallible cure for snake bites or wounds caused by poisoned arrows. We judge from his description that these "snake stones" were tabasheer. The almost unbelievable capacity of these stones for absorbing fluid would undoubtedly render them efficacious for the purpose of drawing poison from open wounds. It is interesting to note that they are still included in the pharmacopoeia of the Orientals.

CHAPTER XIV

Extensive Areas of Silicification and Petrified Forests

Many chapters of the earth's history are clearly legible to geologists and are readily deciphered, according to various land formations, through certain types of rocks or the fossilized fauna and flora and fossil woods. However, there are some areas where whole pages of this history in rock are characterized by question marks. We see the results of changes that have occurred, but can only speculate as to the causes which might have brought them about.

Practically every mineralogist and geologist and many a layman, also, have pondered over the manner in which immense areas, even entire forests, have been completely silicified—turned to agate, opal, or jasper. Was this great plateau, where now lie the prostrate giant trees with bejeweled hearts, once an inland sea into which emptied an ancient river, down which floated these thousands of conifers now jasperized? Did they become jammed and waterlogged, sink, and then become buried in silt and sand as the sea receded, back in those Mesozoic times, and did the fallen giants gradually submit to silicification by percolating waters carrying silica in solution? Or, was the whole area of forest suddenly covered by an enormous shower of volcanic ash, protecting the trees from attacks by the elements, later to become turned to solid jasper by the percolating waters?

Whatever theory we may select to account for the petrification of entire forests, the processes must have been very slow.

First, each molecule of the woody substance must have been removed, to be replaced later by some form of silica, preserving in hard mineral the annular rings, the rays, bark, knots, pitch, and numerous other markings common to fossil woods.

Silicification (meaning impregnation by any form of silica, such as agate, chalcedony, jasper, or opal) occurs in two general ways—deposition by surface waters carrying silica in solution or by magmatic waters from great depth. The latter

LOG OF JASPERIZED WOOD

Complete log of jasperized wood, Arizona Petrified Forest. Resistance to erosion has left the fossil logs lying loose upon the surface.

are also referred to as "juvenile" waters. A mass of molten lava (magma), cooling slowly at some depth below the surface of the earth, is known to give off substantial amounts of water held in chemical combination. Magmatic waters under high temperature and pressure, or perchance heavily charged with alkaline substances, are far better solvents of silica than are surface waters.

Practically all quartz veins filling fissures seen in mine workings, owe their origin, in part at least, to ascending magmatic waters. Likewise, the enormous deposits of siliceous sinter seen in areas like Yellowstone Park are due in part to magmatic waters carrying silica. In both instances, percolating surface waters generally enter into the problem, by mingling with the waters that "see daylight" for the first time. Just how much of the water resting on the surface of the earth and how much of the silica which has been deposited near the surface had its birth in enormous intrusions of magma is a matter of conjecture.

Scientists tell us that if the area under Yellowstone Park was underlain with a cooling mass of lava, a mile in thickness, this enormous body of magma could easily account for *all* the water issuing from the hot springs and geysers within the area. Moreover, a mass of magma of enormous proportions, resting at great depths, would require thousands of years to cool completely. All the huge mounds and basins which have been built up in Yellowstone from nearly pure silica doubtless have their origin largely from magmatic waters, mingled, of course, with surface waters as these are encountered by the ascending solutions. It has been established that a molten magma can carry about 5 per cent of water in chemical combination, to be liberated very slowly as the mass cools. A little calculation will indicate that an intrusion of lava, only a few thousand feet in vertical extent, would, over a period of years, liberate a tremendous amount of "juvenile" water.

Hot springs and geysers carry silica in a colloidal state, which is deposited rapidly and in quantity as the water emerges and cools at the surface. Heated waters at the surface generally deposit a siliceous sinter, a hydrated form of silica—essentially opal, chemically speaking. Unquestionably, surface waters percolate downward and mingle with the rising magmatic waters, to reappear in geysers and hot springs, but since "juvenile" waters are better solvents of silica, it is likely that they play the major role in leaching the mineral from the surrounding rocks through which they pass on their upward journey.

The cryptocrystalline quartz minerals generally have their home in volcanic rocks, or closely associated with them. It is well known that in many instances, following and associated with extensive flows of lava, considerable hot-spring activity is met with. Hence, it would seem that we could very well account for the presence of enormous deposits of silica in some lavas, while other similar areas are nearly barren. In the Western states, the localities where agate, jasper, chalcedony, nodules, and other forms of quartz are found in profusion are invariably in lavas, or else the specimens have been eroded from volcanic rocks of some type. Not all lavas are agate-bearing, by any means; for instance, the lavas of the great "Columbia River Flow," in the Pacific Northwest, originally some 200,000 square miles in extent and in places over a mile in vertical thickness, yield quartz minerals only in limited areas. The noted locality of Antelope, Oregon, is situated in Tertiary lavas, a part of this great flow of "Columbia River lavas," and here in a quite limited area, not over a few square miles in extent, hundreds of tons of excellent material have been gathered, including both crystal and noncrystal varieties.

The moss agates of Montana and Wyoming had their birth in cavities within volcanic rocks. Surprising, too, is the fact that the specimens from both areas are remarkably uniform in size. Those of Wyoming (Sweetwater) are nearly all about an inch in diameter, while the Montana specimens are generally about four inches. South American agates, also, run to a general average size, and the same is true of numerous other localities. In all probability, the average size is governed by the average size of the cavity in the amygdaloidal lavas. Obviously, when no cavities are available, deposition may take place in veins or fissures, if such are present, or may fail to form at all. The agate-filled nodules, from any given area in dozens of localities in the Far Western states also run remarkably uniform in size.

The Tertiary lavas appear to be the favorite places for the deposition of quartz minerals. In the Far Western states, practically all the great areas of silicification which yield good specimens are either within the Tertiary lavas or have a capping, intrusion, or contact with them. The largest deposit of precious opal in the United States—Virgin Valley, Nevada —was at one time deeply covered with Tertiary lavas, ash, scoria, and similar outpourings; but the home of the opal appears to be in an Eocene formation resting just under the later Tertiaries.

Some of the great petrified forests of the United States are much older in age than Tertiary; some, like those of Arizona, thrived possibly 100,000,000 years ago; but here again we find them covered by later Tertiary formations.

Few areas of petrified forests are known in the eastern part of the country, and few hot springs are found in the Atlantic states, compared to the number in the West. Moreover, the Eastern states were not subjected to great outpourings of lava during the Tertiary period. It is possible that this may account for the lack of similar great areas of silicification in the Eastern states. Seemingly, the great forests which grew in the eastern part of the United States ages ago have undergone carbonization—turning to coal—while similar forests of the West were turned to solid stone.

"Petrified forests" have been found in various parts of the world, yet comparatively few areas exhibit widespread silicification involving entire forests. It seems somewhat strange that very little research has been carried on to account for the phenomenon.

FORESTS TURNED TO QUARTZ

The great areas in some parts of the world where entire forests of trees have been almost completely petrified and thus preserved for millions of years should be considered among the great wonders of the world. In addition to their spectacular beauty, the fossil forests and woods have preserved for us important scientific data concerning climatic conditions during the various geologic periods.

The process by which each molecule of the wood substance was removed and carefully replaced by some form of silica—agate, opal, or jasper—has preserved the wood structure, making it possible readily to determine the species. In the oaks and other hardwoods, even the medullary rays running across the annular rings are plainly visible on the unpolished cross section. The length of time required to silicify fully a complete tree up to fourteen feet in diameter is, of course, a matter of speculation, but certainly it must have taken a long time. While we have noted that laboratory experiments can duplicate practically every variety of quartz and imitate nearly every kind of agate, yet we have so far failed to petrify wood by any artificial means—only nature knows this secret.

The general term "petrified wood" is applied to all forms of replaced wood, regardless of the agent or mineral which has permeated the wood. Generally, silica in some form or other is the petrifying or fossilizing agent, but some twenty or more minerals have been recorded, including calcite, native copper, pyrite, chalcopyrite, gypsum, and dolomite. As a rule, all the logs, limbs, or fragments seen in a single forest area are of the same type of silicification, having, of course, been subjected to the same conditions; thus, the great fossil forest of Arizona is largely jasper; in central Washington we find mostly common colored opal; in Patagonia, South America, jasper predominates. The Virgin Valley, Nevada, area is quite distinctive, for that is the only place in the entire world where so much and such colorful fossil wood has been found, where the petrifying agent has often been gem-quality "fire" opal. Limb sections of wood or casts of wood turned completely to blazing red, green, and purple precious opal are indeed the first desire of every connoisseur of fossil woods.

How They Petrified. There are three general types of so-called petrified forests: (1) In one kind, the trees, standing in a vertical position, were overwhelmed and completely covered by a shower of volcanic ash or some other covering. Lava in a molten state will sometimes submerge an entire forest; but in such cases the heat generally consumed the wood, leaving perhaps only a hollow cast in the solidified lava. On Specimen Ridge, in the southern part of Yellowstone Park, forest after forest is seen in vertical cross section exposed by erosion, undoubtedly covered by showers of volcanic ash, to be petrified later. Some of the early forests exposed at Specimen Ridge are millions of years old and all of them are standing upright, not like the fallen monarchs of Arizona. (2) In another type, perhaps, log jams collected at the mouth of a river entering a lake and, sinking into the mud, later became petrified. It is thought that the Arizona forest is of this type. Driftwood on a lake may be carried to one shore by prevailing winds and thus large deposits of fossil wood may accumulate; the woods of central Washington and those of Virgin Valley, Nevada, are good examples. Generally, fossil wood which at one time has been driftwood is lacking in bark, and more or less rounded. Some think this accounts for the lack of bark on the wood of the Arizona forest. (3) Scattered woods may also have been covered in some manner or other, to become silicified later. Rising waters in a lake or river may completely submerge a forest, protect it from decay, and later on, petrifaction may preserve the trees permanently. Some of the woods of central Washington, Oregon, California, and Nevada, are of this type.

Surface or Magmatic Waters. The great problem in a study of the mode of silicification is the determination of the roles played by percolating ground waters, waters originating from cooling lavas, and any surrounding water in which the wood may be submerged. In all probability, complicated chemical reactions enter into the problem, for the wood substance must be taken into solution, carried away, and replaced by silica. Waters charged with *acids* tend to "digest" wood (cellulose), and this factor must be taken into consideration. As has been previously stated, until we can petrify wood in the laboratory, we shall probably never know with certainty the mechanism of the process.

In the great areas of silicification, magmatic waters undoubtedly played a prominent role. It cannot be conceived how thousands of tons of silica could be concentrated into a small area by the lean silica-bearing, ground waters. Magmatic waters are frequently heavily charged with silica, strongly acid in reaction, and definitely capable of attacking the wood substance and replacing it with silica. Probably, the very presence of organic matter is a factor in the deposition. Ground waters can mix freely with rising magmatic waters, but the part played by the former is, likely, only a minor one.

261

Identifying Fossil Woods. The determination of the type or species of fossil wood is of importance, as it gives the student a valuable clue to climatic and other conditions prevalent at the time when the tree was growing. Woods, for example, that are found in a drift accumulation or along an old lake-shore line, may be types that thrived only at higher elevations and away from swampy ground. This would yield further proof of the

PETRIFIED WOOD—TREE SECTION

Note medullary rays running from center and crossing annular rings at right angles— typical of the hard woods like oak, walnut, and hickory.

"driftwood" theory. In a drift accumulation, we may expect to find a wide range of species.

The skilled observer, viewing the rough or polished surface of the cross section, can determine the species or type of wood in many instances by the naked eye or the aid of a low-power hand lens. Hardwoods like oak, walnut, and hickory have prominent medullary rays radiating out from the center of the cross section and cutting across the annular rings. The size and arrangement of the cells in some types are characteristic and can often be determined with a lens of ten or fifteen power.

262

In the more detailed determinations, and in some types of wood, a thin section and a low-power microscope are needed for accurate work. The cross section is the most valuable single cut, but in some woods a radial or tangential section is needed, in addition. For microscopic purposes, the wood section is cemented to a glass slide with Canada balsam and ground until light will pass through the wood; darker and more opaque woods must be reduced to a thousandth of an inch or less. A microscope of about fifty magnification is ample for all ordinary work, but the instrument should have good resolution to give a clear picture.

Do not be satisfied to label your specimens merely as petrified wood, but learn the species or type of wood, as well. The polished surface, especially across the grain, will often yield valuable information when examined with a low-power hand lens. In this manner the type of wood can often be determined. Fossil woods are intensely interesting, and the collection and study of them are rapidly becoming a popular avocation. The beauty, romance, and scientific importance attached to these beautiful examples of Mother Nature's art make them worthy of their popularity. Some of the private collections of polished and rough fossil woods are remarkable for their beauty.

Petrified woods usually take a high polish and are well adapted to cutting into gem stones and ornaments of many kinds. Large book ends cut from fossil wood make attractive and useful objects, the grain and other markings being well brought out by the art of the lapidarist.

Although not particularly rare or scarce, petrified woods are not nearly so widely distributed as agate and some of the other forms of quartz. It seems as though conditions were favorable for the silicification of wood in relatively few parts of the world, even though forests may have been abundant. In the United States, the fossil woods are largely confined to the western part of the country; no large silicified forests are known in the eastern section.

The great coal measures of the Atlantic states represent forests of the past which have carbonized, with but little silicification noted, although in nearly every coal mine there may be found examples more or less perfectly preserved. Here, also, are frequently seen splendid casts of logs or stumps preserved in sandstones.

Like other types of quartz, water-worn specimens of petrified wood can be found in stream gravels, associated with agate, chalcedony, and jasper. Specimens may be transported long distances by this means, far from the original source, yet the forests, or original sources of supply, occupy limited areas and are restricted in their distribution. Since the Arizona petrified forest is perhaps the best known in the world, we shall describe it first.

WESTERN LOCALITIES

Arizona Petrified Forest. The colorful jasperized forest of Arizona is unquestionably the best known of those in America; for years it has been the Mecca for millions of visitors, although removal of specimens is now forbidden within the park area. Much of the present commercial supply of specimens comes from adjacent areas, outside of the National Park boundaries. Ranchers and local Indians bring in large quantities of specimens exposed in the open country by erosion. Prior to the establishment of the park, many tons of fine specimens were removed and vandalism destroyed some of the finest logs.

There are three general types of fossil wood found in the Arizona forest: (1) The fully jasperized wood, with bright-red colors predominating, some being more translucent, owing to carrying a mixture of agate, which gives a pleasing variegated appearance. This type of wood is generally a riot of colors and shading. It is seen in large sections, some of the logs being four feet or more in diameter. When polished on the cross section, they make spectacular museum specimens. This wood is by far the most common and tends toward a deep, maroon-red color. (2) Minor amounts of bright-red wood are found, often with areas of nearly colorless quartz. This material is very suitable for gem-cutting purposes. (3) The sections of dark or nearly black wood are found sparingly, the dark color no doubt being due to a partial carbonization or the presence of an abnormal amount of organic carbonaceous matter.

Practically all the wood of the forest belongs to the conifer family, including various redwoods and sequoias. The structure of the wood resembles that of the Araucanian pines, a group of conifers now confined to Norfolk Island, near Australia, and

JASPERIZED WOOD
Cut and polished section of log, fifteen inches in diameter. Arizona Petrified Forest.

a single locality in the Andes of Chile. The forest thrived under semitropical climatic conditions, with plenty of rainfall —much more than the area receives today. The logs are all found in sedimentary formations, which would lend further credence to the driftwood theory. In a forest of cone-bearing trees, one would expect to find numerous fossil cones, but these are very rarely seen in the Arizona or any other fossil forest, with the exception of the Patagonia forest of South

America. Why fossil cones should be lacking is a matter of conjecture and speculation.

Washington. While not nearly so well known as the Arizona forest, the opalized-wood forests and deposits of central Washington justify a rating close to that of Arizona and Utah. Moreover, the Washington area is outstanding, in that here we find the only fossil ginkgo trees known in the world. Fossil leaves of this primitive type of tree are known in numerous localities, but it remained for the state of Washington to produce the first petrified tree.

In central Washington, some twenty-eight miles east of Ellensburg, on a modern highway, the state has set aside an area known as the "Ginkgo Petrified Forest," and is rapidly developing the area. Many of the huge tree sections were partly covered by debris and lava rock, which has been removed, the better to expose these beautifully opalized specimens. The Ginkgo forest is of the drift type, as indicated by the various types of wood found; some grew at higher elevations, while others thrived in low swampy ground—all to be carried into a small area, where final opalization took place.

Not all the trees in this forest are ginkgo; in fact, only a few are of this type. The species present include oak, maple, walnut, redwood, swamp cypress, Douglas fir, and a number of others. It has been estimated that no less than 10,000 fossil trees exist or have actually been seen in the central Washington area, yet not more than six Ginkgo trees have been authentically reported. Perhaps this growth was originally limited or thrived in an area where conditions for preservation were not favorable. The ginkgo tree of today, *Ginkgo biloba*, is not found in its native habitat, but has been preserved and handed down to us from the Sacred Gardens of the Orient, where it has been kept for thousands of years. The ginkgo, one of our oldest and most primitive types of trees, is one of the direct ancestors of our modern tree, and is remarkable in that it has survived through millions of years, while numerous other species have perished.

The distribution of opalized woods in central Washington ranges from Roosevelt, bordering the Columbia River, northward nearly to the Canadian border. Specimens are found as "float" almost anywhere in that great area. On the south, the Horse Heaven Hills are well known; the area around Vantage and Saddle Mountain to the north has also yielded many tons of this colorful fossil wood. So far, no tree standing in a vertical position where it originally grew has been authentically reported. Generally, the tree sections or driftwood fragments are found in the sediments of old shallow lakes, between the great flows of Miocene lavas which cover much of this area. Most of the specimens are perhaps some 15,000,000 years old, but their age will vary according to the horizon in which they are found.

In some instances, huge logs five feet or more in diameter are found, where they appear to rest directly in the Miocene lava, but a close investigation will generally indicate that these trees rested in a sediment and were thus protected when the molten lavas or red-hot ash covered them. Digging in a sediment between the layers of lava may yield a great variety of types of wood and colors, with yellows, browns, and white predominating. Red and black colors are also found, but these are more rare and often most beautiful. The conifer type of wood seems to be dominant, but swamp cypress and American elm rank a close second.

Just why there is practically no agatized or jasperized wood in this great area is a problem of considerable interest, but the fact remains that specimens found a hundred miles or more apart all bear the same general characteristics. Being opalized, the wood is not so hard as other varieties, but it takes an excellent polish, is easy to work, and is widely utilized for lapidary work, being cut into cabinet specimens and ornaments of various types. Like the Arizona region, central Washington is quite devoid of present-day forests, and specimens are found on the rolling, sage-covered hills, or in small canyons, where the logs are exposed by vertical erosion.

The locality known as Saddle Mountain in south-central Washington produces some excellent opalized-wood specimens and affords a convenient collecting place. The mountains are a range of low, rounded hills, extending in an east and west direction from Beverly and Bend to the town of Taunton. Collecting can be done most conveniently on the north slope of the hills, for here the highway extends along the foothills. Saddle Mountain is only some ten miles south and east of the noted Ginkgo Forest State Park.

At Saddle Mountain, good specimens are frequently found loose upon the surface slopes, where they have weathered from the surrounding shallow sedimentaries or basalts. Some logs are encountered, and the woods are often beautiful, with brown, yellow, red, and white shades predominating. Most of the material is sufficiently translucent to render it well suited for gem or specimen-cutting. The locality is especially noted for the fine examples of American elm, in the form of circular limb sections. Saddle Mountain extends over a considerable area, and petrified wood is likely to be found at any place, the southern portion being more difficult to reach and farther from a highway. For this reason, intensive collecting has not been done in that great area of opalization.

Oregon. Fossil woods are common to many parts of this state, being found mainly in the central part, where the woods are more colorful and suitable for gem purposes. The woods of western Oregon are for the most part of a drab and unattractive color. In the eastern part of Oregon, in the Stein Mountains, a very sparsely settled area, a new fossil forest has been found recently, but it is still unexplored. In many of the agate-filled nodule deposits around Madras there are petrified logs in profusion, but the color is usually not attractive.

The remarkable agate casts of wood found in the lavas around Bend are suitable for cabinet purposes; often these fillings of agate and chalcedony, in the cavity left by the tree in the once molten lava, reach a diameter of two feet or more. The wood structure is, of course, completely lacking, but the bark may leave its imprint on the walls of the cavity. In the recent lavas around Bend are numerous large, hollow sections left by trees; some are prone and others are standing vertical, but seemingly they were too young to have become filled with agate.

Idaho. The area south of Caldwell, Idaho, produces some excellent petrified wood, but it has not been extensively worked by collectors. Good specimens are found along Succor Creek, in Oregon, adjoining the region, and around Rockville. This field also yields quartz-crystal-lined geodes, with jasper, agate, and small but colorful fire opal in the matrix; considerable silicification took place in the lavas which cover the greater part of this locality.

Utah. A little-known but spectacular fossil forest is located in the Circle Cliffs, southeastern Utah. Owing to lack of highways (1936) into the area, it can be visited only by foot or on horseback, and is seldom seen except by cattlemen and sheepherders. Huge and colorful trees are found throughout a large area; some of these "fallen monarchs of the past" have diameters of from ten to thirteen feet. An effort has been made to preserve the forest as a state or national park and construct a suitable highway into the region.

California. Several petrified forests are known in this state, and one in the north-central part has been developed for tourists. In the southern part of California, notably in Kern County, are enormous areas where fossil palm woods are found and utilized for specimen purposes.

Nevada. So far as can be learned, Nevada has the distinction of boasting the largest petrified tree known anywhere in the world. Located in the desert, and partly covered by sand, rests a specimen some fourteen feet in diameter, which has been traced for a length of nearly 300 feet. It is near the town of Coaldale, just across the California border line. This giant is a member of the Sequoia family, which now thrives in a limited area to the West, in California.

We cannot mention Nevada without thinking of the woods of Virgin Valley in Humboldt County, just across the Oregon boundary line. Since this area was discovered by a range rider in 1908, numerous limbs and casts of wood, fully opalized, with splendid "fire," have been found and mined from the shallow open cuts made by prospectors. Field evidence would indicate that all the opal found in Virgin Valley is a replacement of

269

wood, but in many specimens the wood structure and shape have been wholly lost. In some specimens the entire central core has been transformed into a miracle of opal, but proof of the wood may be noted in small patches, where it still remains, only partly silicified. Again, in other examples, the central core may be merely common white opal, but the original bark gives off elusive flashes of red, green, and purple flame. Limb sections will range in size from quite small up to about six inches in diameter. Small two-inch sections have sold for $1,000 or more, showing this fossil wood to be the most valuable of all.

The opalized wood of Virgin Valley is of the drift type, as evidenced by its distribution in a loosely consolidated sandstone and occurrence on only one side of the valley. An ancient lake once filled this valley, and the prevailing winds carried the driftwood into the Eocene and early Miocene sediments deposited at one side. Most of the wood is of the conifer type, with redwoods predominating. Again, fossil cones are almost lacking, but at times cones have been found very well preserved in flashing flames of precious opal.

In Nye County, Nevada, beautiful opalized and agatized wood is found, often in complete limb and tree sections. This wood has been identified as a redwood related to the living species, *Sequoia sempervirens*. Conifers, including cypress and spruce, are found with the redwood.

Wyoming. Petrified woods, mainly in the form of small sections of limbs, are found on the high, sage-covered plateaus of Wyoming. Eden Valley, north of Rock Springs, is the best known locality, where contrasting black, brown, and colorless agatized wood is available. Cut across the grain, these woods make excellent specimens. Some of the Wyoming agatized woods show a good fluorescence, due to a secondary deposition of common opal. Agatized wood of good quality is also found on the Red Desert, north of Wamsutter, and north of the radium and uranium deposits on Lost Creek.

Texas. From Texas comes a bright-yellow opalized wood, showing the structure fully as clearly as ordinary wood. It is in part opalized but is not translucent like that of Washington. In many ways, the Texas wood greatly resembles that of southwestern Idaho, although the localities are widely separated. Oak types are dominant in both Texas and Idaho and are well suited to lapidary purposes.

WIDELY SCATTERED REGIONS

Black Hills Cycad Forest. One of the most remarkable of the outstanding petrified forests of the world is the Cycad Forest National Monument, Black Hills, South Dakota. Dr. G. R. Wieland, a noted authority on paleobotany, has made an extensive study of this area and was one of the first to urge the permanent preservation of the locality. The Cycad Forest consists mainly of flowering gymnospermous plants, which grew and thrived under the tropical or subtropical conditions prevalent in this region more than 100,000,000 years ago. Silicified examples of the sago palm are also included in the forest area.

The South Dakota cycads are of greater geological age than the oldest of our present true-flowering plants, the only surviving close rival and relative of the cycad being the "Sacred Ginkgo" tree of the Orient. The cycad may be looked upon as the ancestor of our modern flowering plants, while the ginkgo developed into or was the forerunner of some present-day conifers. In the South Dakota forest, specimens of beautifully petrified complete plants have been found, including those showing development of fruit and young crowns of fronds. These cycads are found in the Lakota sandstones, which are thought to be of Cretaceous age.

Central States. Petrified wood is of common occurrence in the region of the "Coal Measure" shales of the Upper Mississippi basin. In several places, as near Wilmington, Illinois, where "strip mining" is practiced, silicified logs are often brought to the surface by the shovels. Some are of considerable size, two or more feet in diameter. These logs, while very interesting because they throw light on the nature of the forests in the coal-making period, present little material suitable for cutting pur-

271

poses. However, the "Coal Measures" are not entirely devoid of good material for such purposes, for along Sugar Creek, some eight or ten miles south of Zanesville, Ohio, very fine specimens of jasperized wood have been found, showing splotches of jet black which make it very attractive for polished cabinet speci-mens. Presumably, they represent the inclusion of carbonaceous material from the original log.

In Missouri, scattered along the Mississippi River, logs of jasper and chalcedony are found from time to time. Since the source of this material has not been definitely ascertained, some think that, possibly, it has been carried in from some consider-able distance. What the transporting agent chanced to be, is left to our imagination. The Bad Lands of South Dakota are also a prolific source of silicified wood, much of which is colorful and some opalized. At several places in the coal-mining region of Oklahoma, one may see large petrified logs and stumps that have been raised from the mines and are displayed in public parks, etc. The plains of Kansas and Nebraska have yielded fine examples of silicified wood, some so beautifully preserved in translucent chalcedony as to show the growth structures of the tree very plainly. In the states bordering upon the Gulf of Mexico, petrified wood is also commonly met with, scattered through the sandy or marly sediments of Cretaceous or Tertiary age. Much of this is so well preserved that the identity of the wood can be readily ascertained from a thin section.

Eastern States. Along the Atlantic Seaboard, silicified wood abounds in the Tertiary sediments, New Jersey probably furnishing the largest number of specimens. Various types of petrified wood have been found in the "Pine Barrens," and near Princeton. Semipetrified logs are met with from time to time in the glauconite mines. These have considerable interest, from the fact that they throw some light on the process of petrification.

The oldest known petrified forest is located near the little village of Gilboa, in the Catskills (Schoharie County, New York). In this locality numerous stumps and logs have been recovered from strata of the Upper Devonian Age. Thus far, no forest of that age so extensive as this has been reported from any other locality. So important is this find considered that the New York State Museum has prepared a unique exhibit of the material. The trees, very naturally, being so extremely old, present very primitive forms. In fact, they represent the giant seed ferns, the probable ancestors of our present-day ferns, and perhaps furnished the off-shoots from which, later, developed our gymnosperms.

Foreign Localities. There are numerous petrified forests outside of the United States, but no attempt will be made to describe them, other than a few of the most noted ones.

The Patagonia forest, of South America, is one of the most interesting in the world from a scientific standpoint. Dr. R. G. Weiland, of Yale University, a noted paleobotanist, has made an extensive study of this forest and calls attention to numerous technical features, among which is the presence of quantities of finely preserved silicified cones. This is the only petrified forest known where cones occur so plentifully. The woods of the forest and the cones are, for the greater part, jasperized.

In the Red Deer Valley, ninety miles east of Calgary, Canada, fossil wood of good quality is found associated with agatized dinosaur bones. The wood is largely in the form of limb sections, and in colors and sizes strongly resembles the specimens of Eden Valley, Wyoming, directly south. In all probability, these two localities are contemporaneous in age and type, although no detailed comparative study has yet been made of the wood species.

WORM HOLES PRESERVED IN FOSSIL WOOD

Petrified wood showing worm- or teredo-bored holes, is found in very few localities in the world; this fact has been noted by Dr. R. G. Weiland in his recent book, "The Cerro Cuadrado Petrified Forest" (South America). He calls attention to the fact that in all his field observations he has encountered very few examples of worm holes in fossil wood and calls attention to one log found in South Dakota.

Several localities, including California and Colorado, are known where single specimens have been found. In Eden Valley, north of Rock Springs, Wyoming, a number of choice examples were discovered by Rev. O. P. Avery, local collector. The Eden Valley specimens are quite attractive, with their contrasting colors of black, brown, yellow, and white chalcedony. They show teredo-bored holes penetrating the limb sections. One specimen is so well preserved that the actual sawdust, left immediately under the bark, is to be seen silicified with the bulk of the wood. Possibly, the original bark failed to silicify or was lost through erosion, as it is lacking on the otherwise complete limb section.

A superb ten-pound piece of agatized wood, showing numerous small holes, was found recently on the sage-covered desert, east of Bend, Oregon, and is now in the museum collection of *The Mineralogist* at Portland. The Bend specimen is also impregnated with iron salts, and grades into jasper in some areas. The holes are distinctly of the termite type.

Two types of worm-drilled fossil wood have been found. Those showing small holes were made by termites (ants). Their drillings are about one-fourth the diameter of the teredo drillings. So far as can be learned, the termite has never been found fossilized in wood, only the results of his efforts being evident. The teredo borings are much larger, averaging about one-fourth of an inch in diameter, and will frequently riddle the wood so extensively as to leave little remaining.

In a locality east of Roseburg, Oregon, and in a restricted area along the Oregon coast, numerous and very large sections of silicified wood are found, showing the teredos beautifully preserved within the wood. The teredo-wood locality, some twenty miles east of Roseburg, has yielded an entire waterworn log, weighing over 500 pounds and showing where hundreds of teredo holes once existed, although now they are filled with a light-colored chalcedony. Moreover, numerous teredos, finely preserved by chalcedony, are seen resting in their home. The original holes are filled with silica of a color contrasting with that of the surrounding matrix, thus making it possible to trace easily the passageways as they wind about. Included in the filled holes are sand and other debris, which would indicate that the wood was bogged down and waterlogged, prior to silicification. The wood appears to be mainly conifera, some being identified as redwood. This locality, which is no doubt the most noted of its kind, has yielded hundreds of specimens and is worthy of a more detailed scientific study.

Along the Oregon coast, ranging from Newport on the south to about Tillamook on the north, both large and small fragments of teredo-bored fossil wood are found on the beach sands by agate collectors. The origin of these specimens is not known, for they have not been found *in situ*, like those of Roseburg; but they are identical in appearance. Much of the wood is partly carbonized, as well as silicified; but the chalcedony filling in the cavities stands out in clear contrast.

Generally, specimens are found on the beach more or less accidentally, especially following storms or at very low tides. Hundreds of specimens are picked up every year by tourists and collectors; but, more often than not, the uninitiated will pass by the dull-looking mass as just another "rock." Both the beach specimens and the Roseburg log and limb section show best when cut and polished, the cut surface revealing the many angles at which the teredo worked. Where a fossil teredo is cut lengthwise, the jointed structure of the body is plainly visible. On some specimens, presenting waterworn or fractured surfaces, portions of the body or the rounded head of the worm can be seen.

CHAPTER XV

The Art of Cutting Gem Quartz

EARLY HISTORY

History fails to record when the cutting and polishing of quartz gems first began. Primitive man, ages ago, noted the effect of sand and water wear upon pebbles of quartz and the superior beauty of those worn pebbles over unpolished agate. Very crude and laborious methods were applied by man living in the Smooth Stone Age, to attain a good cutting edge upon a tool or weapon or a smooth surface on an ornament. Sand of various grits was the only abrasive available.

For centuries prior to the introduction of the modern grinding wheel and abrasives, gem stones were ground to shape on lead laps charged with the mineral corundum—better known as emery powder. Grinding wheels were employed by the early gem cutters, but these were made of sandstone, no harder than quartz, and were not suitable for any gem material having a hardness greater than seven. Old textbooks on gemmology give a technique of gem-stone cutting which was in universal use prior to the introduction of the modern abrasives and grits.

Some forty years ago, the modern abrasives, silicon carbide and alumina—electric-furnace products—were first introduced. Silicon carbide, with a hardness equal to that of sapphire, was immediately utilized by the gem-cutting industry, both in the form of molded grinding wheels and as grits. This material was found much more satisfactory than the impure emery, and much more uniform in quality. The other electric-furnace product, fused aluminum trioxide (alumina), is widely used as a polishing agent for the harder class of gems. Until the hard, artificial abrasives were made available at a low cost, the lapidary industry could not and did not advance in speeding up production; for centuries, the technique remained essentially the same.

HOW TO CUT QUARTZ GEMS

The modern method of cutting and polishing quartz into gem stones is essentially the same as the technique applied to other semiprecious stones of similar hardness. All quartz gems have a hardness of seven (or very slightly less), which makes a stone of good wearing qualities. There are two general methods of cutting gem stones. One is used from the "amateur" or hobby viewpoint, and the other is applicable in a commercial way. The former employs simple and inexpensive equipment, while the commercial methods involve the application of more elaborate and costly machinery. Good work can be done with a simple home lapidary unit, but this method will be slower than the high-speed commercial methods, used where time is an important cost factor in mass production. Those who wish to mount into rings, brooches, and other ornaments the stones they cut, are referred to the recent work by W. T. Baxter, "Jewelry, Gem Cutting and Metalcraft."

The working of quartz minerals can be divided into three groups: (1) cabochon cutting, (2) specimen finishing, (3) facet cutting. Cabochon cutting and specimen finishing are similar, in that flat or curved surfaces of large size are involved, while in facet cutting flat surfaces of very small size are cut and polished. Only a general outline of the technique can be given here; for more detailed information the reader is referred to special works and current mineralogical publications, such as the April, 1938, issue of "*The Mineralogist.*"

CABOCHON CUTTING

Cabochon cutting and finishing flat or curved surfaces on a specimen can be divided into four general parts, (1) sawing, (2) grinding, (3) sanding, (4) polishing.

Sawing. If the material from which the lapidarist desires to cut a cabochon is already in suitable-sized fragments, no sawing will be required; the work can start directly on the

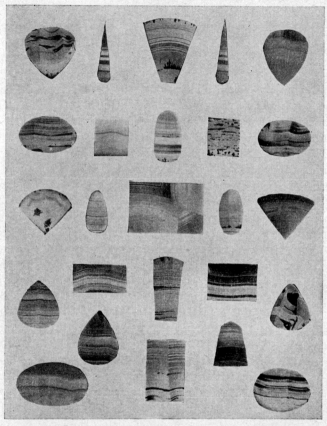

POLISHED RIBBON, BANDED, MOSS, IRIS AGATES
Illustrating various styles of cutting. (*Photograph by Fred S. Young.*)

grinding wheels. Small waterworn pebbles of agate generally need no sawing but can be fashioned into shape directly on the grinding wheels. In the case of larger masses, and where conservation of material is indicated, sawing is resorted to, in order to obtain suitable-sized blanks for the grinding wheels. If it is desired to finish a large flat surface on a specimen or to expose an agate-filled nodule or a cross section of a limb of fossil wood, sawing is also indicated.

There are two general methods of sawing, involving the use of the mud saw or the diamond saw. The mud saw is simply a circular metal disk charged with silicon carbide grit, sold under the trade names "crystolon" and "carborundum," and various others. For a twelve-inch disk, a gauge of twenty is suitable; Armco or auto-fender steel is a suitable metal. The disk should be perfectly round and should revolve at a speed of from 250 to 350 r.p.m. The edge of the disk passes through a mixture of "mud," consisting of number 120 grit, silicon carbide, and water, with clay flour or ordinary flour added to give enough viscosity to the mixture so that it will adhere to the saw blade. The work to be cut is held rigid in a swinging clamping arm, or rests on a movable carriage, both being held against the saw under ten-

SAWING AGATES

Diamond-charged metal disk used in sawing agates to proper shape prior to grinding.

sion from a spring or weights over a pulley. About ten pounds pressure against the saw is suitable for a specimen three inches in diameter. The "mud" saw, while much slower than the diamond saw, is quite effective.

The diamond saw, used for the purpose of sectioning hard gem minerals, is the prime favorite with most lapidarists and will be found in every modern commercial gem-cutting establishment. The speed of the diamond saw is the same as that given for the mud saw, and the same metal is indicated. The disk of the diamond saw is charged with powdered diamond bortz, from one-half to two carats being used to charge a twelve-inch disk. The periphery of the disk is notched to a depth of one thirty-second of an inch, at intervals of one-sixteenth of an inch, using an old knife blade and a light hammer. The diamond bortz, crushed to a grit of approximately 100 mesh, is mixed with a small amount of vaseline (about the size of a pea), and applied to the notches with a toothpick, then rubbed into the notches with the fingertips. A light peen hammer is then used to tap the notches so as to close them tight.

Next, the saw is put into motion under power, and a case-hardened steel roller is held against the edge of the disk, using a rest to steady the hand and roller. This is to close the notches further, grip the diamond grit in the metal, and give the saw a "set," so that the tool will cut its clearance in the work. The circular-running, diamond-charged tool is a very efficient one. With proper charging and use it will give long service and cut thousands of square inches of hard material like the quartz minerals. Details for the charging of the metal diamond saw will be found in current magazines and textbooks on gem-cutting; only the salient points have been given here. The diamond saw is kept lubricated by allowing the edge to run in a mixture of equal parts of kerosene and motor oil.

Grinding Wheels. The use of grinding wheels is quite essential for the shaping of quartz gems which are to be cut into cabochon styles and the shaping of crystal quartz which is to be facet cut. Clear crystal quartz, amethyst, and citrine quartz are usually cut with faceted surfaces, while all agate and practically all the other varieties of quartz are cut with single, smooth, rounded or flat surfaces. Grinding wheels are also utilized to flatten or round the rough surface of a specimen, prior to the sanding and polishing operations.

The grinding wheels in most general use are those made of silicon carbide. Sometimes, these wheels are termed "emery" wheels, but emery (an impure form of the mineral corundum) has now largely been replaced by the product of the electric furnace—silicon carbide. The effective speed of the grinding wheel is a *surface speed* of about 5,000 feet per minute; this means that a wheel twelve inches in diameter should run at an r.p.m. speed of about 1,775. As in mud and diamond sawing, these wheels should be shielded with sheet metal, to prevent splashing. A small spray of water should be run on the periphery of the wheel during operation, to prevent dust and keep the surface of the wheel flushed and free of clogging and excessive heating.

Two grinding wheels are mounted on the arbor, one on each side, a number 100 grit for fast cutting and roughing out, and a number 220 for final shaping and special kinds of work. The wheels should have a sufficient spray of water to keep them fully wet. The water can be carried to the wheels by small copper tubing or rubber hose, under the sheet-metal shield. A drain is provided in the grinding compartment of the lapidary bench, to carry away the water. Smaller wheels require less water, and for them a drip arrangement can be made by using a container suspended above the grinding wheels. For the cutting of quartz gems, a wheel of medium-hard bonding is indicated, the "J" bond in the *Crystolon* wheel being satisfactory, or, if the *Carborundum* wheel is in use, an "M" bond is indicated. If the bonding is too soft for the work at hand, the wheel will cut rapidly but will show excessive wear. On the other hand, a very hard bonding will mean less wheel wear but slower cutting and the generation of excess heat, unless the wheel is flooded with water.

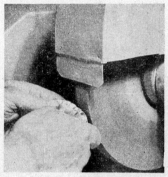

GRINDING AGATE TO SHAPE
Silicon carbide wheels, with grits of from number 100 to number 220, are used. (*Photograph by The Mineralogist Magazine Laboratories.*)

The grinding to proper shape of a cabochon is generally carried out by holding the work in the fingers, using a rigid rest for the forearm and elbow. A little practice will enable one to gain the skill properly to shape the stone to the desired outline and size. For cabochon-shaping, most of the grinding is done on the periphery of the wheel, but the sides can be used to flatten the back of a cabochon or to obtain a flat surface on a specimen.

Sanding. Prior to any attempt to polish either a cabochon-style cut gem, or a flat or rounded surface on a specimen, all deep scratches and saw or grinding-wheel marks must be removed by "sanding." The sanding operation is carried out dry, no water being needed.

Silicon-carbide-charged cloth ("emery" cloth) of number 220 grit is fastened over the side of a wooden disk, with a felt pad to give a soft base underneath the cloth. The wooden disk can be from eight to ten inches in diameter and about two inches thick; the working face should be slightly convex at the center. This convexity should amount to about one-fourth of an inch and will enable the more ready sanding of large, flat surfaces. The wooden sanding disk should be so mounted on the arbor that there will be no projecting nut or bolt on the working surface, and that the entire surface may be left available for working.

SANDING OPERATION

Removing scratches prior to polishing. Silicon carbide ("emery") cloths, stretched over a wooden disk. (Photograph by Fred S. Young.)

The speed of the sander should be from 1200 to 1500 r.p.m. for a disk eight inches in diameter. A cabochon stone, to be sanded prior to polishing, should be mounted on a small wooden stick by the use of special lapidary cement. Larger specimens can be sanded while they are held in the hand. After all deep scratches are removed and the surface has a smooth, velvetlike finish, the final polishing operation can be started. Less time will have to be spent in the final polishing if the sanding operation is properly carried out.

Polishing. Felt buffs are generally used to place the final, high, glossy polish on all cabochon styles of quartz gems. Flat or rounded surfaces on specimens can be polished by the use of felt buffs; the size of the surface which can be handled will be governed by the diameter and width of the felt. For ordinary cabochon work, a "rock-hard" type of buff (about one inch by six inches) will suffice; commercial establishments use larger felt buffing wheels.

The speed of the felt buff should be about the same as that given above for sawing; hence, the polishing can be done on the same arbor with the saw. The average peripheral speed given for polishing operations is 900 surface feet per minute; this is the speed at which the periphery of the buff should travel, and will, of course, mean a variation in the revolution per minute (r.p.m.) speeds of different-sized buffs or wheels. The stone to be polished has already been mounted ("dopped") on a stick and should not be detached until the final polish is attained. For hard minerals like quartz, the "rock-hard" type of buff will give better results, as heavier pressure against the buff can be applied. A buff which is too soft will tend to develop deep grooves on the periphery and sides.

HARD FELT POLISHING BUFFS
Cabochon-style gems and specimens are polished on felt buffs. Note that the stone is cemented to dop stick to facilitate handling.

Polishing agents of a very wide variety have been used in the lapidary industry. Prior to the introduction of the modern abrasives, materials like tripoli, rottenstone, rouge, tin oxide, pumice, chalk, and similar natural abrasives were the only ones available. Some of these, especially tripoli and tin oxide, are still favorites among both commercial and amateur gem-stone cutters. However, there are available now a large number of manufactured polishing agents and these are very satisfactory; they generally cost no more (even less) and are very reliable, in that they are free from grit and always uniform in quality. The *Norton Alumina* polishing powders are widely used for polishing the quartz minerals, *Alumina* of grades E-67 and E-111 being excellent. The *Levigated Alumina* is of still finer grit and is used for opal or agate, to produce a very high, final glossy finish. Dixon *Ruby Powder* is excellent for polishing facets on quartz gem stones. Waldru *Final Polishing Agent* and Carborundum Company *Buffing Powders* are also in general use.

A small amount of any of the above polishing powders is mixed with water to form a thin paste and applied to the felt buff with a brush, the felt being kept well-coated with the mixture. Polishing is not a slow and tedious operation, unless deep scratches are present. Remember, it takes much longer to wear away a deep scratch with polishing powder than with the sander; hence, more time spent in proper preparation of the surface means less time needed for polishing.

FACET CUTTING

Transparent quartz minerals, like amethyst, citrine, and clear crystals, are cut with numerous small, flat surfaces, to bring out brilliance and sparkle through the refraction and reflection of light entering or touching the gem. The standard "brilliant" cut, like that seen on diamonds, has 57 small, polished faces, divided as follows: Crown facets, one row of sixteen at girdle, one row of eight main facets, and one row of eight crown table facets, making thirty-three, including the large table facet. Below the girdle, on the "bottom" portion of the gem, are twenty-four pavilion facets. The girdle of a facet-cut gem is the line around the circumference. There are numerous variations of the standard "brilliant"-style cut, with a greater or smaller number of facets. Other styles of cutting are given various technical terms.

Roughing out the Stone. The first procedure in facet cutting is to obtain a suitable-sized fragment to start grinding. Small water-worn pebbles or crystals will require no sawing but can go immediately to the grinding wheels. In dealing with larger crystals or fragments of valuable gem material, sawing is indicated, to obtain as many stones as possible and waste a minimum amount in the grinding operation. The mud saw or the diamond can be used to reduce the rough stone to proper sizes for facet cutting.

The suitable-sized fragment is then shaped on the regular grinding wheels, leaving enough excess material to allow for further reduction, when the facets are cut on the gem. Proper shaping of a stone for facet cutting requires a little more care and skill than shaping under cabochon work.

Cutting Facets. The shaped gem is then mounted on a metal stick called a "dop," by use of a special lapidary cement and gentle heat. It is customary to cut and polish the large table facet first, then the pavilion facets, and finally the crown facets. Facets of a given row are cut to proper size and placed in their correct position, and then polished, before the next row is started. Fine-grit silicon carbide and water are used to cut the facets, and, for quartz gems, number 400 grit will work rapidly enough, although commercial cutters who have developed great skill may use coarser grit powder.

Some commercial facet cutters, of long experience, find the old "jamb-peg" arrangement quite satisfactory for placing facets in proper position and angle. The beginner and amateur will find the various mechanical devices for obtaining the correct angles and division of the facet areas a great aid, if not an actual necessity. There are various mechanical facet-cutting attachments, for use with the horizontal running lap, to aid in proper cutting of the facets. One type is illustrated here. For cutting the facets, an iron lap is frequently used, charged with a thin mixture of water and the abrasive grit. Since only a small amount of material is to be removed, this operation is one of care rather than heavy grinding; a slight touch may be sufficient to reduce one of the small crown facets.

Polishing Facets. All the facets on the pavilion are cut and then polished, without the stone's being removed from the dop. The gem is then reversed on the dop, and all the crown facets are cut and polished, and the task is thus completed. This means three separate cementings, one for the large table, one for the pavilion, and finally one for the crown. In the cutting of small gems, some skill is required in mounting the gem accurately, to avoid having a stone with the table off center or similar mechanical defects. Mechanical devices are often used to aid in correctly recementing the gem to the dop.

The polishing operation is carried out on horizontal running laps, separate from those on which silicon carbide has been used. Pewter, tin, lead, and zinc laps are used in the polishing of

facet-cut gems. A felt or similar soft surface is not suitable for facet-cutting work. As in the work of polishing cabochon-style gems, wide varieties of polishing agents are employed in facet polishing. Tripoli, tin oxide, Alumina, Levigated Alumina, Ruby Powder, Waldru Powder, and the Carborundum Company Buffing Powders are all in use and have their special applica-

FACET CUTTING GEM STONES

Type of mechanical device used in cutting facets on quartz gem stones. Obtaining proper angles of facets and placing in proper position can be done by raising or lowering arm and turning dop to which stone is cemented. Low-speed, horizontal-running, metal laps are used for both cutting of facets and polishing.

tions. Quartz is not a difficult gem to polish, and good work can be done with these polishing agents; various lapidarists have their preferences, favorite formulas, or "secret" methods.

In both cutting and polishing, low speeds are indicated; an eight- or ten-inch lap is generally used and need not run over 100 r.p.m. The polishing agent is mixed quite thin with water and applied to the metal-lap surface quite sparingly, only a very small amount being required for proper polishing. Considerably more skill is required for facet cutting, but many amateurs are doing very creditable work, using quartz and the numerous other gem minerals which make beautiful and valuable cut stones.

TYPES OF EQUIPMENT

Most of the equipment illustrated here can be used for commercial work, if so desired. For those who do not wish to purchase or construct the more elaborate equipment, small ready-made home units are available, ready to plug into any socket and operate. Do not forsake this fascinating and delightful hobby, merely for lack of room or other facilities. Quite complete and compact units can be purchased which could be set up in an apartment house parlor, create very little noise or dirt, and yet turn out satisfactory work. A small one-fourth-horsepower motor is often all the home unit required for power.

Thousands of people throughout the United States collect and polish gem stones as a useful, practical, and fascinating avocation. Since quartz gem minerals are to be found in practically every part of the country, it is only natural that this type of material should be the prime favorite with the lapidarist. Placing a cut and polished surface on an otherwise rough and unattractive specimen will greatly enhance its beauty, as well as its value. The colorful, agate-filled nodules are virtually worthless as cabinet specimens without the skilled touch of the lapidarist. The delicate lines of bandings, the remarkable dendritic growths, the elusive illusion of depth and color, and numerous other features in agate, are all brought out to the best advantage on the polished surface. Many of these superb specimens would be wholly unfit for cabinet purposes without this dressing up.

There are very likely to be numerous localities in your vicinity where, at no cost other than the visit and time, you can obtain quartz minerals suitable for cutting and polishing. In some parts of the country, collectors have built up remarkably beautiful and valuable collections solely through their spare-time efforts. It is a real recreation to search the field, stream gravels, ocean beaches, and vast expanses of sage-covered deserts, for these treasures. The hobby of gem cutting takes you into the field in pleasant weather, and during the long winter evenings the whirl and hum of the grinding wheels will prove a pleasant relaxation from your daily routine tasks. Moreover, your time will not be wasted, for many of these cut and polished pieces will have a real material value, aside from furnishing you with pleasure and recreation. Some lapidarists specialize solely in the quartz minerals and exhibit thousands of beautiful and valuable specimens in their cabinets, all obtained at little cost other than their personal efforts. Moreover, some varieties of quartz are practically worthless for specimen purposes unless cut and polished, as we have noted in the case of the agate.

HOME GEM-CUTTING SHOP

Type of equipment which can also be used for commercial work. Grinding wheels at left; diamond saws, polishing buffs at right. (*Photograph, courtesy Fred S. Young.*)

QUARTZ GEMS PRODUCED IN AMERICA

According to the estimates made by the United States Bureau of Mines, the value of the quartz gems produced in the United States in the year 1921 amounted to only about $11,000. This estimate appears rather low, even for that year, but since then the production has been greatly increased, especially in the Far Western states.

A great part of the quartz, agate, and jasper stones used in costume jewelry are still produced in foreign cutting centers, especially at Idar, Germany, where agate cutting has been an important industry for centuries. At one time, the area about Idar produced excellent agate in quantity, but these deposits were exhausted over fifty years ago. Since then, rough material has been imported largely from South America, going to Germany as ballast in ships.

Most of the agate of South America lacks color and is unsuited for gem cutting, unless artificially colored, hence a great deal of the agate shipped from German cutting centers has been colored by being soaked and dyed in chemicals or by heat treatment. Both facet and cabochon stones are subjected to some form of treatment to improve the color and appearance. Large polished specimens of dyed or treated agate can generally be detected readily by the agate connoisseur.

While dyed agate is suitable for some purposes, the naturally colored material is certainly more desirable in many respects. Specimens of dyed agate, particularly the shades of green and blue, often seem to clash in their combinations—mixtures never seen in nature. The artificial colors that seem to be the most satisfactory are the reds, yellows, and black.

During the last five years, a great many new localities producing well-colored agate, jasper, jasp-agate, moss agate, and a host of similar varieties in quantity have been found in the Western states, including California, Oregon, Washington, Wyoming, Montana, Idaho, and Nevada. A great deal of this newly discovered material is being collected on a commercial scale and is rapidly finding its way into the American markets, to replace the artificially colored material previously imported.

In recent years, many new commercial cutting establishments have been put into operation. Thus, with the thousands of home lapidary shops, it is safe to estimate that the value of quartz gems and specimens now being produced in America is at least several hundred thousand dollars worth annually.

Glendive, Billings, and Livingston are the leading producing agate centers in Montana, while Portland, Oregon, is by far the leading production center of the Pacific Northwest. Some ten or more regular commercial lapidary shops are operated in Portland, in addition to approximately 300 home shops. A large number of commercial agate-cutting shops are to be found in southwestern Oregon and along the Oregon coast, where agates and jasper are found in great abundance. The establishments along the beaches cater mainly to the tourists.

While Idar, Germany, continues to produce large quantities of facet- and cabochon-cut gem stones, the cutting center of Portland, Oregon, leads in the production of superb cabinet specimens of agate and jasper. With the recent discovery of numerous deposits of agate and jasper in the Oregon country, rough material is readily available to the Portland establishments. The art of coloring, dyeing, or treating agates by heat, appears to be unknown in the Portland center; the quality of the naturally occurring material does not warrant resorting to artificial means to improve its quality.

San Francisco, Los Angeles, San Diego, and Long Beach, in California, have also greatly increased their production of quartz gem stones since 1921. A great deal of high-quality jasper of various types is produced and cut at the several cutting centers of California. It is conservatively estimated that at least 800 home lapidary shops are in operation in the state of California; the production of quartz gems from these establishments alone amounts to thousands of dollars annually. This includes the value of facet-cut stones, cabochons, ornaments, book ends, paper weights, polished specimens for museums and cabinets, and similar examples of the lapidary art. Some of this finished product finds its way into the markets, while other specimens are retained in private collections or placed in museums and educational institutions.

California produces a very large variety of quartz minerals, but the jasper type of material is perhaps outstanding and is plentiful in numerous localities. The private collection of cut and polished ornaments and semiprecious stones belonging to William B. Pitts, on display at Golden Gate Park, San Francisco, well exemplifies the great variety of quartz gems found in California. The Pitts collection, consisting of thousands of pieces, is unquestionably the leading one of its kind in America.

The Art of Cutting Gem Quartz

The growing public demand for American quartz gems is being felt throughout the lapidary industry, and new cutting establishments are being opened in areas wherever the raw mineral is found. According to a United States Bureau of Mines Information Circular, *Quartz Gem Stones*, "The finish given these domestic stones has proved that the craftsmanship of American workmen is equal to that of the foreign expert." With this in mind, and in order to promote development and

MODERN GEM-CUTTING LABORATORY

Cabochon-grinding equipment in background and to left. Facet-cutting lap in foreground. (*Photograph, courtesy The Mineralogist Gem-Cutting Laboratories, Portland, Oregon.*)

utilization of the American deposits of quartz gem minerals, it is expected that the American lapidary industry will in the near future undergo expansion, supplying the greater part of the millions of dollars' worth of semiprecious gems consumed annually in America.

INDUSTRIAL AND OTHER USES OF QUARTZ

While articles of jewelry and other ornaments constitute the widest range of use for the many varieties of quartz minerals, there are, of course, numerous practical applications and purposes for which the mineral is employed in the arts and in industries. Obviously, it will be impossible to discuss fully so broad a subject; such a discussion would require a large volume.

One of the very important uses to which crystal quartz is put is in the controlling of the wave length for radio broadcasting. Prism sections are cut from quartz crystals, of optical quality, which are of various thicknesses and of proper orientation in relation to the crystallographic axis. It has been found that sections oriented at right angles to the optic (C) axis of the crystal will give definite electrical oscillations, while those oriented at other angles respond in a different frequency. Thus, the manner in which the sections are cut and the thickness to which they are ground influence their response to electrical impulses. In this way, it is possible to control the wave length of a broadcasting station more accurately than by any other known means.

Rock crystal (quartz) and sands carrying a high silica content find wide use in the manufacture of various types of glass, including common window glass, as well as the higher grades of laboratory apparatus and optical lenses. Lenses ground from quartz crystals find use in special types of microscopes and optical instruments where ultraviolet light is employed, since pure quartz will transmit a much greater percentage of ultraviolet light than ordinary glass. Specially made glass carrying a high silica content is fitted into the windows of solariums where the passage of ultraviolet light is needed, and the glass tubes used in some types of ultraviolet lamps are practically pure fused quartz.

Quartz, both crystalline and amorphous, is utilized in the construction of numerous kinds of scientific instruments, of which only a few of the most important will be mentioned. The quartz "wedge," ground from a large quartz crystal, is used on the polarizing petrological microscope, for studying interference figures in the determination of minerals, which is, indeed, a very important scientific use. Spectroscopic prisms are, likewise, ground out of the clearest rock crystals. Analytical balances of the better grade are equipped with knives ground from the finest agate, upon which the balance beam rides. Small mortars and pestles used in laboratories are ground from quartz. Like-wise, spatulas used in mixing corrosive cements and porcelain plastics are frequently ground from a flawless section of agate. Your dentist makes daily use of instruments of this kind. Bearings of all sorts, where an extremely hard, smooth, and noncorrosive material is required, are usually made of quartz or some mineral of similar properties.

Crystal quartz fuses at a very high temperature (1750°C.), becoming a molten mass of considerable viscosity in which numerous gas bubbles are included. Casting lens blanks, rods, tubing, and sheets of pure quartz was, therefore, not a success-ful commercial venture until quite recently, when methods were discovered whereby these bubbles can be largely elimi-nated. Castings of extremely large size, even, can now be made successfully. The large 200-inch astronomical telescope lens recently cast was by far the largest ever successfully attempted. When the telescope is finally completed and installed on Mount Palomar, in southern California, in about 1940, astronomers will peer farther out into space, with the aid of this remarkable lens made of practically pure quartz, than man's vision ever penetrated before.

One of the most recent and astounding discoveries for the use of quartz is that tubes of pure quartz glass will conduct beams of light in much the same way that pipes will conduct water. If the tube be bent, even to an angle of 90°, a light flashed into one end of it will round the bends and come out at the other end with practically undiminished strength. Ordinary glass, being amorphous, permits light in rounding bends to be scattered by reflection from its surface, while in the pure quartz tube it is completely refracted around the bend by the prismlike crystals composing its structure. This discovery may not have any revolutionary effect upon society; yet, aside from its novelty, there are ample purposes for which it may be employed to great advantage, such as per-mitting surgeons conveniently to introduce cold light into remote recesses of the human anatomy without fear of injury.

Yet many other uses of quartz are listed in the *Minerals Year-book* (1936), some of which are the following: Quartz is used in the manufacture of ferrosilicon, an iron-silicon steel-alloy product of the electric furnace; for whiteware and enamel; as packing in acid towers and water filters; for refractory purposes (in the manufacture of firebrick); as a filler; as an abrasive agent in some kinds of sandpaper, soaps, and scouring compounds, metal polishes, and safety matches. Ground sand, or "pulverized silica," is used widely in the ceramic trades; as a silica wash for molds in steel foundry works; as a filler in preparing roofing, paint, and other similar products; and as an abrasive agent in various cleaning and scouring compounds.

Much "sharp sand" is used in sawing and rubbing granite, limestone, marble, slate, and soap stone. It is also used in rough-grinding plate glass previous to smoothing and polishing, and for sandblasting castings, cutting letters on monuments, cleaning the outer walls of buildings, etc. By railroads "sharp sand" is used to give the locomotives a firmer grip on the rails in wet or slippery weather, or in climbing heavy grades. It is used in profusion for the same purpose upon the highways of the Northern states, in the sleety weather when everything is coated with ice. The use of sand as a plaster, cement, and concrete aggregate is so common that it need not be discussed here, although many chapters have been written upon the subject in engineering texts and magazines.

Water glass has become so important an article of commerce that it is now shipped about the country in tank cars. By the fusing of silicon dioxide with sodium carbonate, carbon dioxide is liberated and a new substance known as sodium silicate is formed. It is very soluble in water, and in a concentrated solution tremendous amounts are used as an adhesive in making paper cartons, as an egg preservative, a filler in cheap soaps, a weatherproof coating for disintegrating stone buildings, fire-proofing for both wood and cloth, cementing materials, and for many other purposes. It is one of the most versatile substances in the entire range of quartz materials, having almost unlimited commercial possibilities.

Appendix

SELECTED REFERENCE BOOKS

BAXTER, W. T. "Jewelry, Gem Cutting, and Metalcraft." New York, 1938.

BURNHAM, S. M. "Precious Stones." Boston, 1886.

CLARKE, FRANK WIGGLESWORTH. "Data of Geochemistry." (*U. S. Geological Survey Bulletin 770*), 1924.

CROOK, A. R. "Guide to the Mineral Collections of the Illinois State Museum." Springfield, 1920.

DANA, EDWARD S. "A Text-book of Mineralogy." New York, 1904.

ENGLISH, GEORGE LETCHWORTH. "Getting Acquainted with Minerals." Rochester, N. Y., 1934.

FARRINGTON, OLIVER CUMMINGS. "Gems and Gem Minerals." Chicago, 1903.

KRAUS, EDWARD HENRY, and HOLDEN, EDWARD FULLER. "Gems and Gem Minerals." New York, 1931.

KUNZ, GEORGE FREDERICK. "Gems and Precious Stones of North America." New York, 1892.

PIRSSON, LOUIS V. "Rocks and Rock Minerals." New York, 1908.

SOSMAN, ROBERT B. "Properties of Silica." *American Chemical Society Monograph 76*, New York.

SPENCER, L. J. "Key to Precious Stones." London, 1935.

STREETER, EDWIN W. "Precious Stones and Gems." London, 1898.

VAIL, JAMES G. "Soluble Silicates in Industry." *American Chemical Society Monograph 85*, New York.

WHITLOCK, HERBERT P. "The Story of the Gems." New York, 1936.

WODISKA, JULIUS. "A Book of Precious Stones." New York, 1909.

SELECTED REFERENCE TOPICS

BECK, GEORGE F. "Determination of Fossil Woods." *The Mineralogist*, (a series of articles), Vol. IV, 1936, and Vol. V, 1937. Consult index.

Quartz Family Minerals

DAKE, H. C., and F. S. YOUNG, "Art of Gem Cutting." *The Mineralogist*, April, 1938.

EARDLEY, V. L. "Diatomite." *Canadian Department of Mines, Publications* 691, 1928. Contains selected bibliography.

FARRINGTON, O. C. "Agate." *Field Museum Natural History Geological Leaflet* 8, 1927.

GOODWIN, N. "Diatomaceous Earth." *Chemical and Metallurgical Engineering*, 1920, Vol. XXIII, pp. 1158–1160.

HASTINGS, C. "The Jeweled Forests of Arizona." *American Forests*, 1936, Vol. XLII, pp. 208–210.

HOWARD, J. W. "Agates." *Journal of Chemical Education*, 1933, Vol. X, pp. 67–70.

JORDAN, D. S. "A Miocene Catastrophe." *Natural History* (Journal of the American Museum of Natural History) 1920, Vol. XX, No. 1.

KEYS, CHARLES. "Lost Mountains of the Prairies." (Sioux Quartzite) *Scientific Monthly*, 1917, Vol. IV, 369–377.

LARSON, DR. ESPER. "Quartz the Geologic Thermometer." *U. S. Geological Survey Bulletin* 848, 1934.

LENNON, P. O. "Knapping Flints—The Oldest Industry." *Sands, Clays and Minerals Magazine*, 1934, Vol. II, No. 1.

NEWLAND, D. H. "Herkimer County Quartz Crystals." *Rocks and Minerals Magazine*, 1937, Vol. XII, No. 67.

SEWARD, N. H. "Australian Opals." *Sands, Clays and Minerals Magazine*, Vol. I, No. 2, pp. 20–22.

SHEPHERD, G. F. "Bibliography of Opal." *Rocks and Minerals Magazine*, 1933, Vol. VIII, No. 8.

THOMPSON, M. "How to Tell Right-handed and Left-handed Quartz Crystals." *Rocks and Minerals Magazine*, 1937, Vol. XII, No. 67.

VAN TUYL, DR. F. "Origin of the Geodes of the Keokuk Beds." *Science*, N.S. 1912, Vol. XXXVI, pp. 569–572.

WALCOTT, A. J. "The Cause of Asterism in Gems." *Field Museum Natural History Geological Leaflet*, 1938.

WHITLOCK, H. P. "Concerning Phantoms." *Natural History* (journal of the American Museum of Natural History), 1933, Vol. XXXIII, pp. 271–272.

WILD, GEORGE O. "The Treatment of Gem Stones by Heat." *Rocks and Minerals Magazine*, March, 1932.

Index

298

Index

Index

Index

303